MATHEMATICS FOR ELEMENTARY SCHOOL TEACHERS

A FIRST COURSE

MATHEMATICS FOR ELEMENTARY SCHOOL TEACHERS

A FIRST COURSE

James W. Armstrong

Assistant Professor of Mathematics
University of Illinois

Harper & Row, Publishers
New York, London, and Evanston

CONTENTS

CHAPTER 3
Elementary Set Theory 84

CHAPTER 4
Elementary Number Theory 112

CHAPTER 5

The System of Fractions

CHAPTER 6

The System of Integers

CHAPTER 10
Systems of Numeration

PREFACE

Mathematics for Elementary School Teachers: A First Course consists primarily of an algebraic treatment of the number concept. Number systems are introduced in roughly the same order that they are introduced in the elementary grades. The book also includes a detailed discussion of decimal numerals and a briefer discussion of other systems of numeration. A chapter on sets is included even though the text is not dependent upon set-theory language or notation. The development of the number systems is sequential, each system being founded on its predecessor in a way which is both natural and reasonable from the students' point of view. Indeed, naturalness and reasonableness are the factors which have controlled the presentation of the number concept. Digressions from the mainstream of ideas have been kept to a minimum so that the natural flow of ideas can be fully emphasized and exploited. A goal of the book is to present arithmetic as a unified whole, not simply as a collection of apparently disjointed and unrelated facts.

The selection of topics represents what the author feels is an optimal core of ideas suitable for a one-semester five-, four-, or three-hour first course in mathematics for prospective elementary school teachers. The approaches to the various topics have been tested in the classroom more than eight times in various forms and with various manners of presentation. This experimentation was directed toward identifying the most rigorous mathematical development commensurate with the students' backgrounds.

It is assumed that this book will be used as a text in a terminal course for students who will not again receive instruction in these same topics. Consequently the text provides many reinforcement experiences in addition to initial learning experiences. To accomplish this, the text has been organized in such a way that each idea can be considered at least twice. Successive presentations of an idea are handled differently and in different contexts, thus allowing for development of the idea and not simply its restatement.

The exercises range from routine computational and theorem-proving exercises to those which call for some imagination. It is expected that prospective teachers will occasionally be called upon to provide complete and detailed exposition of ideas. Therefore review questions are designed to elicit such expositions as well as the restatement of definitions, theorems, and so on.

Also available to teachers is a guide which contains a supplementary list of answers, suggestions on how the text might be used in three-, four-, and five-hour semester courses, and a detailed analysis of interdependency relations existing between the various parts of the text.

I would like to express my appreciation to the following individuals who aided or guided me in one way or another as I wrote this book. (1) To Professor John Harvey, who read the manuscript during its final stages and whose comments and criticisms added substantially to any quality this book may possess. (2) To Professor Paul Bateman, for his encouragement. (3) To my colleagues at the University of Illinois, whose interest in the project was of great help. Specifically, thanks to Professor Ralph Alexander, Dr. Stephanie Alexander, and to Professors Hiram Paley, Joseph Rotman, and John Wetzel. (4) To Mrs. Joan Peressini, who typed the manuscript, tolerated my indecisions and delays, and did a superb job. (5) To Harper & Row, Publishers, who kept me happy during the preparation of the manuscript. (6) To the young ladies who by their interest and enthusiasm provided the initial and continuing motivation for writing this book.

JAMES W. ARMSTRONG

MATHEMATICS FOR ELEMENTARY SCHOOL TEACHERS

A FIRST COURSE

CHAPTER 1

Preliminaries

Before we begin our study of mathematics it is necessary to discuss some preliminary ideas. Mostly these preliminary ideas are matters of logic, and partly they are nothing more than the careful statement of the meanings of certain words and ideas. Little in this chapter is actually mathematics, but it will all be used in talking about mathematics.

DEDUCTIVE SYSTEMS

The study of mathematics is carried on within the logical framework of what is called a *deductive system*. Very roughly speaking, a deductive system is a kind of logical hatrack upon which the various ideas of mathematics are hung. Each idea has its own place on this hatrack and it is therefore necessary to learn something about the hatrack itself so that later we may be able to put the right ideas in the right places.

The reader is more or less familiar with one deductive system already, namely, the deductive system of plane Euclidean geometry which he studied in high school.* If we analyze this geometry course, we see that the study of plane geometry consists in its fundamentals of

1. The identification of certain geometric concepts (*point, line, triangle, angle,* and so on).
2. The discovery of true statements about those concepts (*through two distinct points there is one and only one line; the sum of the interior angles of a triangle is 180°,* and so on).

---

* This part of mathematics is named after the Greek mathematician Euclid (circa 300 B.C.). Euclid's fame rests with his authorship of a book on geometry known today as *Euclid's Elements.* The *Elements* is a remarkable book for many reasons, but primarily its fame derives from the way that Euclid organized his presentation of geometry. Even though it contains many serious errors of logic, in this book we see the first awareness that mathematics could be formulated in a precise and logical way. It is from Euclid's organization of geometry that the present concept of a deductive system stems.

1

In fact, this is all that any mathematical study amounts to, the identification and listing of concepts, and the discovery and listing of true statements about those concepts. A deductive system, then, consists of these two parts: concepts and true statements about the concepts. Let us examine each of these two parts in greater detail.

Concepts

Suppose we were to make a complete list of all the known concepts of plane Euclidean geometry. This list might consist of many thousands of concepts, but it would be a finite list. After listing these concepts, we could attempt to construct a precise definition for each concept on the list in terms of other concepts on the list. We say we could *attempt* to construct these definitions because it can be shown that it would be impossible to give every concept on the list a definition without committing the logical error of using what is called a *circular definition*. A circular definition is one which either directly or indirectly uses the concept being defined in its own definition. For example, the following entries at one time appeared in a well-known encyclopedia:

Memorial Day: *See Decoration Day*
Decoration Day: *See Memorial Day*

Now if we knew nothing about American holidays and we wanted to know what Memorial Day was all about, this encyclopedia would be of no help whatsoever. In essence this encyclopedia says that Memorial Day means Memorial Day. This is not very helpful. Because we recognize the futility of using circular definitions we outlaw their use in mathematics.

Let us now return to the list of all known geometric concepts which we had written out. We asserted that if we could not employ circular definitions, then we would not be able to define all the concepts on this list. To see why this is so let us simplify the situation by assuming that our list of all geometric concepts contains only four concepts. (The number four is chosen simply because it is small. Any larger number would do just as well but the discussion would be much more complicated.) Label these four concepts A, B, C, and D. Now let us try to supply a definition for every one of these concepts in such a way that circular definitions will not occur. Keep in mind that this list is a *complete* list of known geometric concepts and so the definition of any one concept must be phrased in terms of other listed concepts. We may as well begin by trying to define concept A. We know that we cannot use A in its own definition, so a definition of A would have to be phrased in terms of one or more of the concepts B, C, and D. For concreteness suppose that a definition of concept A is found which involves only concept B. Next let us try to find a definition of B. This definition could not involve either concept A or B or we would have constructed a circular definition. Hence a definition of B could involve only C or D. For concreteness suppose a definition of B is found which involves only concept C. Now we try to define C and we know that such a definition could not involve any one of the concepts *A*, *B*, or *C*. (Why?) This means that a definition of *C* could involve only concept *D*. For concreteness suppose we can find a definition of *C* in terms of concept *D*. We have now defined all the concepts except concept *D*. Certainly we are not going to use *D* in its own definition and so a definition of *D* could only involve *A*, *B*, or *C*. But if a definition of *D* were to involve any one of these three concepts, we would have a circular definition. If *D* were to be defined in terms of, say, *B*, then we would have the following circular definition:

D is defined in terms of *B*

B is defined in terms of *C*

C is defined in terms of *D*

and so we see that, ultimately, *D* has been defined in terms of itself. We leave it to the reader to show that if *D* were defined in terms of either *A* or *C*, other circular definitions would appear.

Thus the concept *D* cannot be defined in terms of *A*, *B*, *C*, or *D*. But there are no other concepts than these! Therefore there is no alternative but to leave concept *D* without any definition at all.

The moral of this argument is that in any mathematical study there will always be some concepts which cannot be defined without introducing circular definitions. It is therefore necessary to leave some concepts without definition. In general there will be many different ways to select the concepts which will be left undefined, and the actual selection is usually made on the basis of naturalness and convenience. After the undefined concepts have been selected, the other concepts of the study may then be defined in terms of the undefined concepts.

True Statements About the Concepts

Assuming that we have completed the identification of at least some of the concepts pertinent to the branch of mathematics we wish to study, we may now begin the search for true statements about those concepts. But before we begin this search we had better make sure that we know what we mean by a true statement.

First of all we should remark that in mathematics truth need bear no relation to the real world in which we live. There are just two kinds of true statements and neither one of these need relate either directly or indirectly to the real world. The first kind of true statement is the *assumed true statement*, or *axiom*. An axiom is true simply because we say that it is true; its truth is assumed without any kind of logical argument to support it. The second and more familiar kind of true statement is the *proved true statement*, or *theorem*. We do not want to go into the question of what it means to prove a theorem is true at this time for the idea is not a simple one and it will be one of the objects of our study throughout this book. Suffice it to say that to prove a theorem is true means to verify (somehow) that the truth of this theorem follows in a logically acceptable way from the truth of other statements already known to be true. These other true statements which are used to establish the truth of the given statement may be either axioms or previously proven theorems. The *proof* of the given theorem is this verification. If the reader will think back to his high school plane Euclidean geometry course, he will recall that a substantial part of that course was devoted to proving the truth of theorems.

Of the two kinds of true statements, axioms and theorems, it may be felt that somehow the theorems are the more "satisfying." Theorems are proved in accordance with logical principles but axioms are only assumed to be true. The question therefore arises of why we should use axioms at all. Wouldn't it be better to prove all the true statements? The answer to this lies in the fact that it is impossible to prove every true statement. To see why this is so let us return to the list of true statements that we were about to begin before we digressed to discuss axioms and theorems. We had listed some concepts and were ready to begin compiling a list of true statements. Consider whether the first statement to be put on this list could possibly be a theorem. If this first statement were a theorem it would mean that the statement could be proved true. To say it could be proved true means that the truth of the statement follows from the truth of other statements *which are already known to be true*. The first statement therefore could not possibly be a theorem since there are no other statements already known to be true at the time we are trying to establish the truth of the first statement. It follows that the first statement to be put on the list of true statements is not a theorem and so must be an axiom; it must be true for no other reason than that it has been assumed to be true.

Thus in every mathematical study the list of true statements must contain axioms, and, in particular, the first true statement on this list must be an axiom. For example, among the axioms of plane Euclidean geometry are the following:

1.   Through two distinct points there passes one and only one line.
2.   A straight line measures the shortest distance between two points.
3.   Given a line and a point not on that line there is one and only one line passing through the given point which is parallel to the given line.

These are not all the axioms of plane Euclidean geometry nor are these always included in the list of axioms for this mathematical study. In general there will be a variety of different ways to select the axioms, and the actual selection is usually made on the basis of convenience and naturalness. By *naturalness* we mean that in some sense the axioms ought to express the most fundamental or primitive truths possible. Observe that the three geometric axioms listed above express very primitive truths.* It is almost always true that the axioms are

---

* Greek geometers thought that the third of these statements expressed a self-evident and primitive truth about geometry, but later geometers have disagreed. This axiom, called Euclid's Parallel Postulate, was thought by some mathematicians (notably C. F. Gauss, J. Bolyai, and N. Lobachevsky, all about 1825) to be sufficiently nonprimitive that there was question of whether or not it should be an axiom. Studies relating to this particular axiom subsequently resulted in an important and new branch of mathematical geometry called non-Euclidean geometry.

chosen from among the most primitive true statements on the list of all true statements.

There is a great deal more that can be said about the separation of the true statements into axioms and theorems, but we have all we need to prepare us for our study of mathematics. We shall close this discussion with one final comment. Ultimately the truth of every theorem rests upon the assumed truth of the axioms. That is, ultimately every theorem is justified in terms of axioms alone, and so there is no "truth" in mathematics that is any "truer" than the "truth" of the axioms. We have included an exercise to guide the reader in discovering for himself why this is true.

Exercises

1. In a certain mathematical study there are precisely five concepts, which we shall label A, B, C, D, and E. Suppose that we have defined concept A in terms of concepts C and E and have defined concept E in terms of concepts B and D.
    (a) What are the only concepts that could possibly be used in defining concept D?
    (b) What are the only concepts that could possibly be used in defining concept C?
    (c) Suppose we find a definition for concept B which involves only concept C. If concept C can be defined, which concepts could be involved in this definition? Which could not be involved?
    (d) Suppose we find a definition for concept D in terms of concept C. Explain why we could not then define concept C in terms of concept E.
2. Suppose that we are constructing a list of true statements and that we have already constructed this much of the list:

    True statement 1:   Axiom 1
    True statement 2:   Axiom 2
    True statement 3:   Theorem 1
    True statement 4:   Axiom 3
    True statement 5:   Theorem 2
    True statement 6:   Theorem 3

    (a) Explain why the truth of Theorem 1 must necessarily rest upon the assumed truth of one or both of Axioms 1 and 2.
    (b) Explain why the truth of Theorem 2 must ultimately rest upon the assumed truth of one or more of Axioms 1, 2, and 3.
    (c) Explain why the truth of Theorem 3 must ultimately rest upon the assumed truth of one or more of Axioms 1, 2, and 3.

The Four Parts of a Deductive System

When a body of thought is organized in such a way that the concepts and true statements have been classified by whether they are undefined or defined concepts and axioms or theorems, we refer to that body of thought as a deductive system. Formally a deductive system consists of four parts:

1. The undefined concepts
2. The defined concepts

3. The axioms
4. The theorems

Our first contact with a deductive system will be in Chapter 2 where we shall lay the foundations for the deductive system of counting numbers by listing some of the undefined concepts and axioms of that system. However, since our primary interest lies in the concepts and true statements themselves rather than the way these are organized in the deductive system, we shall not permit the logical considerations attendant with the deductive system to intrude into our study except at the very beginning. The further we progress the less attention we shall pay to the specific logical foundations upon which the particular branch of mathematics that we are studying is built.

LOGIC

In order to study a deductive system meaningfully one must have a reasonably firm grasp of the basic parts of logic. In this section we shall discuss a few logical ideas that are prerequisite to our discussion of mathematics.

Numbers and Numerals

One of the fundamental notions of logic that we shall use from time to time is that *an object or concept is different from the name of that object or concept.* This notion is not at all unusual, but generally we do not pay much attention to it. To say that the name of a thing is different from the thing being named implies, for example, that the piece of paper on which these words are printed is not itself a page, but something which is called a page.

Our interest in this notion lies in the way it applies to numbers. We shall call a symbol which names (represents, symbolizes, denotes) a number a *numeral*. We can write numerals on a blackboard, but we cannot write numbers on a blackboard. We can turn a numeral upside down, but we cannot turn a number upside down.

Now it is true that most of the time it is inconvenient to distinguish between numbers and numerals. No one would say, "The number whose numeral is 4 multiplied by the number whose numeral is 6 is the number whose numeral is 24," when he could say, "4 multiplied by 6 is 24." To distinguish between numbers and numerals in such instances would be pointless. On the other hand, there are times when it is extremely useful to distinguish between numbers and numerals. Whenever an idea can be more easily expressed by making this distinction, we shall do so.

Because symbolism is so important in mathematics, it is very easy for the student to develop an overdependence upon symbols; that is, he tends to think too much in terms of the symbols themselves and not enough in terms of the ideas the symbols represent. The student who cultivates a healthy disregard for the symbols that are used and centers his attention primarily on the ideas those symbols represent cannot go far wrong.

Exercises

1. List four different numerals for the number named by the numeral 4.
2. List five different names for this book.
3. Which is the larger number? Which is the larger numeral?

5   3

4. Can a number be written? Can a numeral be written?
5. Frequently numerals are chosen so as to convey information about the number being named.
   (a) Find a numeral for the number named by the symbol 4 which conveys the information that this number is even.
   (b) Find a numeral for the number named by the numeral 7 which conveys the information that this number is three greater than four.
   (c) Find a numeral for 15 which conveys the information that this number is evenly divisible by 5.

Statements

A *statement* is an idea represented by means of a *sentence* and is either true or false but is not both true and false. A sentence is the name of a statement. For example, the different sentences "Hank is smart" and "Heine ist klug" represent the same statement. It is sometimes useful to make the distinction between statements and the sentences which name them, but most of the time no particular purpose is served by making this distinction.

Statements may be classified by whether they are *simple* or *compound*. Without trying to define a simple statement (examples are, "It is raining," "I do," and "This course is easy") we can describe a compound statement as being compounded of one or more other statements using the *logical connectives* "and," "or," "not," and "if—then." Examples of compound statements are, "It is raining *and* I am getting wet," "*Either* it is raining *or* someone has turned on the sprinklers," "*It is not true that* this is an easy course," and "*If* I do, *then* I'll regret it later."

We shall discuss the first three of these logical connectives only briefly but shall discuss the "if—then" connective in greater detail since it is the one of most frequent application in mathematics.

THE CONNECTIVE *And*

Given two statements A and B (which may be either simple or compound) we may use them to form the statement

A and *B*

The compound statement "*A* and *B*" is true or false depending upon the truth or falsity of statements *A* and *B* as shown in the following table.

A	B	A and B
True	True	True
False	True	False
True	False	False
False	False	False

The statement "*A* and *B*" is therefore true only when both *A* and *B* are themselves true.

THE CONNECTIVE *Or*

If *A* and *B* are statements, then we can use them to form the compound statement

$$A \text{ or } B$$

As the mathematician uses this connective, the truth or falsity of the compound statement "*A* or *B*" is determined by the truth or falsity of the statements *A* and *B* as shown in the following table.

A	B	A or B
True	True	True
False	True	True
True	False	True
False	False	False

Hence for the mathematician the statement "*A* or *B*" is false only when *A* and *B* are themselves both false and is true in all other cases. Used in this way the connective *or* is called the *inclusive or*.

The other, nonmathematical, use of the connective *or* is called the *exclusive or*. When the connective *or* is used in the exclusive sense, the truth or falsity of the statement "*A* or *B*" is determined by the truth or falsity of the statements *A* and *B* as shown in the following table.

A	B	A or B (exclusive)
True	True	False
False	True	True
True	False	True
False	False	False

The difference between these two uses of the connective *or* is therefore seen to be that when using the *inclusive or* the statement "$2 + 2 = 4$ or $3 + 3 = 6$" is regarded as true, while this statement would be regarded as false if the *exclusive or* were being used.

THE NEGATION CONNECTIVE

Given a statement A we can form the compound statement

$$\text{Not } A$$

Obviously the statements A and Not A have opposite truth value; that is, if A is true, then Not A is false and if A is false, then Not A is true.

A	*Not A*
True	False
False	True

Let us remark while we are here that the negation of the statement "A and B" is the statement "Not A or Not B" and that the negation of the statement "A or B" is the statement "Not A and Not B."

Review Questions

1. What is the difference between a statement and a sentence?
2. What is the difference between the *inclusive or* and the *exclusive or*? Which is used in mathematics?
3. In terms of the truth or falsity of statements A and B, when is the statement "A and B" true? When is the statement "A or B" true? When is the statement "Not A" true? When is "A and B" false? When is "A or B" false? When is "Not A" false?

Exercises

1. Which of the following statements are true?
    (a) $2 + 2 = 5$ and $3 + 4 = 7$.
    (b) $2 + 2 = 4$ and $3 + 4 = 7$.
    (c) $2 + 2 = 5$ and $3 + 4 = 9$.
    (d) $2 + 2 = 4$ and $3 + 4 = 9$.
    (e) $2 + 2 = 5$ or $3 + 4 = 7$.
    (f) $2 + 2 = 4$ or $3 + 4 = 7$.
    (g) $2 + 2 = 5$ or $3 + 4 = 9$.
    (h) $2 + 2 = 4$ or $3 + 4 = 9$.
    (i) $2 + 2 = 5$ or dogs bark.
    (j) Dogs bark or $2 + 2 = 7$.
    (k) $6 = 4$ or $6 = 5$.
    (l) $2 + 3 = 3 + 2$ or $2 + 3 \neq 3 + 2$.
    (m) 2 is less than 4 or 2 is greater than 4.
    (n) 2 is less than 3 or 2 is equal to 3.
    (o) 2 is less than 2 or 2 is equal to 2.
2. If we were to say, "By definition a statement is either true or false," would we be using the *inclusive or* or the *exclusive or*?

The Connective *If — Then*

If A and B are statements, they can be used to form the compound statement

If A, then B

Such compound statements are called *implications*. The statement A in the implication

If A, then B

is called the *hypothesis* of the implication and the statement B is called the *conclusion* of the implication. For example, given the statements

It is raining

and

Dogs generally have only one head

we can form two implications:

If it is raining, then dogs generally have only one head

and

If dogs generally have only one head, then it is raining

The truth or falsity of an implication can be determined from the truth or falsity of the hypothesis and conclusion as shown in the following table.

A	B	*If A, then B*
True	True	True
False	True	True
True	False	False
False	False	True

This table shows that an implication is true in all cases except when the hypothesis is true and the conclusion is false. The reader should pay particular attention to the fact that an implication is true whenever its hypothesis is false.

Implications are of the utmost importance in mathematics and occur probably more often than any other kind of statement. The reason for this is that, as a rule, theorems (which are the stuff of which mathematics is made) are stated in the form of implications. Now since implications, like all other statements, are either true or false, it must follow that one of the most important and useful abilities a mathematician may possess is the ability to prove the truth of implications. Thus we come to the question, how does one go about proving that an implication is true? We shall discuss the notion of proof in more detail in a later section, but for now it will suffice to say that to prove that an implication is true means to supply a convincing argument that the truth of the conclusion follows logically from the assumption of the truth of the hypothesis. The reader should pay particular attention to the fact that in the last sentence we did not say that this proof is a convincing argument that the truth of the conclusion follows from the truth of the hypothesis, we said only that the truth of the conclusion should follow from the *assumption* of the truth of hypothesis. Mathematics is the game of assuming one statement is true and, by using this as a hypothesis, trying to establish the truth of some other statement.

THE CONVERSE OF AN IMPLICATION

Given an implication

$$\text{If } A, \text{ then } B$$

we can form another implication by interchanging the hypothesis and conclusion; namely we form the implication

$$\text{If } B, \text{ then } A$$

The second implication is called the *converse* of the first. For example, the converse of

$$\text{If } 2 + 3 = 5, \text{ then the moon is made of Camembert}$$

is

$$\text{If the moon is made of Camembert, then } 2 + 3 = 5$$

If one implication is the converse of a second implication, then the second is also the converse of the first.

Suppose that the implication "If A, then B" is a true statement. The converse of this implication need not be true. The converse of the true statement

$$\text{If it will rain, then we will delay the picnic}$$

is false, while the converse of the true statement

$$\text{If a square has a side of length 3 inches, then its area is 9 square inches}$$

is true.

THE CONTRAPOSITIVE OF AN IMPLICATION

Given the implication

$$\text{If } A, \text{ then } B$$

we can form another implication by interchanging and at the same time negating the hypothesis and conclusion:

$$\text{If not } B, \text{ then not } A$$

The new implication thus formed is called the *contrapositive* of the original implication. For example, the contrapositive of

$$\text{If } 2 + 3 = 5, \text{ then the moon is made of Camembert}$$

is

$$\text{If the moon is not made of Camembert, then } 2 + 3 \neq 5$$

If one implication is the contrapositive of a second, then the second implication is also the contrapositive of the first.

We saw that the truth or falsity of the converse of a given implication did not in general bear any relation to the truth or falsity of the given implication. In contrast to this, the truth or falsity of the contrapositive of a given implication is completely determined by the truth or falsity of the given implication. In particular, a given implication and its contrapositive have exactly the same truth value; that is, the contrapositive of a given implication is true exactly when the implication itself is true. In Exercise 5 we guide the reader through a verification of this fact.

LOGICAL EQUIVALENCE

We are especially interested in true implications whose converses are also true. The statement

$$\text{If } 5 = 6, \text{ then } 6 = 5$$

is an example of such an implication. If both implications "If A, then B" and "If B, then A" are true, then we say that the statements A and B are *logically equivalent* and write "A if and only if B." The statements "$5 = 6$" and "$6 = 5$" are logically equivalent, and so we can write "$5 = 6$ if and only if $6 = 5$."

The "if and only if" statement can be regarded as a way of combining two implications into one statement; that is, the statement

$$A \text{ if and only if } B$$

is the combination into one statement of the two implications

$$\text{If } A, \text{ then } B \quad \text{ and } \quad \text{If } B, \text{ then } A$$

EXAMPLE.   The statement "The area of a square is 9 square inches if and only if the length of its side is 3 inches" can be regarded as the combination into one statement of the two implications "If the area of a square is 9 square inches, then the length of its side is 3 inches" and "If the length of the side of a square is 3 inches, then its area is 9 square inches." The two statements "The area of the square is 9 square inches" and "The length of the side of the square is 3 inches" are logically equivalent statements.

Review Questions

1. What is an implication?
2. What is the hypothesis and what is the conclusion of an implication? How can you distinguish between them?

3. What is the converse of an implication? What is the contrapositive of an implication?
4. Is the converse of a true implication true?
5. What is the connection between the truth or falsity of an implication and the truth or falsity of its contrapositive?
6. What does it mean to say that two statements are logically equivalent? What statement expresses the fact that statements A and B are logically equivalent?
7. Every "if and only if" statement gives rise to two different but related implications. How are these two implications related to one another?

Exercises

1. Each of the following statements can be rephrased as a statement of the form "If ... , then ... ." Do this.
   (a) I'll pass the exam tomorrow, if I study.
   (b) $2 + 2 = 4$ implies $3 + 5 = 8$.
   (c) $3 + 4 = 7$ is implied by $2 + 2 = 18$.
   (d) $3 + 3 = 7$ when $4 = 5$.
   (e) When $3 + 5 = 1$, then $3 = 17$.
2. Identify the two implications of which each of these statements is the combination. Are these implications true? Are the given statements true?
   (a) A dog has at least four legs if and only if $6 = 6$.
   (b) A dog has at least three legs if and only if $6 \neq 6$.
   (c) It will rain if and only if the ground gets wet.
3. Consider the following statements.
     (i) B if and only if A.
    (ii) Not A if and only if not B.
   (iii) B if and only if not A.
    (iv) Not A if and only if B.
     (v) Not B if and only if not A.
    (vi) Not B if and only if A.

   (a) Which of these statements are equivalent to "A if and only if B."
   (b) Which of them are equivalent to "A if and only if not B."
4. Write out the converse and the contrapositive of each of the following implications. Compare the truth or falsity of each implication with the truth or falsity of its converse and of its contrapositive.
   (a) If it will rain, then the lawn will get wet.
   (b) If two distinct straight lines intersect, then they have at most one point in common.
   (c) If two distinct straight lines intersect, then they have exactly one point in common.
5. Consider the implication "If A, then B" and its contrapositive "If not B, then not A."
   (a) The contrapositive implication is false when not B is true and not A is false and is true otherwise. Explain.
   (b) The contrapositive implication is false when B is false and A is true and is true otherwise. Explain.
   (c) The given implication is false when A is true and B is false and is true otherwise. Explain.

(d) Both the given implication and the contrapositive implication are false when *A* is true and *B* is false and are true otherwise. Explain.

A REMARK ABOUT DEFINITIONS

Although definitions are not always stated in the "if and only if" form, it is nevertheless true that definitions are by their very nature statements of this form. Consider the following definition of *square*.

A square is a rectangle whose sides are equal in length.

This definition is poorly stated because the definition does not explicitly tell us that a square is the *only* kind of rectangle whose sides are of equal length. This definition is better phrased as follows:

A rectangle is a square if and only if its sides are of equal length.

This formulation of the definition of square in terms of rectangle explicitly exhibits the "if and only if" form and makes it very clear that a square is distinguished from all other rectangles in that the sides of a square are of equal length. Other examples of definitions phrased in the "if and only if" form are

Definition of Even Number *A number is called an even number if and only if that number is exactly divisible by two.*

Definition of the Center of a Circle *A point is the center of a circle if and only if that point is equidistant from every point of the circle.*

Frequently definitions are not put into the "if and only if" form for reasons of clarity or style. It should be kept in mind, however, that phrased in the "if and only if" form or not, all definitions are of this form and can be so phrased if one desires to do so.

Exercises

1. Give a definition in the "if and only if" form for
    (a) rectangle in terms of parallelogram.
    (b) equilateral triangle in terms of triangle.
    (c) digit in terms of less than ten.
2. Rephrase each of these definitions using the "if and only if" form.
    (a) Epsilon: The fifth letter of the Greek alphabet.
    (b) Icosahedron: A polyhedron having twenty faces.
    (c) Factor: To say that a number *n* is a factor of a number *m* means that *m* is equal to *n* multiplied by some other number.

Mathematical Proof

Let us suppose now that we are engaged in a study of some area of mathematics and that we have identified an implication that for one reason or another we believe is probably a theorem.* The next step is to try to find a proof that this implication is true. We must somehow verify that the truth of the conclusion of this implication follows logically from the assumption of the truth of its hypothesis. There are two methods by which we might do this. The first is called the method of *direct proof* and the second the method of *indirect proof*. Because we will not become actively concerned with the method of indirect proof until Chapter 4, we will delay the discussion of this method of proof until that time. The method of direct proof will be used in the next chapter and so we will discuss this method now.

To establish the truth of an implication by the method of direct proof we proceed as follows: Starting with the assumption of the truth of the hypothesis we somehow find a sequence of true statements which provides a logical path leading from the assumption of the truth of the hypothesis to the truth of the conclusion. The truth of each of these statements must follow from known true statements in the deductive system in which we are working. Thus the truth of these statements must follow logically from (1) axioms, (2) previously proven theorems, or (3) definitions of defined concepts. Here is a sample of the form such a direct proof might take when we write it out.

Theorem   *If A, then B.*
Hypothesis: A.
Conclusion: B.
The Proof: (by direct method)

Statements of the Proof	*Justifications of the Statements of the Proof*
(1) *A*	(1) Hypothesis
(2) Statement	(2) This statement follows logically from (1) by virtue of an axiom
(3) Statement	(3) This statement follows logically from (2) by virtue of a previously proven theorem
(4) Statement	(4) This statement follows logically from (3) by virtue of the definition of one of the defined concepts
(5) *B*	(5) The conclusion *B* follows logically from (4) by virtue of an axiom

END OF PROOF

* We say that this statement is an implication because most theorems are stated as implications. Those theorems which are not stated as implications can be rephrased as implications if we want to do this.

Such a proof may consist of any number of steps but it will always have the same general appearance. The first step will be the hypothesis of the implication to be proved and the last step will be the conclusion of this implication. The intermediate steps will consist of true statements each of which is true by virtue of an axiom, a previously proven theorem, or a definition of one of the defined concepts.

If the reader will think back to his high school geometry course, he will recall that the proving of theorems in this way comprised a substantial part of that course. We shall see a number of these proofs in the next chapter, so if the notion of direct proof is not completely clear in the reader's mind we urge him to be patient—the examination of a few concrete examples of such proofs will cause these ideas to fall into place.

Universal Statements

Statements of the form

All *A*'s are *B*'s

are called *universal* statements. For example, the statements

All men are mortal

and

All true implications have true contrapositives

are universal statements. Universal statements may be found phrased in other ways too. The following are different phrasings of the statement "All *A*'s are *B*'s."

1. Every *A* is a *B*.
2. If a thing is an *A*, then that thing is a *B*.
3. Whenever a thing is an *A*, then that thing is a *B*.
4. There are no *A*'s which are not *B*'s.
5. No matter which *A* we consider, it is a *B*.

EXAMPLE.   The universal statement "All men are mortal" may be rephrased as

1. Every man is mortal.
2. If a thing is a man, then that thing is mortal.
3. Whenever a thing is a man, then that thing is mortal.
4. There are no men who are not mortal.
5. No matter which man we consider, that man is mortal.

Consider the universal statement

All numbers divisible by 2 are also divisible by 4

This statement can be proved false simply by finding a number which is divisible by 2 but not by 4. The number 6 is such a number. The number 6 is said to be an example counter to the assertion made by the statement and is therefore called a *counterexample* to the statement. The statement

All numbers are even

is false and to prove this it is sufficient to exhibit an example counter to the assertion made by the statement. The number 3 is not an even number and is therefore a counterexample to the statement.

It should be clearly understood that the exhibition of a *single* counterexample is all that is required to prove a universal statement false. The exhibition of additional counterexamples cannot add to the falsity of what is already a false statement.

In contrast to this, the exhibition of an instance of the truth of a universal statement does not prove the statement true. To exhibit examples wherein the statement

All implications have converses

is true is irrelevant insofar as establishing the truth or falsity of the statement is concerned. Indeed to show that there are sixty trillion implications which have converses does not contribute at all toward proving that the statement is true. To prove that the universal statement "All A's are B's" is true, it is necessary to prove somehow that the statement is true in every possible case; that is, it is necessary to prove that every single A *without exception* is also a B.

Exercises

1. Rephrase each of the following statements in the five other ways mentioned.
   (a) All theorems have proofs.
   (b) All axioms are assumed truths.
   (c) All true implications have true contrapositives.
2. Prove that each of these statements is false.
   (a) Every member of your immediate family has blue hair.
   (b) If there is a page of this book which contains the letter e, then that page also contains the number 67 mentioned somewhere on it.
   (c) The first name of every president of the United States between 1790 and 1890 was George.

Existential Statements

Statements of the form

Some A's are B's

are called *existential* statements. The statements

Some men are good

and

Some true implications have true converses

are existential statements. Existential statements may be phrased in other ways which include the following:

1. At least one *A* is a *B*.
2. One or more *A* is a *B*.
3. A few *A*'s are *B*'s.
4. There exists an *A* which is a *B*.

It is from the phrasing of (4) that the name *existential* derives.

EXAMPLE. The existential statement "Some men are good" may be rephrased as:

1. At least one man is good.
2. One or more men are good.
3. A few men are good.
4. There exists a man who is good.

Observe that the words *some* and *few* have exactly the same meaning as *at least one*. Also, to say that some *A*'s are *B*'s does not preclude the possibility that *all A*'s are *B*'s. For example, to say that some mathematicians are educated does not rule out the possibility that all mathematicians are educated.

To prove that an existential statement is true it is necessary only to exhibit one example of the truth of the assertion made by the statement. The existential statement

> Some true implications have true converses

is proved true by the exhibition of one true implication which has a true converse. The exhibition of the implication

> If two distinct straight lines intersect, then
> they have exactly one point in common

therefore proves the existential statement true.

On the other hand, exhibiting an instance of the falsity of an existential statement does nothing toward proving the statement is either true or false. Thus to give an example of a true implication whose converse is false does nothing toward proving that the statement

> Some true implications have true converses

is either true or false. To prove that the existential statement "Some *A*'s are *B*'s" is false it is necessary to verify somehow that no matter which *A* one considers, *A* is not a *B*. One must verify that the statement is false in every possible instance.

Exercises

1. Rephrase each of the following statements in the four other ways mentioned.
    (a) Some concepts are undefined.

    (b) Some implications have false converses.

    (c) Some girls have red hair.

2. Prove each of the following statements is true.

    (a) Some numbers are even.

    (b) Some universal statements are false.

    (c) Some universal statements are true.

    (d) Some existential statements are true.

    (e) Some true implications have true contrapositives.

    (f) Some numbers which are less than 10 are less than 5.

Equations

There are many different kinds of equations but in this book we are going to be concerned with only three kinds of equations.

ABSOLUTE EQUATIONS

An *absolute equation* is a true statement of equality between numbers. Examples of absolute equations are

$$5 = 2 + 3$$
$$6 + 1 = 4 + 3$$
$$10 - 9 = 2 - 1$$

CONDITIONAL EQUATIONS

Conditional equations differ from absolute equations in that they involve what we are going to call *unspecified numerals*. Examples of conditional equalities are

$$2 + n = 6$$
$$x - 3 = 7$$
$$2a - 6 = a + 1$$

In each of these equations the letter is not meant to represent any special number but instead is used to represent an unspecified number. In a sense the letter occupies a place into which we may put any number we desire. It is because each conditional equation contains this unspecified numeral that a conditional equation is neither true nor false. However, a conditional equation will yield true or false statements upon specification of the unspecified numeral. For example, if we specify that the unspecified numeral in the conditional equation

$$2 + n = 6$$

should represent the number 5, then the statement which results, $2 + 5 = 6$, is a false statement. On the other hand, if we specify that n should represent the number 4, then the statement which results, $2 + 4 = 6$, is true. The reason these equations are called *conditional* equations is that whether or not they give rise to true statements is conditional upon the proper specification of the unspecified numeral.

Some conditional equations possess *solutions*. By a solution of a conditional equation we mean a specification of the unspecified numeral which gives rise to a true statement. For example, we have already seen that the number 4 is a solution of the conditional equation $2 + n = 6$.

Some conditional equations do not have any solutions and others have many different solutions. The conditional equation

$$n + 1 = n + 2$$

does not have any solutions. That is to say, there is no specification of the unspecified numeral n for which this equation will produce a true statement. On the other hand, the equation

$$(n - 3)(n - 2)(n - 1)(n) = 0$$

has four different solutions. If the numeral n were to represent any one of the numbers 0, 1, 2, or 3, then the resulting statement would be true.

IDENTITIES

An *identity* is a conditional equation which yields a true statement for all possible specifications of the unspecified numeral. Thus every number is a solution of an identity. The conditional equation

$$n + 2 = 2 + n$$

yields a true statement no matter which number n represents and is therefore an identity.

Identities play a very important role in mathematics and we shall see quite a few of them. Most of these will involve more than one unspecified numeral. For example, the conditional equation

$$n + m = m + n$$

is an identity because no matter which numbers the numerals n and m represent the resulting statement is true.

Review Questions

1. What is an absolute equation?
2. What is a conditional equation, and why is it called that?
3. What is an identity?
4. Are all equations true statements? Can an equation be neither true nor false?
5. What is meant by a solution of an equation?

Exercises

1. Label the following equations by whether they are absolute equations, conditional equations which have solutions, or conditional equations which have no solutions. Are any of these equations identities?

   (a) $2 + n = n + 2$.
   (b) $3 + 5 = 5 + n$.
   (c) $2 \times n = 8$.
   (d) $n \times 2 = n$.

   (e) $4 - n = 4$.
   (f) $15 + 5 = 20$.
   (g) $n \times 1 = n + 1$.
   (h) $n \times m = m \times n$.

CHAPTER 2

The System of Counting Numbers

We begin our study of arithmetic with the most elementary class of numbers, the *counting numbers*. In the first section we use these numbers to discuss one of the major concepts of mathematics, the concept of a *relation*.

A second major concept of mathematics is that of an *operation*. This idea is discussed in the remainder of the chapter, starting with the second section. In this section we discuss, on an intuitive level, the operations of addition and multiplication of the counting numbers. The properties of an operation are then introduced in terms of these familiar examples.

The third section introduces the concept of the *deductive system of counting numbers* and lays the foundations for a development of this system. These foundations are discussed and a few theorems are proved to demonstrate how true statements are verified in a deductive system.

In the fourth section subtraction and division of counting numbers are defined and investigated within the framework of the deductive system we have previously defined.

Finally, in the fifth section we examine the general concept of a binary operation using the two arithmetic operations already discussed as models. Numerous examples of binary operations are investigated.

The purpose of this chapter is therefore threefold. First, we want to discuss some of the specific relations and operations of the arithmetic of the counting numbers. Second, we use these familiar ideas to study the general ideas of relation and operation. Third, we lay the foundations for a deductive system and carry out a short program of typical mathematical investigations within that deductive system. The last objective provides some insight into the nature of mathematics as a science.

EQUALITY OF COUNTING NUMBERS AND OTHER RELATIONS

The *counting numbers* are the simplest kind of numbers in the sense that it is from these numbers that all other numbers are derived. Their most common symbolic names are 0, 1, 2, 3, ...* We shall not define these numbers even though it is possible to do so. This will cause no difficulty because we are all as familiar with these numbers as we are with our own names.

Equality of Counting Numbers

Equality is one of the most frequently used concepts in mathematics and therefore deserves our immediate attention. Most often equality, symbolized by $=$, is used in the following way. *If A and B are symbols representing some quantity or thing, then to write A = B means that A and B are names for the identical quantity or thing.* For example,

Sacramento $=$ Capitol of California	(Equality of cities)
$1 = 6 - 5$	(Equality of numbers)
Memorial day $=$ Decoration day	(Equality of days)

This is the way equality is used in mathematics.

The concept of equality of counting numbers is so primitive an idea that it may appear difficult to find much to say about it. However, every use to which this concept will be put in our study of the counting numbers can be justified by using one or more of three particular properties called the *reflexive*, *symmetric*, and *transitive* properties of equality of counting numbers. As he reads the statements of these properties the reader will find that he is already familiar with them.

The Reflexive Property *No matter which counting number the numeral n represents, $n = n$.*

This statement says that $0 = 0, 1 = 1, 2 = 2, 3 = 3, 4 = 4$, and so on.

The Symmetric Property *No matter which counting numbers the numerals n and m represent, if $n = m$, then $m = n$.*

This statement says that, for example, since $6 = 2 \times 3$ it is true that $2 \times 3 = 6$. It may be interpreted as saying that a statement of equality of counting numbers may be read from left to right ($n = m$) or from right to left ($m = n$).

The Transitive Property *No matter which counting numbers the numerals n, m, and p represent, if $n = m$ and if $m = p$, then $n = p$.*

For example, according to this property if we know that $2 \times 3 = 6$ and that $6 = 4 + 2$, then we may conclude that $2 \times 3 = 4 + 2$. This property may be verbalized as "Things equal to the same thing are equal to each other."

---

* The three dots following the symbol 3 comprise what is called the *ellipsis symbol*. The mathematician uses this symbol to instruct the reader to continue to list the numbers in the indicated way without stopping. They might be interpreted as meaning "etc."

The terminology here is not standardized. Some books do not call zero a counting number.

Generalizing the Concept of Equality

The concept of equality of counting numbers is in itself simple enough. But equality is only one specific instance of a much more general idea, the concept of *relation*. Relations play a large part in our study of arithmetic and provide a most important unifying device by means of which we can tie together many apparently separate ideas. Roughly speaking, a relation on a collection of objects is a way of comparing objects in that collection.

Let us begin by considering the collection of all people and discussing some of the ways that members of this collection may be compared. If *A* and *B* represent two people (members of the collection of all people), then we may ask whether or not

1. *A* is related to *B* in that *A* is the father of *B*,
2. *A* is related to *B* in that *A* is the mother of *B*,
3. *A* is related to *B* in that *A* is the sister of *B*,
4. *A* is related to *B* in that *A* is taller than *B*.

These are just four of the many ways in which two people may be compared. Each of these ways of comparing two people is called a *relation*. Let us look at some specific examples.

Consider the family tree in Fig. 1. This family tree is somewhat unusual in that the height of each member of the family has been recorded. Consider now the relation of "is the father of" defined on the collection of people in this family tree. Which of these people are related by this relation?

John is related to Will by the relation "is the father of"
John is related to Mary by the relation "is the father of"
Will is related to Hank by the relation "is the father of"
Hank is related to Nancy by the relation "is the father of"
Hank is related to Jim by the relation "is the father of"
Hank is related to Nick by the relation "is the father of"

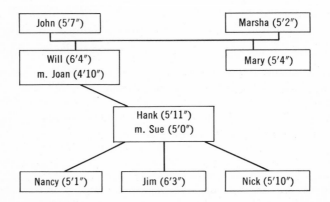

Figure 1

We can simplify these statements by introducing some symbolism. Let us use the symbol $\mathfrak{F}$ to denote the relation "is the father of." Then these six statements can be written in the form

$$\text{John} \quad \mathfrak{F} \quad \text{Will}$$
$$\text{John} \quad \mathfrak{F} \quad \text{Mary}$$
$$\text{Will} \quad \mathfrak{F} \quad \text{Hank}$$
$$\text{Hank} \quad \mathfrak{F} \quad \text{Nancy}$$
$$\text{Hank} \quad \mathfrak{F} \quad \text{Jim}$$
$$\text{Hank} \quad \mathfrak{F} \quad \text{Nick}$$

The symbol John $\mathfrak{F}$ Will means that John is the father of Will or that John is related to Will by the relation "is the father of." Hank $\mathfrak{F}$ Jim means that Hank is father of Jim, and so on.

If we next use the symbol $\mathfrak{M}$ to denote the relation "is the mother of," then we can list all the pairs of people who are related by this relation:

$$\text{Marsha} \quad \mathfrak{M} \quad \text{Will}$$
$$\text{Marsha} \quad \mathfrak{M} \quad \text{Mary}$$
$$\text{Joan} \quad \mathfrak{M} \quad \text{Hank}$$
$$\text{Sue} \quad \mathfrak{M} \quad \text{Nancy}$$
$$\text{Sue} \quad \mathfrak{M} \quad \text{Jim}$$
$$\text{Sue} \quad \mathfrak{M} \quad \text{Nick}$$

Marsha is related to Will by the relation "is the mother of," and so on.

If the symbol $\mathfrak{J}$ denotes the relation of "is taller than," then the following symbols state that the people mentioned are related by this relation:

$$\text{John} \quad \mathfrak{J} \quad \text{Marsha}$$
$$\text{Will} \quad \mathfrak{J} \quad \text{John}$$
$$\text{Will} \quad \mathfrak{J} \quad \text{Hank}$$

If $\mathfrak{G}$ represents the relation of "is the grandmother of," then Marsha $\mathfrak{G}$ Hank is true since Marsha is the grandmother of Hank. However, Marsha $\mathfrak{G}$ Will is false since Marsha is not the grandmother of Will. In this case we would write Marsha $\not\mathfrak{G}$ Will to indicate that Marsha is *not* related to Will by this relation. If $\mathfrak{J}$ represents "is taller than," then Nancy $\not\mathfrak{J}$ Jim since Nancy is *not* taller than Jim.

Observe that no person in the family tree is related to himself (herself) by any of the relations discussed above. Thus, for example, John is not related to himself by the relation of "is taller than" or by the relation of "is the father of." However, if the relation is "is no taller than," then John is related to himself for certainly John is no taller than himself. Thus if $\mathfrak{R}$ represents the relation of "is no taller than," then each of these statements is true:

$$\text{John} \quad \mathfrak{R} \quad \text{John}$$
$$\text{Mary} \quad \mathfrak{R} \quad \text{Mary}$$
$$\text{Nancy} \quad \mathfrak{R} \quad \text{Nancy}$$
$$\text{Nick} \quad \mathfrak{R} \quad \text{Nick}$$

Exercises

1. If $\mathcal{Y}$ represents the relation of "is younger than," find four pairs of people from the family tree such that $n \mathcal{Y} m$. Find four pairs of people such that $n \not{\mathcal{Y}} m$. Is it possible that there might be a person n such that $n \mathcal{Y} n$?
2. Find four pairs of people from the family tree such that $n \mathcal{S} m$ if $\mathcal{S}$ represents the relation of "is shorter than." Find three pairs of people such that $n \not{\mathcal{S}} m$. Is it ever possible that $n \mathcal{S} m$ if n and m represent the same person?
3. Find all possible pairs of people from the family tree such that $n \mathcal{R} m$ if $\mathcal{R}$ represents the relation "is taller than but not more than two inches taller than."

We see that whenever objects are compared with one another, a relation is involved. We have just finished comparing the members of a certain family, the basis for the comparisons being certain ancestral relationships, height, and so on. Here are some more examples.

EXAMPLE 1.   During football season one is likely to hear statements like, "Peterson is a better quarterback than Standouski." This is a comparison between quarterbacks, and the relation involved is, "is a better quarterback than." If $\mathcal{R}$ is used to denote this relation, then the original statement can be symbolized by

Peterson $\mathcal{R}$ Standouski

EXAMPLE 2.   When more than one section of a certain course is offered, one is likely to hear statements like, "Take the course from Dr. Smith because he is an easier grader than Dr. Henderson." The relation involved here is, "is an easier grader than," and the objects with which the relation deals are the instructors teaching a certain course. Denoting this relation by the symbol $\mathcal{R}$, the statement quoted above is conveniently symbolized by

Dr. Smith $\mathcal{R}$ Dr. Henderson

Some Mathematical Relations

Just as there are many relations between people, there are many relations between counting numbers. A relation between counting numbers that we have already discussed is the relation of *equality of counting numbers*. When we say that two counting numbers n and m are equal, we mean that n is related to m in that n is equal to m. Thus 6 and 2×3 are related and we, in the spirit of the previous paragraphs, could write $6 \, \mathcal{E} \, 2 \times 3$, where the symbol $\mathcal{E}$ represents the relation of equality. Since equality is so frequently used, we have chosen the special symbol $=$ to represent it. Thus instead of writing $6 \, \mathcal{E} \, 2 \times 3$ and remembering the $\mathcal{E}$ means equality, we write $6 = 2 \times 3$. Here are some other relations on the collection of counting numbers, the first two of which are important enough to have been given special symbols.

The Relation of Less Than   *If n and m are counting numbers, we say that n is less than m, and write $n < m$, if there is a nonzero counting number p such that $n + p = m$.*

For example, 3 is less than 5 (3 < 5), since there is the nonzero counting number 2, and $3 + 2 = 5$. On the other hand, 6 is not less than 5 (6 ≮ 5), since there is no nonzero counting number p such that $6 + p = 5$. Also, 5 ≮ 5 since there is no nonzero counting number p such that $5 + p = 5$. Thus 3 is related to 5 by this relation, 6 is not related to 5 by this relation, and 5 is not related to itself by this relation.

The Relation of Greater Than *If n and m are counting numbers, we say that n is greater than m, and write n > m, if there is a nonzero counting number p such that n = m + p.*

For example, 5 > 4 and 5 > 0, but 6 ≯ 7 and 6 ≯ 6.

The Relation of Equal to One More Than *If n and m are counting numbers, we say that n is equal to one more than m if n = m + 1.*

Thus 5 is equal to one more than 4 and 6 is equal to one more than 5, but 7 is not equal to one more than 8. If we let $\Re$ represent this relation, then we can symbolize these statements by the symbols 5 $\Re$ 4, 6 $\Re$ 5, and 7 $\not\Re$ 8. This relation is not a standard one and there is no special symbol to represent it.

Exercises

1. Consider the relation "is less than" for the collection of all counting numbers.
    (a) Are there any counting numbers related to themselves by this relation? That is, is it ever true that $n < n$?
    (b) Is it possible to find counting numbers n and m such that both $n < m$ and $m < n$?
2. Consider the relation "is greater than" for the collection of all counting numbers. Answer parts (a) and (b) of Exercise 1 for this relation.
3. Consider the relation "is equal to one more than" for the collection of all counting numbers. Answer parts (a) and (b) of Exercise 1 for this relation.

The Properties of a Relation

The relation *equality of counting numbers* possesses the properties of reflexivity, symmetry, and transitivity. It is reasonable to ask if it might be meaningful for an arbitrary relation to possess some of these properties. Below are the statements of these properties in terms of an unspecified relation on an unspecified collection of objects. The symbol $\Re$ represents the unspecified relation.

The Reflexive Property *No matter which object the symbol n represents, n $\Re$ n.*

The Symmetric Property *No matter which objects the symbols n and m represent, if n $\Re$ m, then m $\Re$ n.*

The Transitive Property *No matter which objects the symbols n, m, and p represent, if n $\Re$ m and m $\Re$ p, then n $\Re$ p.*

The reader should compare these properties with the corresponding properties of equality to see that they are the same as the properties originally given for equality when the relation ℛ is specified to be equality and the collection of objects to be the collection of counting numbers. That is, replace the symbol ℛ in the above statements with the symbol = and compare with the statements on page 23.

Let us examine some of the nonmathematical relations mentioned earlier to see which properties they possess.

EXAMPLE 1.   If we consider the collection of all people and the relation "is the father of," then the three properties of reflexivity, symmetry, and transitivity when phrased for this relation look like this:

Reflexivity.   No matter which person n represents, n is the father of n.

Symmetry.   No matter which people n and m represent, if n is the father of m, then m is the father of n.

Transitivity.   No matter which people n, m, and p represent, if n is the father of m and if m is the father of p, then n is the father of p.

None of these properties is possessed by this relation, for not one of these statements is true. In order to show that this relation is not reflexive, it suffices to find one person who is not his own father. The reader is such a person. In order to show that this relation is not symmetric, it is only necessary to find one pair of people such that n is the father of m but m is not the father of n. Noah and Shem provide such an example. To show that the relation is not transitive we need only find three people n, m, and p such that n is the father of m and m is the father of p, but n is not the father of p. We leave it to the reader to provide a counterexample to the transitivity of this relation.

EXAMPLE 2.   Again consider the collection of all people. Let the relation be "is an ancestor of." Here are the statements of the three properties phrased for this relation:

Reflexivity.   No matter which person n represents, n is an ancestor of n.

Symmetry.   No matter which people n and m represent, if n is an ancestor of m, then m is an ancestor of n.

Transitivity.   No matter which people n, m, and p represent, if n is an ancestor of m and if m is an ancestor of p, then n is an ancestor of p.

The first property, reflexivity, is not possessed by this relation and all that is needed to show this is to find one person who is not an ancestor of himself. Since the reader is not an ancestor of himself, we have found such an example. To show that this relation is not symmetric we need to find two people such that one of them is an ancestor of the other, but not vice versa. Henry I and Henry II of England provide such a counterexample. To show that the relation is transitive it is necessary to show that whenever n is an ancestor of m and m is an ancestor of p, then it is necessarily true that n is an ancestor of p. But in view of the meaning of the word *ancestor* this is obvious. Therefore the only property possessed by this relation is that of transitivity.

EXAMPLE 3.   Again consider the collection of all people. The relation is "loves." Here are the three statements written out in full:

Reflexivity.   No matter which person *n* represents, *n* loves *n*.

Symmetry.   No matter which people *n* and *m* represent, if *n* loves *m*, then *m* loves *n*.

Transitivity.   No matter which people *n*, *m*, and *p* represent if *n* loves *m* and if *m* loves *p*, then *n* loves *p*.

Which of these are true statements? Certainly the reader can think of examples which make the second and third statements false. Sydney Carton loved Miss Manette, but Miss Manette did not love Carton. This example shows that the relation of "loves" is not symmetric. (Love would be of considerably less interest to authors if it were symmetric!) The reader can find counterexamples which show that this relation is not transitive. But is this relation reflexive? If we believe that *every* person loves himself, then the relation is reflexive. However, if we believe that there is *at least one* person who does not love himself, then we would have to conclude that this relation is not reflexive.

Exercises

1. Consider the collection of all people and the relation "is older than" defined on this collection. Denote this relation by ℛ. Then to write *n* ℛ *m* means that *n* is older than *m* and to write *n* ⊄ *m* means that *n* is not older than *m*, which is the same as saying that *n* is the same age or younger than *m*.
    (a)   As in Examples 1, 2, and 3 immediately preceding these exercises, write out the statements of reflexivity, symmetry, and transitivity for this relation.
    (b)   Which of the statements in part (a) are true? Explain, giving counterexamples where appropriate. Which of the properties of reflexivity, symmetry, and transitivity are possessed by this relation?
2. Consider the collection of all people and the relation "is the son of" defined on this collection.
    (a)   As in the examples immediately preceding these exercises, write out the statements of reflexivity, symmetry, and transitivity for this relation.
    (b)   Which of the statements in part (a) are true? Give counterexamples where appropriate.
3. Consider the collection of all people and the relation "is the sister of" defined on this collection. Which of the three properties of reflexivity, symmetry, and transitivity are possessed by this relation? Give counterexamples where appropriate.
4. Consider the collection of all people and the relation "has not less money but has less than one dollar more than" defined on this collection. Denote this relation by ℛ.
    (a)   If George has $23.00 and Harry has $23.00, is George ℛ Harry?
    (b)   If Slim has $16.50 and Bill has $16.00, is Slim ℛ Bill? Is Bill ℛ Slim?
    (c)   From your answer to part (b), what can you say about this relation?
    (d)   If Mary has $13.00, Mike has $12.50, and Will has $12.00, is Mary ℛ Mike? Is Mike ℛ Will? Is Mary ℛ Will?
    (e)   From your answer to part (d), what can you say about this relation?
    (f)   Are you related to yourself by this relation? Is your mother related to herself? Can you conclude from these two answers that this relation is reflexive? Explain.
5. Below is a list of relations on certain collections of objects. Write out the statements

of reflexivity, symmetry, and transitivity for each relation and tell which of these properties are possessed by each relation. In each case give some examples of objects which are related by the relation and give some examples of objects which are not related by the relation.

(a) The relation "is taller than" for the collection of all people.

(b) The relation "has darker hair than" for the collection of all people in your immediate family.

(c) The relation "is not more than five years older" for the collection of all people. (*Careful:* This relation is reflexive.)

(d) The relation "is no older than but is taller than" for the collection of all people.

(e) The relation "eats no more than" for the collection of all animals.

(f) The relation "is more beautiful than" for the collection of all paintings.

PROPERTIES OF THE MATHEMATICAL RELATIONS

Now let us examine the three mathematical relations we defined on pages 26 and 27 to determine which of them are *reflexive*.

LESS THAN.   The question we must answer is whether or not it is true that no matter which counting number n represents, $n < n$. The answer is no, since for example $5 \not< 5$. Hence this relation is not reflexive.

GREATER THAN.   If n is a counting number, is $n > n$? Again the answer is no, hence this relation is not reflexive.

EQUAL TO ONE MORE THAN.   If n is a counting number, is n equal to one more than n? Certainly not. Therefore this relation is not reflexive.

Let us now examine these relations for *symmetry*.

LESS THAN. If n and m are counting numbers and if $n < m$, is $m < n$? No, since if $n = 4$ and $m = 5$, then $n < m$ but $m \not< n$. This relation is not symmetric.

GREATER THAN.   If n and m are counting numbers and if $n > m$, is $m > n$? No, and therefore this relation is not symmetric.

EQUAL TO ONE MORE THAN.   If n and m are counting numbers and if n is equal to one more than m, is m equal to one more than n? The answer is no and this relation is not symmetric. A counterexample which shows that this relation is not symmetric is easily found. The counting number 5 is one more than 4 ($5 \, \Re \, 4$) but 4 is not one more than 5 ($4 \not{\Re} \, 5$).

Lastly, which of these relations are transitive?

LESS THAN.   If n, m, and p are counting numbers and if $n < m$ and $m < p$, is $n < p$? Surely. Hence the relation has the transitive property.

GREATER THAN.   If n, m, and p are counting numbers and if $n > m$ and $m > p$, is it true that $n > p$? The answer is yes and therefore this relation is transitive.

EQUAL TO ONE MORE THAN. If n, m, and p are counting numbers such that n is equal to one more than m and m is equal to one more than p, then is n equal to one more than p? No, since n is equal to two more than p. This relation is therefore not transitive. A counterexample which specifically demonstrates this is found when $n = 5$, $m = 4$, and $p = 3$. Then n is related to m and m is related to p. However it is not true that n is related to p since 5 is not equal to one more than 3; that is, $5 \mathrel{\mathcal{R}} 4$, $4 \mathrel{\mathcal{R}} 3$, but $5 \mathrel{\not{\mathcal{R}}} 3$.

Of the relations of *equality, less than, greater than*, and *equal to one more than* the only one which has all three properties is *equality*. When a relation has all three of these properties, it is called an *equivalence relation*. Hence *equality* is an equivalence relation, but the other three relations are not.

There are many useful relations on the collection of all counting numbers, but there are five which are the most important. We have already mentioned three of these, *equality, less than*, and *greater than*. The other two are defined below. They are very similar to *less than* and *greater than*.

Definition of the Relation of Less Than or Equal to *If n and m represent counting numbers, then we say that n is less than or equal to m if there is a counting number p such that $n + p = m$. If n is less than or equal to m we write $n \leq m$.*

The only difference between this and the definition of *less than* is that here we permit the possibility that the counting number p may be zero. Thus, according to this definition, $6 \leq 8$ because there is a counting number p such that $6 + p = 8$. Also, $6 \leq 6$ since there is a counting number p (namely, zero) such that $6 + p = 6$. Any pair of numbers which are related by the relation *less than* will also be related by the relation *less than or equal to*. However, some numbers are related by this new relation which are not related by *less than*. For example, $6 \mathrel{\mathcal{R}} 6$ if $\mathcal{R}$ represents $\leq$ but $6 \mathrel{\not{\mathcal{R}}} 6$ if $\mathcal{R}$ represents $<$.

We leave it as an exercise to show that the relation $\leq$ is reflexive and transitive, but is not symmetric.

Definition of the Relation of Greater Than or Equal to *If n and m represent counting numbers, then we say n is greater than or equal to m if there is a counting number p such that $n = m + p$. If n is greater than or equal to m, we write $n \geq m$.*

The only difference between this definition and the definition of *greater than* is that here we permit the possibility that p might be zero. Thus while $6 \mathrel{\not{>}} 6$, it is true that $6 \geq 6$ because there is a counting number p (namely, zero) such that $6 = 6 + p$. It is a consequence of the definitions that if $n > m$ then $n \geq m$.

We leave it as an exercise for the reader to show that this relation is reflexive and transitive but not symmetric.

Exercises

1. Find a relation for the collection of all counting numbers such that $4 \mathrel{\mathcal{R}} 5$, $6 \mathrel{\mathcal{R}} 9$, but $7 \mathrel{\not{\mathcal{R}}} 5$. (Such a relation has been mentioned in the text.)

2. Find a relation for the collection of all counting numbers such that $4 \not{\mathcal{R}} 5$, $6 \not{\mathcal{R}} 3$, but $5 \mathcal{R} 4$.

3. Find a relation for the collection of all counting numbers such that $3 \mathcal{R} 5$, $7 \mathcal{R} 9$, $11 \mathcal{R} 13$, but $5 \not{\mathcal{R}} 3$ and $6 \not{\mathcal{R}} 5$.

4. Consider the relation for the collection of all counting numbers described as follows: If n and m are counting numbers, then $n \mathcal{R} m$ means that either $n = m$ or the result of subtracting the smaller of n and m from the larger is an even number. For example, $6 \mathcal{R} 4$ because $6 - 4 = 2$ is even. $1 \mathcal{R} 7$ since $7 - 1$ is even. But $4 \not{\mathcal{R}} 9$ since $9 - 4$ is odd. $8 \mathcal{R} 8$ since $8 = 8$.

   (a) Insert $\mathcal{R}$ or $\not{\mathcal{R}}$ depending on whether or not the numbers are related by this relation.

6 [ ] 7	8 [ ] 4	9 [ ] 5	19 [ ] 6
0 [ ] 0	7 [ ] 17	1 [ ] 2	2 [ ] 10
5 [ ] 5	100 [ ] 10	0 [ ] 4	9 [ ] 0

   (b) To which counting numbers is 1 related? To which numbers is 11 related? To which numbers is 0 related? To which numbers is 6 related?

   (c) Write out the statements of reflexivity, symmetry, and transitivity for this relation.

   (d) Explain why this relation is reflexive.

   (e) Explain why this relation is symmetric.

   (f) This relation is transitive. Find a few triples of counting numbers n, m, and p such that $n \mathcal{R} m$ and $m \mathcal{R} p$ and observe that in each case $n \mathcal{R} p$.

   (g) In light of your answers to parts (d), (e), and (f), what kind of a relation is this?

5. Find a relation for any collection of objects that you want which is reflexive but not symmetric and not transitive.

6. Consider the relation "ends in the same digit" for the collection of counting numbers. For example, $67 \mathcal{R} 107$ since both 67 and 107 end in the digit 7, but $45 \not{\mathcal{R}} 13$ since these numbers do not end in the same digit.

   (a) Find some pairs of counting numbers which are related by this relation. Find some pairs which are not related.

   (b) To which counting numbers is 16 related?

   (c) Explain why this relation is an equivalence relation.

7. Find a relation for the collection of all people which is an equivalence relation.

8. Consider the relation defined for the collection of all counting numbers as follows: $n \mathcal{R} m$ if and only if "either n evenly divides m or m evenly divides n." For example, $6 \mathcal{R} 2$ since 2 evenly divides 6 and $5 \mathcal{R} 45$ since 5 evenly divides 45, but $17 \not{\mathcal{R}} 45$ since 17 does not evenly divide 45 and 45 does not evenly divide 17.

   (a) Insert either $\mathcal{R}$ or $\not{\mathcal{R}}$ according as the given numbers are or are not related.

1 [ ] 5	6 [ ] 18	9 [ ] 45
7 [ ] 7	6 [ ] 44	11 [ ] 100

   (b) Explain why this relation is reflexive.

   (c) Explain why this relation is symmetric.

   (d) Find three counting numbers n, m, and p for which $n \mathcal{R} m$ and $m \mathcal{R} p$, but $n \not{\mathcal{R}} p$. The exhibition of these counting numbers will show that this relation is not transitive.

9. Explain why the relation "less than or equal to" is reflexive and transitive. Give an example to show that it is not symmetric.
10. Explain why the relation "greater than or equal to" is reflexive and transitive but not symmetric.
11. What properties are possessed by the relation defined on the collection of all counting numbers as follows: $n \, \Re \, m$ if and only if "either $n = m$ or $n = m + 1$."
12. Two important relations on the collection of all triangles that are studied in high school geometry are "is similar to" and "is congruent to." Which of these is an equivalence relation? Explain.
13. Two important relations on the collection of all lines that are studied in high school geometry are "is parallel to" and "is perpendicular to." What properties are possessed by these relations? Is either of them an equivalence relation?
14. Which of the relations of "has the same center as" and "has the same radius as" is an equivalence relation on the collection of all circles?

In this section we have examined the concept of a *relation*. We have discussed relations on various collections of objects (people, counting numbers, etc.) and we have discussed the properties of reflexivity, symmetry, and transitivity. In particular, we have studied the equality and inequality relations on the collection of all counting numbers. This concludes our discussion of relations. We shall encounter many more relations and we shall always be interested in determining their properties, for it is by means of its properties that a relation is used.

In the next three sections we shall examine a second major concept of arithmetic, the concept of an *operation*.

Review Questions

1. In your own words, what is a relation on a given collection of objects?
2. If $\Re$ is a relation defined on a given collection of objects, what does it mean to say that the relation $\Re$ possesses the reflexive property? To say that $\Re$ possesses the symmetric property? To say that $\Re$ possesses the transitive property?
3. What is an equivalence relation?
4. We have discussed five important relations on the collection of all counting numbers. What are they? What are their properties?
5. Define the four inequality relations of *less than, greater than, less than or equal to,* and *greater than or equal to* for counting numbers.
6. In what way do the definitions of *less than* and *less than or equal to* differ?
7. If n and m are counting numbers and $n > m$, need it be true that $n \geq m$? If it is true that $n \leq m$, need it be true that $n < m$?

ADDITION AND MULTIPLICATION OF COUNTING NUMBERS

In this section we shall investigate the operations of addition and multiplication of counting numbers. We shall study the properties of each of these operations and then display the properties in explicit form. The reader must become thoroughly familiar with these properties, for when we formulate the axioms for the deductive system of counting numbers in the following section we shall include these properties in the list of axioms.

Addition of Counting Numbers

The reader is familiar with addition as a process for operating upon two given counting numbers to produce a third counting number. The addition table (Fig. 2) describes the effect of this process upon the counting numbers 0 through 9. The table is used as follows. To add 6 to 7 find the counting number in row 7 and column 6. This number is 13 and therefore $7 + 6 = 13$. To add 4 to 8 find the number in row 8 and column 4: 12. Hence $8 + 4 = 12$. To add n to m, find the counting number which lies in row m and column n. If this counting number is s, then $m + n = s$.

Our immediate aim is to introduce the reader to the basic properties of the addition process. Later, when we begin to prove theorems, we will see how these properties are used to explain other less basic properties of addition.

PROPERTIES OF ADDITION OF COUNTING NUMBERS

The first observations we want to make about addition of counting numbers are that (1) it is a process which can be performed upon every pair of counting numbers and (2) the result of performing the process upon a pair of counting

Columns

+	0	1	2	3	4	5	6	7	8	9
0	0	1	2	3	4	5	6	7	8	9
1	1	2	3	4	5	6	7	8	9	10
2	2	3	4	5	6	7	8	9	10	11
3	3	4	5	6	7	8	9	10	11	12
4	4	5	6	7	8	9	10	11	12	13
5	5	6	7	8	9	10	11	12	13	14
6	6	7	8	9	10	11	12	13	14	15
7	7	8	9	10	11	12	13	14	15	16
8	8	9	10	11	12	13	14	15	16	17
9	9	10	11	12	13	14	15	16	17	18

Rows

Figure 2 The addition table.

numbers is a unique counting number. We call this property of addition of counting numbers the *closure property* and formally state it as follows.

1. The Closure Property of Addition of Counting Numbers   *No matter which counting numbers the symbols n and m represent, the symbol n + m represents one and only one counting number.*

To say that the symbol $n + m$ represents *one* (which means *at least one*) counting number means that the process can be performed upon n and m and to say that $n + m$ represents *only one* counting number means that the result of performing the addition process upon n and m is a *unique* counting number.

It is important to distinguish between these two parts of the closure property: First, the addition process can be applied to every pair of counting numbers and, second, the result of this application is always a unique counting number. The second part of the closure property, the uniqueness part, can be viewed from another angle. Consider the two counting numbers which we represent by the numerals 3 and 5. What is the result of performing the addition process upon these two numbers? We may express this question in the form

$$3 + 5 = ?$$

Now according to the closure property the sum of these two counting numbers is unique. This means that if we change the numerals representing the summands* by using, for example, the numerals III and V, then we should not change the number which is the sum. That is, it will be true that

$$3 + 5 = III + V$$

This illustrates that *changing the names of the summands does not affect the number which is their sum.* Thus if n, m, a, and b are counting numbers such that $n = m$ and $a = b$, then $n + a = m + b$. That is, if n and m are names for the same counting number ($n = m$) and if a and b are names for the same counting number ($a = b$), then the sum of the two counting numbers does not depend upon the particular choice of names so that the number represented by $n + a$ and the number represented by $m + b$ are equal. This particular formulation of the uniqueness part of the closure property is called the *well-definedness property*. The reason we give a name to this formulation is because it is used so often in arithmetic and it is convenient to have a special name for it.

The Well-Definedness Property of Addition of Counting Numbers   *If n, m, a, and b are counting numbers such that n = m and a = b, then n + a = m + b.*

We must emphasize that the well-definedness property is simply a particular phrasing of the uniqueness part of the closure property. Logically there is no reason to give this particular phrasing a special name. However this particular

---

* When two numbers are added, the numbers being added are called *summands* and the number produced is called their *sum*. Synonyms for summand are *addend* and *term;* e.g., the sum of the summands (addends, terms) 2 and 3 is 5.

formulation of the uniqueness part of the closure property has very wide application in the study of addition of counting numbers and it is decidedly convenient to have this concept phrased in this way and given a special name. We
shall refer to the well-definedness property many times and when we do the
reader should remind himself that what is meant is a particular way of stating
the uniqueness part of the closure property.

Perhaps the statement "Equals added to equals are equal" is familiar. This
statement is in fact simply another way of stating the well-definedness property.
For n and m are equals ($n = m$) which when added to equals ($a = b$) yield
equal sums ($n + a = m + b$).

Let us see how this property is used in arithmetic.

EXAMPLE 1.   Is the statement

$$5 + 4 = (3 + 2) + (2 + 2)*$$

true? If so, why is it true?

Solution: This statement is true and its truth is explained by the well-definedness
property of addition. For we know that $5 = 3 + 2$ and that $4 = 2 + 2$. Using the
fact that addition is well-defined, it is then possible to conclude that the counting
number represented by the symbol $5 + 4$ is the same as the counting number represented by the symbol $(3 + 2) + (2 + 2)$.

EXAMPLE 2.   The statement $4 + 7 = 4 + (5 + 2)$ is true. Why?

Solution: Since $4 = 4$ (why?) and since $7 = 5 + 2$, the well-definedness property
of addition assures us that the sum of the two counting numbers when represented
by 4 and 7 is the same as the sum of these counting numbers when represented by
4 and $5 + 2$.

This property of addition justifies a kind of *substitution* that is commonly
employed in elementary mathematics. That is, looking at Example 2 above,
we have used well-definedness to justify the substitution of $5 + 2$ for 7 in the
symbol $4 + 7$. In Example 1, we saw how we can justify the substitution of
$3 + 2$ for 5 and $2 + 2$ for 4 in the symbol $5 + 4$.

Exercises

1. Which operations are to be performed first?
    (a) $5 + (3 + 1)$.   (b) $(5 + 3) + 1$.
    (c) $[(5 + 1) + 6] + 8$. (The brackets are used instead of parentheses because
         we do not like to use more than one set of parentheses at a time. Too many
         sets of parentheses cause confusion.)
2. Which operations are performed last?
    (a) $5 + (8 + 3)$.   (b) $(5 + 2) + (7 + 5)$.
    (c) $[6 + (8 + 1)] + 5$.

* Parenthesis are symbolic instructions to perform *first* the operations *inside* the parentheses.   After performing these operations, the operation *between* the parenthesis should be
performed.   Thus the symbol $(3 + 2) + (2 + 2)$ is to be regarded as the sum of $3 + 2$ or 5
and $2 + 2$ or 4.

3. The statement $3 + 5 = 3 + (4 + 1)$ is true. Why?

4. Why is the statement $8 + (9 - 2) = (4 + 4) + 7$ true?

5. Upon entering a classroom, you see the following symbols written on the blackboard:

$$ ⁄ + 尺 \quad = 川 $$

Assuming that the addition problem was worked correctly, in order to identify each of the three traditional Chinese numerals used in this expression it is sufficient to know which counting numbers the symbols ⁄ and 尺 represent. Explain.

6. The closure property says two things about addition of counting numbers. It says that (1) the symbol $n + m$ is the name of *at least* one counting number no matter which counting numbers n and m represent, and (2) the symbol $n + m$ represents *at most* one counting number no matter which counting numbers n and m represent. If we replace addition of counting numbers by subtraction of counting numbers, are these two statements still true? Explain. Does subtraction of counting numbers possess the closure property?

Consider the counting numbers 2 and 3. We can use addition of counting numbers to produce a new counting number in two different ways. We can add 3 to 2 obtaining $2 + 3$, or we can add 2 to 3, obtaining $3 + 2$. No doubt the reader's reaction on reading this is to think to himself, "So who cares; the numbers $2 + 3$ and $3 + 2$ are equal anyhow." Exactly!

2. The Commutative Property of Addition of Counting Numbers *No matter which counting numbers the symbols n and m represent, $n + m = m + n$.*

Thus the result of adding m to n ($n + m$) is the same as the result of adding n to m ($m + n$).

We express the fact that $2 + 3 = 3 + 2$ by saying that 2 and 3 *commute with respect to addition of counting numbers*. The commutative property of addition states that *every* pair of counting numbers commute with respect to addition of counting numbers. If it were true that even one pair of counting numbers did not commute, then addition would not be commutative.

The next property of addition of counting numbers is involved in problems calling for the addition of more than two summands. For example, what is the sum of the numbers 2, 3, and 7? Obviously the answer is 12. But let us examine this computation more carefully. *Exactly*, how is the sum of these three numbers computed? One person might find their sum in this way:

$$ 2 + 3 = 5 $$

and

$$ 5 + 7 = 12 $$

therefore

$$ 12 \text{ is the sum} $$

while another person might find their sum like this:

$$3 + 7 = 10$$

and

$$2 + 10 = 12$$

therefore

12 is the sum

Each of these people has recognized a very important fact about addition: *It is not possible to add more than two counting numbers at a time.* If the sum of three counting numbers is to be found, then *two* additions must be performed. If the sum of four counting numbers is required, then *three* additions must be performed.

The first person to work this problem found his sum like this:

$$(2 + 3) + 7 = 5 + 7 = 12$$

The second person found the sum in the following way:

$$2 + (3 + 7) = 2 + 10 = 12$$

The fact that these two people obtained the same sum is expressed by saying that addition of counting numbers is *associative*.

3. The Associative Property of Addition of Counting Numbers   *No matter which counting numbers n, m, and p represent, $(n + m) + p = n + (m + p)$.*

We express the fact that $(2 + 3) + 7$ is equal to $2 + (3 + 7)$ by saying that the counting numbers 2, 3, and 7 *associate with respect to addition*. Thus the associative property of addition states that *every* triple of counting numbers associates with respect to addition.

We may observe that in the statement of associativity

$$(n + m) + p = n + (m + p)$$

the symbols *n*, *m*, and *p* occur in the same order from left to right on both sides of the equality symbol. The only difference in the symbols $(n + m) + p$ and $n + (m + p)$ is that the set of parentheses has been "shifted." Each of the symbols involves two additions and in $(n + m) + p$ the leftmost addition has been performed first, while in $n + (m + p)$ the rightmost addition has been performed first.

We can sum up what we have said as follows: If it were not for the associative property we would not know which counting number the symbol $2 + 3 + 7$ represents. The sum we would obtain by performing the leftmost addition first might be different from the sum obtained by performing the rightmost addition first. But because of the associative property if one person interprets $2 + 3 + 7$ as $(2 + 3) + 7$ and another interprets it as $2 + (3 + 7)$, both people will obtain the same sum in spite of the difference in their interpretations. This is not true of, say, subtraction. The symbol $8 - 4 - 2$ is ambiguous. Performing the leftmost subtraction operation first, we get $(8 - 4) - 2$ or $4 - 2$ or 2. Performing the rightmost operation first, we get $8 - (4 - 2)$ or $8 - 2$ or 6.

Exercises

1. Which of the following symbols are ambiguous? Explain.
   (a) $5 + 4 + 2$.   (d) $8 - 2 \times 2$.
   (b) $15 - 4 + 2$.   (e) $9 + 4 - 2$.
   (c) $6 \times 4 - 2$.
2. Consider the addition problem:

$$
\begin{array}{r}
2 \\
3 \\
+7 \\
\hline
?
\end{array}
$$

The addition can be performed from top to bottom or from bottom to top; that is,

$$(2 + 3) + 7$$

is equal to

$$(7 + 3) + 2$$

Supply justifications for each step in the following demonstration of this fact.

$$
\begin{aligned}
(2 + 3) + 7 &= 2 + (3 + 7) && \text{Why?} \\
&= (3 + 7) + 2 && \text{Why?} \\
&= (7 + 3) + 2 && \text{Why?}
\end{aligned}
$$

The counting number zero plays a particularly distinguished role relative to addition. What is the sum of 6 and 0? What is the sum of 25 and 0? What is the sum of an unspecified counting number n and 0? Of course, the property we are talking about is:

4. The Zero Property of Addition of Counting Numbers *No matter which counting number the symbol n represents, $n + 0 = n$.*

Because of this property we give a special name to the counting number zero; we call zero the *additive identity*. This name refers to the fact that if we start with a counting number and add zero to it, the new number so obtained is *identical* to the number with which we began.

Is there any other counting number with this special property? That is, if x is a counting number such that no matter which counting number n represents it is true that $n + x = n$, can x be any number other than zero? Certainly not. Hence zero is the *only* additive identity.

The fifth and last basic property of addition is called the *cancellation property* of addition.

5. The Cancellation Property of Addition of Counting Numbers   *If n, m, and p represent counting numbers such that*

$$n + p = m + p$$

then it is true that n = m.

This property is called the cancellation property because if the p's are "erased" from both sides of the equation

$$n + p = m + p$$

then we are left with

$$n = m$$

This "erasure" of the p's is called *canceling* the p's.

One of the applications of the cancellation property is to the solving of certain kinds of equations. We are going to give the reader such an equation and ask him to give the solution as quickly as he can. Here is the equation:

$$n + 2 = 3$$

Surely the reader has given the solution as 1. Now the reader should ask himself how he arrived at this solution. It is possible that he will answer that he subtracted 2 from 3 to obtain the solution. This is not incorrect, and we shall discuss this sort of procedure presently. However, we do not think that this is the way the reader really solved the equation. Rather, we think that he recognized that the solution required was some number which when increased by 2 gave 3 and that he also immediately recognized that when 1 is increased by 2 the result is 3. Consequently he would conclude that the solution is 1. This is a very straightforward procedure for solving this particular equation.

This method of solving the equation in fact makes use of the cancellation property of addition of counting numbers. Let us see how. Here is the solution written out step by step.

(1)	$n + 2 = 3$	(1) The given equation
(2)	$3 = 1 + 2$	(2) From the addition table
(3)	$n + 2 = 1 + 2$	(3) This follows from (1) and (2) by using the transitivity property of equality
(4)	$n = 1$	(4) This follows from (3) by using the cancellation property of addition

Review Questions

1. State the five properties of addition of counting numbers.
2. State the well-definedness property of addition of counting numbers. What is the

connection between this property and the closure property of addition of counting numbers?

3. How is the cancellation property used in solving equations? Can you describe in general terms the kind of equations that can be solved by using this property; that is, what do these equations look like?
4. Why is zero called the additive identity?
5. In using the addition table to find the sum of 4 and 5 it is irrelevant whether one looks for the entry in the fourth row and fifth colunm or the fifth row and fourth column. Explain this in terms of a property of addition of counting numbers.

Exercises

1. Consider the statement, "If $n + 3 = m + 3$, then $n = m$." This statement is true by reason of the cancellation property of addition. State the *converse* of this implication. Is this converse true? Why?
2. Use the cancellation property to find the counting number x such that the statement $x + 3 = 7$ is true.
3. As in Exercise 2 find all counting numbers x such that the statement $x + 6 = 17$ is true.
4. Use properties of addition to justify each statement.

(a) $8 \times (2 + 0) = 8 \times 2.$ (h) $3 + (2 + 7) = (3 + 7) + 2.$
(b) $16 + 7 = 7 + 16.$ (i) $(5 + 19) + 0 = 19 + 5.$
(c) $3 + (2 + 7) = 3 + (7 + 2).$ (j) $6 + (3 + 7) = 7 + (3 + 6).$
(d) $3 + (2 + 7) = (2 + 7) + 3.$ (k) $(6 + 3) + 4 = 9 + 4.$
(e) $3 + (2 + 7) = (3 + 2) + 7.$ (l) $6 + (3 + 4) = 9 + 4.$
(f) $3 + (2 + 7) = (2 + 3) + 7.$ (m) $6 + (3 + 4) = 4 + 9.$
(g) $3 + (2 + 7) = 2 + (3 + 7).$

Multiplication of Counting Numbers

Multiplication, like addition, is a process which can be applied to two counting numbers to produce a third. The numbers to which the process is applied are called the *factors* and the number produced is called the *product* of the factors.

The multiplication table is similar to the addition table and is used in the same way.

There are a number of ways to symbolize the process of multiplication of counting numbers. If n and m are counting numbers, then the product of these factors is represented by any one of these symbols,

$$n \times m \qquad n \cdot m \qquad (n)(m) \qquad n(m) \qquad (n)m \qquad nm$$

We shall use these notations interchangeably. The last of these is perhaps the most convenient, but there are some restrictions upon its use. For example, it is not possible to use this notation (called *juxtaposition* or *concatenation*) to denote the product of 5 and 2, for obviously the symbol 52 does not represent the counting number ten.

PROPERTIES OF MULTIPLICATION OF COUNTING NUMBERS

The properties of multiplication of counting numbers are very similar to the properties of addition of counting numbers. Here they are.

1. The Closure Property of Multiplication of Counting Numbers *No matter which counting numbers the symbols n and m represent, the symbol n × m represents one and only one counting number.*

This property indicates two things: First, it is always possible to perform the multiplication process, and, second, the result of performing the multiplication process is always a unique counting number. We find it convenient to rephrase the uniqueness part of this property as follows.

The Well-Definedness Property of Multiplication of Counting Numbers. *If n, m, a, and b are counting numbers such that n = m and a = b, then n × a = m × b.*

The well-definedness property states that changing the names of the factors does not change the number which is the product. This is simply another way of stating that the result of applying the multiplication process to a pair of counting numbers is a unique counting number.

We have seen that the well-definedness property of addition has important applications to the substitution of one symbol for another in a given expression. The same is true of the well-definedness property of multiplication. As an example, consider the symbol

$$(4 + 3) \times (4 \times 2)$$

To find the counting number represented by this symbol we would first write

$$(4 + 3) \times (4 \times 2) = 7 \times 8 \tag{1}$$

and then we would use the multiplication table to find out that

$$7 \times 8 = 56$$

Using transitivity of equality we could then combine the last two equations to obtain

$$(4 + 3) \times (4 \times 2) = 56$$

which is just what we wanted. But we should be sure to notice that equation (1) is obtained by using the well-definedness property of multiplication. That is, from the equations

$$4 + 3 = 7 \quad \text{and} \quad 4 \times 2 = 8$$

we use this property to conclude that

$$(4 + 3) \times (4 \times 2) = 7 \times 8$$

EXAMPLE. Simplify $(4 + 2) \times 3$.

Solution: According to the well-definedness property of multiplication of counting numbers since $4 + 2 = 6$ and since $3 = 3$ (why?), the statement

$$(4 + 2) \times 3 = 6 \times 3$$

is true. Then from the true statements

$$(4 + 2) \times 3 = 6 \times 3 \quad \text{and} \quad 6 \times 3 = 18$$

we can obtain the true statement

$$(4 + 2) \times 3 = 18$$

by using the transitivity property of equality of counting numbers.

The very ordinary computation in the preceding example involves two fundamental facts: Equality of counting numbers is transitive and multiplication of counting numbers is well-defined. Perhaps now the reader is beginning to see that these properties are very basic, for they are involved in justifying even the most elementary kind of arithmetic procedures.

2. The Commutative Property of Multiplication of Counting Numbers *No matter which counting numbers the symbols n and m represent,* $n \times m = m \times n$.

We say that n and m *commute with respect to multiplication.* Thus to say that multiplication is commutative means that *every* pair of counting numbers commute with respect to multiplication.

Like addition, multiplication is a process performed on *two* counting numbers to produce a third. In order to find the product of three counting numbers it is necessary to perform *two* multiplications. It is therefore legitimate to question whether the order in which these two multiplications are performed will have any effect upon the final answer. But we all know that the answer does not depend upon the order in which these multiplications are performed. This is exactly the content of the associative property of multiplication.

3. The Associative Property of Multiplication of Counting Numbers *No matter which counting numbers the symbols n, m, and p represent,* $(n \times m) \times p = n \times (m \times p)$.

Because of this property the symbol

$$n \times m \times p$$

is unambiguous. The leftmost multiplication may be performed first, obtaining $(n \times m) \times p$, or the rightmost multiplication may be performed first, obtaining $n \times (m \times p)$, and the associative property guarantees that the same number will result from each of these computations.

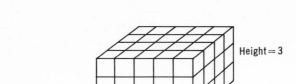

Figure 3

Consider the problem of finding the volume of the solid shown in Fig. 3. The volume of the solid is found by determining the product of its length, width, and height. We may first multiply length and width, and then multiply the resulting number by the height,

$$(\text{length} \times \text{width}) \times \text{height} = (5 \times 4) \times 3$$

or we may multiply width by height, and then multiply the length by this result,

$$\text{length} \times (\text{width} \times \text{height}) = 5 \times (4 \times 3)$$

and the associative property guarantees that either procedure will yield the correct volume.

These two different methods for finding the volume can be visualized as shown in Fig. 4. We express the fact that each of these volumes is equal to 60 cubic units by saying that the counting numbers 5, 4, and 3 *associate with respect to multiplication of counting numbers.*

Is there a counting number which plays a role relative to multiplication analogous to the role played by zero relative to addition?

4. The Unit Property of Multiplication of Counting Numbers *No matter which counting number the symbol n represents, $n \times 1 = n$.*

We call the counting number one the *multiplicative identity* just as zero is called the *additive identity.* The reason for calling this property the unit property is that the counting number one is often referred to as the *unit.* We could just as well have called this property the *One Property.*

Suppose we know that $n \times 2 = 4 \times 2$. What is n? Obviously $n = 4$ and we obtain the equation $n = 4$ from the equation $n \times 2 = 4 \times 2$ by "cancelling" the 2's: $n \times \not{2} = 4 \times \not{2}$. This is a specific example of the cancellation property of multiplication.

5. The Cancellation Property of Multiplication of Counting Numbers *No matter which counting numbers the symbols n, m, and p represent, as long as p does not represent zero, if $n \times p = m \times p$, then it is true that $n = m$.*

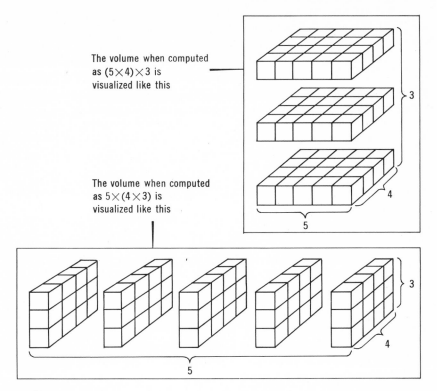

The volume when computed as $(5 \times 4) \times 3$ is visualized like this

The volume when computed as $5 \times (4 \times 3)$ is visualized like this

Figure 4

This property is similar to the cancellation property of addition. However, there is one significant difference: It is not permissible to cancel zero relative to multiplication, but it is possible to cancel zero relative to addition. Let us see why we cannot cancel zero relative to multiplication. Since $7 \times 0 = 0$ and $8 \times 0 = 0$ we know that $7 \times 0 = 8 \times 0$. If it were possible to cancel 0, then from the statement $7 \times 0 = 8 \times 0$ we conclude that $7 = 8$, which is absurd. This shows that we cannot expect to cancel zero relative to multiplication and must therefore require in the statement of this property that the number to be cancelled be other than zero.

Multiplication has five basic properties very similar to the five basic properties of addition. The five properties of multiplication form the basic knowledge needed to work with the operation of multiplication. Other true facts about multiplication can be logically derived from these. There are only two differences between the properties for addition and the properties for multiplication, namely, (1) the multiplicative identity is 1 while the additive identity is 0; and (2) it is possible to cancel any counting number relative to addition, but only nonzero counting numbers can be cancelled relative to multiplication.

Review Questions

1. What do the terms *factor* and *product* mean?
2. Sum is to product as summand is to _____.
3. We express the fact that the symbol $n \times m \times p$ is unambiguous by saying that multiplication of counting numbers has the _____ property.
4. List the five fundamental properties of multiplication of counting numbers.
5. The cancellation property of multiplication can be used to solve certain kinds of equations. Discuss this. Give an example.
6. Addition is to multiplication as 0 is to _____.
7. Compare the properties of addition and multiplication of counting numbers.
8. Why do we not cancel zero with respect to multiplication?

Exercises

1. Construct a multiplication table for the digits 0 through 9.
2. Consider the statement

$$(2 \times 3) \times 6 = 2 \times (3 \times 6)$$

Visualize this statement by means of a problem of finding the volume of a rectangular solid. Draw pictures.
3. Use properties of multiplication to justify the following statements.
   (a) $9 \times 1 = 9$.
   (b) $(1 \times 3) \times 9 = 1 \times (3 \times 9)$.
   (c) $(1 \times 3) \times 9 = (3 \times 1) \times 9$.
   (d) $(1 \times 3) \times 9 = 1 \times (9 \times 3)$.
   (e) $(1 \times 3) \times 9 = (9 \times 1) \times 3$.
   (f) $(1 \times 3) \times 9 = (3 \times 9) \times 1$.
   (g) $(3 \times 1) \times 7 = 3 \times 7$.
   (h) $(1 \times 3) \times 7 = 3 \times 7$.
   (i) $(1 \times 3) \times (4 \times 5) = (4 \times 5) \times (1 \times 3)$.
   (j) $(1 \times 3) \times 2 = 2 \times 3$.
   (k) $3 \times 6 = 3 \times (5 + 1)$.
   (l) $(2 + 3) \times 7 = 5 \times (4 + 3)$.
   (m) $(2 \times 4) \times 7 = 8 \times (3 + 4)$.
4. If n is a counting number such that

$$n \times 3 = 18$$

then we may conclude that $n = 6$. Justify this conclusion by using the cancellation property of multiplication and the transitivity property of equality.

The Distributive Property

The operations of addition and multiplication of counting numbers are interrelated in a number of ways. For example, the reader is no doubt aware that multiplication can be regarded as repeated addition. This is in fact the way desk computers perform multiplication. A desk computer multiplies 56 by 8 by adding

56 to itself 8 times. Euclid defined multiplication in terms of addition as follows: "A number is said to *multiply* a number when that which is multiplied is added to itself as many times as there are units in the other, and thus some number is produced."

Of the many statements which connect these two processes, there is one which has been selected as the most basic in the sense that from this one all the others may be logically derived. This most basic statement relating addition and multiplication is called the distributive property for addition and multiplication.

The Distributive Property for Addition and Multiplication   *No matter which counting numbers n, m, and p represent, $n \times (m + p) = (n \times m) + (n \times p)$.*

This property has the widest possible application in arithmetic. For instance, suppose we want to find the product of 3 and 125. The fastest way to perform this multiplication is to multiply 3 and 100, obtaining 300, and then to multiply 3 and 25, obtaining 75, and then to add 300 and 75, obtaining the answer: 375. In doing this we have used the distributive property,

$$3 \times (125) = 3 \times (100 + 25) = (3 \times 100) + (3 \times 25)$$
$$= 300 + 75 = 375$$

Another application of the distributive property is to justify the ordinary algorithm for multiplying counting numbers. Let us multiply 34 by 16. The algorithm involves placing the numeral 16 below the numeral 34 and then drawing a line. Below this line other numerals are arranged in a particular pattern on the paper. After enough numerals have been written below the first line, another line is drawn. Then the numbers represented by the numerals between the two lines are added, and their sum is written below the second line. This last numeral represents the product of 34 and 16.

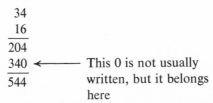

$$
\begin{array}{r}
34 \\
16 \\
\hline
204 \\
340 \\
\hline
544
\end{array}
$$

340 ⟵——— This 0 is not usually written, but it belongs here

Now what is there about this particular arrangement of the numerals on the paper that leads to the correct result? If we perform the multiplication "horizontally," the reason why this process does in fact provide the correct answer is seen to rest with the distributive property:

$34 \times 16 = 34 \times (6 + 10)$	(Well-definedness of multiplication)
$= (34 \times 6) + (34 \times 10)$	(Distributive property)
$= 204 + 340$	(Well-definedness property of addition)
$= 544$	(Performing addition)

The ordinary multiplication algorithm may therefore be viewed as a "vertical" way of writing down the distributive property. The numerals between the lines are obtained by multiplying 34 by 10 and by multiplying 34 by 6.

The distributive property can be visualized geometrically as well. Figure 5 consists of an arrangement of five rows of squares, each row being 12 squares long. This area of this rectangle of squares is 60 square units, the area of one square being called a *square unit*. Now let us separate this rectangular arrangement into two smaller arrangements as shown in Fig. 6. The area of the left-hand arrangement is 5×10 square units and the area of the righthand arrangement is 5×2 square units. But if simply separating the rectangle of squares in this way into two smaller rectangles of squares does not change the total area, then it must be true that

$$5 \times 12 = (5 \times 10) + (5 \times 2)$$

This equation may be rewritten in the form

$$5 \times (10 + 2) = (5 \times 10) + (5 \times 2)$$

This is exactly the statement of the distributive property when $n = 5$, $m = 10$, and $p = 2$. Consequently, in light of this example, we may interpret the distributive property as saying that separating a rectangular region into two rectangular regions does not change the total area.

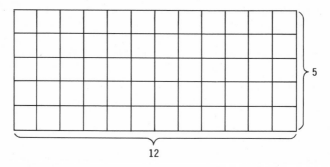

Figure 5

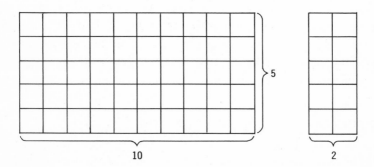

Figure 6

Exercises

1. Is it true that no matter which counting numbers the symbols n, m, and p represent

$$n + (m \times p) = (n + m) \times (n + p)$$

   Explain. Compare this statement with the distributive property and describe the difference between the two.

2. The symbol $(2 \times 3) + (2 \times 5)$ should be regarded as a *sum* of two numbers. The symbol $2 \times (3 + 5)$ should be regarded as a *product* of two numbers.

   (a) Write each of these *sums* as a *product:*

$$(3 \times 7) + (3 \times 6)$$
$$(13 \times 2) + (13 \times 4)$$
$$(2 \times 7) + (7 \times 5)$$
$$(3 \times 4) + (4 \times 5)$$

   (b) Write each of these *products* as a *sum*:

$$2 \times (4 + 5)$$
$$18 \times (6 + 1)$$
$$6 \times (100 + 7)$$
$$(18 + 7) \times 3$$

3. $16 \times 14 = (16 \times 10) + (? \times 4)$.
4. $24 \times 18 = (24 \times ?) + (24 \times 10)$.
5. Demonstrate by using rectangles that

$$4 \times (3 + 5) = (4 \times 3) + (4 \times 5)$$

   is a true statement.
6. Explain how the distributive property is involved in the multiplication of 45 by 37.
7. Generalize the distributive property and complete the equations

$$n \times (m + p + q) = \text{_____}$$
$$n \times (m + p + q + r) = \text{_____}$$

8. The distributive property is used to explain why multiplication can be regarded as repeated addition. For example, to multiply 5 by 3 we compute as follows:

$$5 \times 3 = 5 \times (1 + 1 + 1)$$
$$= (5 \times 1) + (5 \times 1) + (5 \times 1)$$
$$= 5 + 5 + 5$$

   (a) Justify each step in the preceding argument. (Refer to Exercise 7.)
   (b) Explain why $7 \times 4 = 7 + 7 + 7 + 7$.

THE DEDUCTIVE SYSTEM OF COUNTING NUMBERS

We have discussed the equivalence relation of equality of counting numbers and the processes of addition and multiplication of counting numbers together with their properties. This relatively small body of facts will provide us with a foundation upon which to build the arithmetic of the counting numbers.

Laying the Foundations

We are now ready to begin laying the foundations for the arithmetic of the counting numbers. This means that we are ready to specify some of the *undefined concepts* and *axioms* upon which the deductive system of counting numbers will be built. Before we do this, however, a few comments about this foundation are necessary.

First, we are not going to identify all the undefined concepts and axioms right at the beginning. But we will begin with enough undefined concepts and axioms to enable us to start the study of the arithmetic of the counting numbers. We can add to the lists of undefined concepts and axioms whenever we feel the need.

Second, there are many ways to select these first undefined concepts and axioms. For example, we are going to take the concept of *counting number* as undefined, even though there are a number of definitions available for this concept. But each of these definitions involves a fair amount of preparation which after the definition of counting number has been given is not used again. For the purposes of our study this would be a considerable waste of time and effort. But be assured that we are not cheating when we take *counting number* as an undefined concept. The process of reaching down to more and more basic concepts is in a sense unending, and consequently we shall begin at a level of "basicness" that enables us to obtain the results we want in a minimum of time and with a minimum of effort.

THE FOUNDATIONS OF THE DEDUCTIVE SYSTEM OF COUNTING NUMBERS

The Undefined Concepts
1. Counting number.
2. The relation of equality of counting numbers.
3. The process of addition of counting numbers.
4. The process of multiplication of counting numbers.

The Axioms
1. Equality of counting numbers is an equivalence relation.
2. Addition of counting numbers:
   Has the closure property,
   Is commutative,
   Is associative,
   Has the zero property, and
   Has the cancellation property.

3. Multiplication of counting numbers:
    Has the closure property,
    Is commutative,
    Is associative,
    Has the unit property, and
    Has the cancellation property.
4. The distributive property for addition and multiplication holds.

These axioms are reasonable, for if in the deductive system of counting numbers these statements were not all true, then the resulting logical system would not properly reflect our experience of the real world. In order to satisfactorily explain our real surroundings the system of counting numbers ought to contain these statements as true statements. (The reader can easily find examples in the real world which illustrate this.) Therefore we shall *assume* their truth.

Building upon the Foundations

We are now ready to begin the development of the arithmetic of the counting numbers within the logical framework of the deductive system we have just set up. The logical consequences of the foundation are now completely determined. In the following pages we present some of these consequences. There are literally hundreds of theorems we could prove, but we have selected only a few. Most of these were selected because we need them later in our investigations. Others were chosen simply to drive home to the reader the fact that *every* statement which is not an axiom should be proven if it is to be accepted as a true statement.

The reader is not expected to invent proofs of theorems; but given the statements which lead from the hypothesis to the conclusion he should, after observing a few examples, be able to supply justifications for the statements we present. For this reason in some of the following proofs the justifications are omitted. In every such instance the reader should supply these justifications himself.

The reader should pay particular attention to the kinds of justifications that we are allowed to use. Justifications are either

1. axioms,
2. hypotheses,
3. theorems previously proven, or
4. definitions.

Here is our first theorem. We have chosen it because of its simplicity.

Theorem 1   *If n is a counting number, then $0 + n = n$.*
Hypothesis: n is a counting number.
Conclusion: $0 + n = n$.

The Proof:

Statements	Justifications
(1) *n* is a counting number	(1) Hypothesis
(2) $n + 0 = n$	(2) Zero property and (1)
(3) $0 + n = n + 0$	(3) Commutivity of addition
(4) $0 + n = n$	(4) Follows from (3) and (2) by using transitivity of equality

Statement (4) is the desired conclusion and therefore the proof is complete.

The theorem just proved was very obvious. But this does not mean that we can assume that it is true without proving it. It is not only the difficult and nonobvious facts that must be proved in a deductive system. Any statement which is not an axiom must be *proved* true if it is to be accepted as a true statement. No statements are true simply because we believe them or because they are so obvious that we cannot imagine how or why they should be proven. The only statements that can properly be regarded as true are the axioms, which are *assumed* to be true, and the theorems, which are *proved* to be true. The reader must appreciate this if he is to develop a proper understanding of a deductive system and of the importance of a deductive system as a framework in which to study mathematics.

Our next theorem is the analog of Theorem 1 for multiplication.

Theorem 2   *If n is a counting number, then* $1 \times n = n$.
Hypothesis: n is a counting number.
Conclusion: $1 \times n = n$.
The Proof:

Statements	Justifications
(1) *n* is a counting number	(1) Hypothesis
(2) $n \times 1 = n$	(2) Unit property and (1)
(3) $1 \times n = n \times 1$	(3) Commutivity of multiplication
(4) $1 \times n = n$	(4) Follows from (3) and (2) by using transitivity of equality

Statement (4) is the desired conclusion and therefore the proof is complete.

The next two theorems are almost the same except that one deals with addition and the other with multiplication. These theorems show us that we can "cancel" on the left. The axioms tell us that we can "cancel" on the right.

Theorem 3   *Let n, m, and p represent counting numbers. If* $p + n = p + m$, *then* $n = m$.
Hypothesis: $p + n = p + m$.
Conclusion: $n = m$.

The Proof:

Statements	Justifications
(1) $p + n = p + m$	(1) Hypothesis
(2) $n + p = p + n$	(2) Commutivity of addition
(3) $n + p = p + m$	(3) Follows from (2) and (1) by using transitivity of equality
(4) $p + m = m + p$	(4) Commutivity of addition
(5) $n + p = m + p$	(5) Follows from (3) and (4) by using transitivity of equality
(6) $n = m$	(6) Follows from (5) by using cancellation property of addition

Statement (6) is the desired conclusion and therefore the proof is complete.

Theorem 4 *Let n and m represent counting numbers and let p represent a non-zero counting number. If $p \times n = p \times m$, then $n = m$.*
Hypothesis: $p \times n = p \times m$ and $p \neq 0$.
Conclusion: $n = m$.
The Proof:

Statements	Justifications
(1) $p \times n = p \times m$ and $p \neq 0$	(1) Hypothesis
(2) $n \times p = p \times n$	(2) Commutivity of multiplication
(3) $n \times p = p \times m$	(3) Follows from (2) and (1) by using transitivity of equality
(4) $p \times m = m \times p$	(4) Commutivity of multiplication
(5) $n \times p = m \times p$	(5) Follows from (3) and (4) by using transitivity of equality
(6) $n = m$	(6) Follows from (5) by using cancellation property of multiplication, since $p \neq 0$ by (1)

Statement (6) is the desired conclusion and therefore the proof is complete.

Exercises

1. Use Theorem 4 to solve these equations. Explain what you are doing and justify each step.
   (a) $2x = 30$. (*Suggestion:* Write $30 = 2 \times 15$.)

   (b) $3x = 9$.
2.   Use the cancellation property of addition and Theorem 4 to solve these equations. Justify each step.
   (a) $2x + 15 = 45$. (*Suggestion:* Write $45 = 30 + 15$ and use cancellation of addition first.)
   (b) $3x + 4 = 19$.
   (c) $16x + 2 = 18$.

The next theorem looks very much like the distributive property but it is actually a different statement.

Theorem 5   *Let n, m, and p represent counting numbers. Then $(n + m) \times p = (n \times p) + (m \times p)$.*
Hypothesis: n, m, and p represent counting numbers.
Conclusion: $(n + m) \times p = (n \times p) + (m \times p)$.
The Proof:

Statements	Justifications
(1) n, m, and p represent counting numbers	(1) ?
(2) $(n + m) \times p = p \times (n + m)$	(2) Commutivity of multiplication
(3) $p \times (n + m) = (p \times n) + (p \times m)$	(3) Distributive property
(4) $(n + m) \times p = (p \times n) + (p \times m)$	(4) Follows from (2) and (3) by using ?
(5) $p \times n = n \times p$ and $p \times m = m \times p$	(5) Commutivity of multiplication
(6) $(p \times n) + (p \times m) = (n \times p) + (m \times p)$	(6) Follows from (5) by using well-definedness of addition
(7) $(n + m) \times p = (n \times p) + (m \times p)$	(7) Follows from (4) and (6) by using transitivity of equality

Statement (7) is the desired conclusion and therefore the proof is complete.

The counting number 0 has a number of important properties. We have already seen that 0 is the additive identity. The number 0 behaves much differently with respect to multiplication; that is, $n \times m = 0$ if either $n = 0$ or $m = 0$.

Theorem 6   *If n and m are counting numbers and if either $n = 0$ or $m = 0$, then $n \times m = 0$.*

Since the proof of Theorem 6 is somewhat long and not particularly enlightening let us omit it and go on to the companion theorem to Theorem 6. Suppose n and m are counting numbers such that $n \times m = 0$. Can we draw any conclusions?

Theorem 7 *If n and m are counting numbers and if n × m = 0, then either n = 0 or m = 0.*

Hypothesis: n × m = 0.

Conclusion: Either $n = 0$ or $m = 0$.

The Proof: First of all let us observe that if $n = 0$ we are done; for all we are trying to prove is that one of n and m is zero, so if n is zero we are finished. Therefore let us assume that n is not zero. We shall prove that in this case m is zero.

Statements	Justifications
(1) $n \times m = 0$ and $n \neq 0$	(1) Hypothesis and the remark made above
(2) $0 = n \times 0$	(2) Follows from Theorem 6 by using symmetry of equality
(3) $n \times m = n \times 0$	(3) Follows from (1) and (2) by using transitivity of equality
(4) $m = 0$	(4) Follows from Theorem 4 since by (1) n is not zero

⧓*

Go back now and examine carefully the statements of Theorems 6 and 7. Each of these theorems is the converse of the other and so they may be combined into a theorem of the "if and only if" form as follows:

Theorem 8 *If n and m are counting numbers, then n × m = 0 if and only if either n = 0 or m = 0.*

Theorems which are converses of each other are commonly combined into an "if and only if" theorem in this way.

Finally, let us note that Theorem 7 can be rephrased as:

If n and m are counting numbers and if n ≠ 0 and m ≠ 0, then n × m ≠ 0.

This statement is the *contrapositive* of Theorem 7.

Exercises

1. Supply the missing parts of the following proof.

    Theorem 9 *The additive identity is unique. That is, if i is a counting number such that n + i = n for all counting numbers n, then i = 0.*
    Hypothesis: ?
    Conclusion: ?

---

* This symbol will be used to indicate end of proof.

The Proof:

Statements	Justifications
(1) $n + i = n$	(1) ?
(2) $n + 0 = n$	(2) ?
(3) $n = n + 0$	(3) Follows from (2) by using ?
(4) $n + i = n + 0$	(4) Follows from (1) and (3) by using ?
(5) $i = 0$	(5) Follows from (4) by using Theorem ?

‡

2. Here are four theorems whose proofs are relatively elementary. To prove them begin with the expression on the left and change it into the expression on the right by applications of the associative and commutative properties of addition.
   (a) Theorem A. $(n + m) + p = (n + p) + m$.
   (b) Theorem B. $(n + m) + p = p + (m + n)$.
   (c) Theorem C. $(n + m) + p = (m + p) + n$.
   (d) Theorem D. $n + (m + p) = m + (n + p)$.
3. State and prove the analogs of Theorems A through D of Exercise 2 for multiplication of counting numbers. (*Suggestion:* Because of the similarity between the properties of multiplication and addition of counting numbers, these analogs for multiplication can be proved by taking the proofs of the corresponding theorems for addition and replacing addition by multiplication in both the statements and justifications of these proofs.)

There is almost no end to the theorems that are available for us to prove. Having studied a few theorems, however, the reader will have begun to appreciate some of the difficulties involved in presenting a precise verification of a given statement even though the actual content of the statement may be very obvious. He will also have observed that the properties of equality are used over and over again in proofs. Because these properties of equality are needed so often in a proof, they tend to hide the more significant aspects of the proof. We shall therefore minimize their use in subsequent proofs. Thus we shall omit steps involving only the use of reflexivity, symmetry, or transitivity whenever the insertion of these steps would cloud the more significant aspects of the proof or make it overlong.

Review Questions

1. What do we mean by the *foundations* of the deductive system of counting numbers? According to our development of this deductive system, what are the foundations?
2. Each of the proofs that we have seen thus far begins with a statement called the _____ of the theorem and ends with a statement called the _____ of the theorem.
3. If the product of two counting numbers is zero, then _____.
4. There are many different ways to lay the foundations for the deductive system of counting numbers. Why did we choose this particular foundation?

SUBTRACTION AND DIVISION OF COUNTING NUMBERS

We continue our development of the system of counting numbers with the introduction of subtraction of counting numbers and division of counting numbers. These processes are a step above addition and multiplication in the logical hierarchy of concepts. They are defined concepts, and are defined in terms of the undefined concepts of addition and multiplication. After defining them we shall investigate their properties. Then we shall state and prove a few of the more useful theorems involving subtraction and division.

Subtraction of Counting Numbers

Subtraction of counting numbers is defined in terms of addition of counting numbers.

Definition of Subtraction of Counting Numbers   *The process of subtraction, denoted by the symbol* $-$*, is defined as follows: If* n *and* m *are counting numbers, then* n $-$ m *represents that counting number* d *which satisfies the equation*

$$n = m + d$$

If no such counting number d *exists, then* m *cannot be subtracted from* n *and the symbol* n $-$ m *is meaningless.*

For example, $6 - 4$ equals 2 because 2 satisfies the equation $6 = 4 + d$; that is, if d represents 2, then the statement is true. Why is $8 - 5 = 3$? Because $8 = 5 + 3$.

It is important to understand clearly the significance of this definition. *Subtraction is defined in terms of addition.* That is, the equations

$$n - m = d$$

and

$$n = m + d$$

express precisely the same relationship between the three counting numbers n, m, and d. The subtraction process is actually performed by using addition. To subtract m from n, we find the counting number d such that $m + d$ is equal to n. What is the result of subtracting 7 from 15? We try to find the counting number d such that $7 + d$ is equal to 15. Since 7 increased by 8 equals 15, we conclude that $15 - 7 = 8$.

The relation between subtraction and addition as displayed by this definition ought not to be new to the reader. As an example of where he has seen this before, recall how the subtraction problem

$$\begin{array}{r} \text{Minuend} \\ -\ \text{subtrahend} \\ \hline \text{difference} \end{array}$$

is checked. The check is to add the subtrahend and the difference. If the subtraction was performed correctly then this sum should be equal to the minuend. That is

$$\text{Minuend} - \text{subtrahend} = \text{difference}$$

is correct if

$$\text{Minuend} = \text{subtrahend} + \text{difference}$$

This is precisely the definition of subtraction in terms of addition.

There are two kinds of addition problems. First are those problems typified by the problem

$$3 + 5 = ?$$

Second, there is the kind of problem typified by

$$? + 3 = 8$$

Each of these types of addition problem is often encountered in arithmetic. Subtraction is defined only because it is very *convenient* to have available a process by means of which the statement $n + 3 = 8$ can be "solved for n": $n = 8 - 3$.

Exercises

1. Write each of these addition problems as a subtraction problem.
   (a) $n + 23 = 145$.   (c) $15 + 6 + n = 35$.
   (b) $34 + n = 111$.   (d) $34 + 4 = n$.
2. Write each of these subtraction problems as an addition problem.
   (a) $15 - n = 7$.
   (b) $n - 14 = 6$.
   (c) $15 - 4 = n$.
3. Supply justifications for the statements in the proof of the following theorem.
   Theorem   If $n - m = d$, then $n - d = m$.
   Hypothesis: $n - m = d$.
   Conclusion: $n - d = m$.
   The Proof:

Statements		Justifications	
(1)	$n - m = d$	(1)	Hypothesis
(2)	$n = m + d$	(2)	?
(3)	$m + d = d + m$	(3)	?
(4)	$n = d + m$	(4)	?
(5)	$n - d = m$	(5)	?

PROPERTIES OF SUBTRACTION

Now let us examine subtraction to see which properties it possesses. It is important to acknowledge these properties for it is only by means of its properties that we are able to use subtraction in arithmetic.

1. SUBTRACTION OF COUNTING NUMBERS DOES NOT POSSESS THE CLOSURE PROPERTY. If n and m represent counting numbers, then the symbol $n - m$ does not necessarily represent a counting number. For example, the symbol $6 - 9$ does not represent a counting number since there is no counting number d such that $6 = 9 + d$. So subtraction of counting numbers does not possess the first part of the closure property. However, subtraction of counting numbers does possess the uniqueness part of the closure property in the sense that *if* the symbol $n - m$ is meaningful, then it represents a unique counting number. This fact is very important and we shall refer to it often. Consequently it is convenient to give it a special name. To say that the symbol $n - m$ represents a unique counting number when it is meaningful we shall say that subtraction of counting numbers is *well-defined*. We may therefore phrase the well-defined-ness property as follows: *If n and m represent counting numbers such that n − m is meaningful, then n − m represents a unique counting number.* Another more convenient way to phrase this statement is: *If n, m, a, and b represent counting numbers such that n = a and m = b, then the symbols n − m and a − b are either both meaningless or both meaningful, in which case they are equal.* This formulation of the well-definedness property is the most convenient in applications. It is sometimes verbalized as, "Equals subtracted from equals are equal."

2. SUBTRACTION OF COUNTING NUMBERS IS NOT COMMUTATIVE. That is, it is not true that $n - m = m - n$ for every possible pair of counting numbers n and m. The reader can easily supply an example of this.

3. SUBTRACTION IS NOT ASSOCIATIVE. If subtraction were associative, then the symbols $n - (m - p)$ and $(n - m) - p$ would represent the same counting number no matter which counting numbers n, m, and p represent. Hence in order to prove that subtraction of counting numbers is not associative, it is only necessary to find three specific counting numbers for which these symbols are not equal. Such a triple of counting numbers would then be a counter-example to the associativity of subtraction. Consider the counting numbers 6, 4, and 1. We compute:

$$6 - (4 - 1) = 6 - (3) = 3$$

while

$$(6 - 4) - 1 = (2) - 1 = 1$$

Since $1 \neq 3$, the numbers 6, 4, and 1 provide a counterexample to the associativity of subtraction.

4. ZERO IS AN IDENTITY FOR SUBTRACTION.   That is, no matter which counting number n represents, $n - 0 = n$.

5. SUBTRACTION OF COUNTING NUMBERS POSSESSES THE CANCELLATION PROPERTY. That is, if n, m, and p are counting numbers such that

$$n - p = m - p$$

then

$$n = m$$

The cancellation property of subtraction can be used to solve certain kinds of equations. Here is an example.

EXAMPLE.   Solve the equation $n - 4 = 9$.
Solution: Since $9 = 13 - 4$ we use transitivity of equality to write

$$n - 4 = 13 - 4$$

Then using the cancellation property of subtraction we can conclude that

$$n = 13$$

Addition of counting numbers is important in the system of counting numbers because of its many properties. Since only some of these properties are possessed by subtraction of counting numbers, this process is of considerably less importance in the system of counting numbers. The most significant fact about subtraction of counting numbers is that it does not possess the closure property. Because of this we must be careful not to subtract when it is impossible to do so.

Exercises

1. Find three examples which show that subtraction of counting numbers does not possess the closure property. Explain fully using the definition of subtraction.
2. Find four counterexamples which show that subtraction is not commutative.
3. Is it ever possible that $n - m$ is equal to $m - n$?
4. Find four counterexamples to the associativity of subtraction.
5. Is it possible to find counting numbers such that $(n - m) - p$ is equal to $n - (m - p)$?
6. Supply justifications for the following proof that 0 is the subtractive identity.
   Theorem $n - 0 = n$ *for all counting numbers n.*
   Hypothesis: n *is a counting number.*
   Conclusion: $n - 0 = n$.
   The Proof:

Statements	Justifications
(1) n is a counting number	(1) ?
(2) $0 + n = n$	(2) Theorem ?
(3) $n = 0 + n$	(3) From (2) by using ?
(4) $n - 0 = n$	(4) From (3) by using ?

‡

7. Supply justifications for the statements in the proof of this theorem which states that subtraction possesses the cancellation property.

Theorem *If* $n - p = m - p$, *then* $n = m$.
Hypothesis: $n - p = m - p$.
Conclusion: $n = m$.
The Proof:

Statements	*Justifications*
(1) $n - p = m - p$	(1) ?
(2) $n - p = x$ and $m - p = x$, where x is a counting number	(2) This is simply a different way of phrasing statement (1)
(3) $n = p + x$ and $m = p + x$	(3) From (2) by using ?
(4) $n = m$	(4) From (3) by using ?

⁂

THE IMPORTANCE OF SUBTRACTION IN ARITHMETIC

We have already noted that there is no logical necessity for defining subtraction. That is, since subtraction problems are really worked by using addition we could simply omit subtraction from arithmetic and do everything with addition. But this would be decidedly inconvenient. Thus subtraction is introduced and discussed because of its convenience. But just how is this operation convenient? How can subtraction be used to make our thinking about arithmetic problems easier? Let us look at an example.

Suppose n represents a counting number. Add 5 to n and then subtract 5 from this sum. What is obtained? That is, $(n + 5) - 5 = ?$ Or, suppose we begin with n and subtract 5 from n and then add 5 to this difference. What do we obtain? That is, $(n - 5) + 5 = ?$ Obviously in each case the answer is n. This is the content of the following theorems which are of immense use in dealing with problems involving both addition and subtraction.

Theorem 10 *If* n *and* m *represent counting numbers, then* $(n + m) - m = n$.
Hypothesis: n and m represent counting numbers.
Conclusion: $(n + m) - m = n$.
The Proof:

Statements	*Justifications*
(1) n and m represent counting numbers	(1) ?
(2) $n + m = m + n$	(2) An axiom (Which?)
(3) $(n + m) - m = n$	(3) Follows from (2) by using the definition of subtraction

⁂

Theorem 11 *If* n *and* m *represent counting numbers such that* $n - m$ *is meaningful, then* $(n - m) + n$.

Hypothesis: n, m, and $n - m$ represent counting numbers.
Conclusion: $(n - m) + m = n$.
The Proof:

Statements	Justifications
(1) $n - m = d$, where d is a counting number	(1) Hypothesis
(2) $n = m + d$	(2) Follows from (1) by using ?
(3) $d + m = n$	(3) Follows from (2) by using (i) symmetry of equality, (ii) commutivity of addition, and (iii) transitivity of equality
(4) $(n - m) + m = d + m$	(4) Follows from (1) by using ?
(5) $(n - m) + m = n$	(5) ?

⁑

These two theorems display the importance of subtraction in arithmetic; subtraction is useful because of the way it is connected with addition as demonstrated in these theorems. Here are some examples of how these theorems may be used.

EXAMPLE 1.   Consider the equation $n + 3 = 6$. We already know one way to solve this equation using the cancellation property of addition. (Write $6 = 3 + 3$ and cancel the 3's.) The more conventional way to solve this equation is by subtracting 3 from both sides of the equation. This familiar process is in fact justified by the well-definedness property of subtraction. That is, from the equations

$$n + 3 = 6 \qquad \text{and} \qquad 3 = 3$$

we can obtain the equation

$$(n + 3) - 3 = 6 - 3$$

The next step is to apply Theorem 10 to the lefthand side of this equation. We obtain the equation

$$n = 6 - 3$$

from which we conclude that $n = 3$ ($6 - 3 = 3$ since $6 = 3 + 3$).

EXAMPLE 2.   To solve the equation

$$n - 3 = 6$$

we can use the cancellation property of subtraction (writing $6 = 9 - 3$ and cancelling the 3's to obtain $n = 9$) or we can first add 3 to both sides of the equation (justified by the well-definedness property of addition)

$$(n - 3) + 3 = 6 + 3$$

and then apply Theorem 11 to get

$$n = 6 + 3$$

or $n = 9$.

Exercises

1. Solve each of these equations in the manner of Example 1 above. Give reasons for each step.
    (a) $n + 7 = 10$.   (b) $n + 12 = 92$.   (c) $2n + 5 = 11$.
2. Solve these equations in the manner of Example 2 above. Give reasons for each step.
    (a) $n - 6 = 2$.   (b) $n - 7 = 6$.   (c) $3n - 15 = 15$.
3. Solve each of the equations in Exercise 2 using the definition of subtraction, and give reasons for each step.
4. Solve the equations of Exercise 2 using the cancellation property of subtraction, and give reasons for each step.
5. Solve in any way you like and give reasons for each step.
    (a) $2x - 3 = 9$.
    (b) $2(x - 4) = 16$. (*Suggestion:* Begin by writing 16 as 2×8 and using Theorem 4.)
    (c) $3(2x - 1) = 27$.
    (d) $7(3x - 4) = 14$.

SOME OTHER THEOREMS

Here are four more theorems which are often useful. In these theorems n, m, and p represent counting numbers and we assume that all differences are meaningful.

Theorem 12 $(n - m) + p = (n + p) - m$.

Theorem 13 $(n - m) - p = (n - p) - m$.

Theorem 14 $n - (m + p) = (n - m) - p$.

Theorem 15 $n - (m - p) = (n - m) + p$.

These theorems can be useful in computations involving subtraction or subtraction and addition. We shall prove the first theorem and leave the others as exercises.

Proof of Theorem 12:   Since it is assumed that $n - m$ is meaningful, we may begin by putting $n - m = x$ where x is a counting number.

(1) $n - m = x$	(1) Remark above
(2) $n = m + x$	(2) From (1) by using the definition of subtraction
(3) $n + p = (m + x) + p$	(3) From (2) by using well-definedness of addition
(4) $n + p = (x + p) + m$	(4) Theorem C, Exercise (2), page 56
(5) $(n + p) - m = [(x + p) + m] - m$	(5) From (4) by using well-definedness of subtraction
(6) $[(x + p) + m] - m = x + p$	(6) Theorem 10

(7) $x + p = (n - m) + p$

(7)   From (1) by using well-definedness of addition

(8) $(n + p) - m = (n - m) + p$

(8)   From (5), (6), (7) by using transitivity of equality

(9) $(n - m) + p = (n + p) - m$

(9)   From (8) by using symmetry of equality

❀

Exercises

1. Supply the justifications.
    Theorem 13 $(n - m) - p = (n - p) - m$.
    The Proof:

    (1) $(n - p) - m = x$, where x is a counting number

    (1)   The symbol $(n - p) - m$ is meaningful, and so is equal to some counting number

    (2) $n - p = m + x$
    (3) $n = p + (m + x)$
    (4) $p + (m + x) = m + (p + x)$

    (2)   From (1) by using ?
    (3)   From (2) by using ?
    (4)   Theorem D, Exercise (2), page 56

    (5) $n = m + (p + x)$
    (6) $n - m = p + x$
    (7) $(n - m) - p = x$
    (8) $(n - m) - p = (n - p) - m$

    (5)   From (3) and (4) by using ?
    (6)   From (5) by using ?
    (7)   From (6) by using ?
    (8)   From (1) and (7) by using ?

❀

2. Supply the justifications.
    Theorem 14 $n - (m + p) = (n - m) - p$.
    The Proof:

    (1) $n - (m + p) = x$, where x is a counting number

    (1)   The symbol $n - (m + p)$ is meaningful, and so represents some counting number

    (2) $n = (m + p) + x$
    (3) $n = m + (p + x)$
    (4) $n - m = p + x$
    (5) $(n - m) - p = x$
    (6) $n - (m + p) = (n - m) - p$

    (2)   From (1) by using ?
    (3)   From (2) by using ?
    (4)   From (3) by using ?
    (5)   From (4) by using ?
    (6)   From (1) and (5) by using ?

❀

3. Supply the justifications.
    Theorem 15 $n - (m - p) = (n - m) + p$.
    The Proof:

    (1) $n - (m - p) = x$, where x is some counting number

    (1)   The symbol $n - (m - p)$ is meaningful, and so represents some counting number

(2)	$n = (m - p) + x$	(2)	From (1) by using ?
(3)	$n = (m + x) - p$	(3)	From (2) by using Theorem 12
(4)	$(m + x) - p = n$	(4)	From (3) by using ?
(5)	$m + x = p + n$	(5)	From (4) by using ?
(6)	$n + p = m + x$	(6)	From (5) by using ?
(7)	$(n + p) - m = x$	(7)	From (6) by using ?
(8)	$(n - m) + p = x$	(8)	From (7) by using Theorem ?
(9)	$n - (m - p) = (n - m) + p$	(9)	From (1) and (8) by using ?

‡‡

4. Prove that zero is the only identity for subtraction. That is, supply a proof of the
   Theorem *If $n - i = n$ for every counting number n, then $i = 0$.*
   (*Suggestion:* Replace the statement about subtraction ($n - i = n$) with a statement about addition by using the definition of subtraction.)
5. Subtraction and multiplication are related by a distributive property in the same way that addition and multiplication are related by a distributive property. State the distributive property shared by subtraction and multiplication.

For the time being we conclude our discussion of subtraction of counting numbers. The most important things to remember about subtraction are the way it is defined in terms of addition, its properties, and the two very important theorems (Theorems 10 and 11) which display the importance of subtraction in the arithmetic of the counting numbers.

Review Questions

1. How is subtraction of counting numbers defined?
2. What do we mean when we say that subtraction is a less fundamental concept than is addition?
3. What do we mean when we say that subtraction problems are in fact worked by using addition?
4. What are the properties of subtraction? How do these compare with the properties of addition?
5. What are the theorems which display the convenience of subtraction? How are these theorems used in solving equations?
6. "Let n and m represent counting numbers and consider the counting number $n - m$." What is wrong with this statement?
7. Give an example of how the well-definedness property of subtraction is used in solving equations.
8. Give an example of how the cancellation property of subtraction is used in solving equations.

Division of Counting Numbers

The last of the four principal processes defined on the collection of counting numbers is division. Division is defined in terms of multiplication in much the same way that subtraction was defined in terms of addition. Consequently our study of division will closely parallel our study of subtraction.

Definition of Division of Counting Numbers   *If n and m are counting numbers and m is not equal to zero, then the result of dividing n by m, symbolized by n ÷ m, is that counting number q which satisfies the equation*

$$n = m \times q$$

If no such counting number q exists, then n cannot be divided by m and the symbol n ÷ m is meaningless.

Hence, for example, 6 divided by 2 (6 ÷ 2) is equal to 3 because 3 satisfies the equation $6 = 2 \times q$. That is, this is a true statement if the symbol q represents 3. But 5 cannot be divided by 2 and the symbol 5 ÷ 2 is meaningless because there is no number q which makes $5 = 2 \times q$ a true statement.

If $n \div m = q$, we call n the *dividend*, m the *divisor*, and q the *quotient*. Also, when we say that "m divides n" we mean that the symbol $n \div m$ is meaningful—that there is a quotient q such that $n \div m = q$. When $n \div$ m is meaningful we call m a *divisor* of n.

The definition of division of counting numbers avoids the possibility that the divisor m can be equal to zero. This is done because a symbol of the form $n \div 0$, where n is a counting number, cannot be assigned any meaning consistent with the meanings of other symbols $n \div m$ where m is different from zero. Let us see why.

Suppose we were to omit this restriction from the definition. The definition would then look like

Incorrect Definition of Division.   The symbol $n \div m$, where n and m are counting numbers, represents that counting number q such that $n = m \times q$.

Consider the symbol 7 ÷ 0. Is it possible to find a counting number q such that $7 \div 0 = q$? According to the definition above, if it were possible to find such a number q, then it would be true that $7 = 0 \times q$. But since $0 \times q = 0$ (why?), it would then follow by transitivity of equality that $7 = 0$. That is, if there is a number q such that $7 \div 0 = q$, then $7 = 0$. This is absurd. We are therefore forced to conclude that $7 \div 0$ cannot be assigned any meaning. The same is true for any other symbol of the form $n \div 0$ *where n is different from zero*.

But what about the symbol 0 ÷ 0? Can this symbol be assigned meaning? Examine each of the following statements:

$$0 = 0 \times 0$$
$$0 = 0 \times 1$$
$$0 = 0 \times 2$$
$$0 = 0 \times 3$$
$$0 = 0 \times 4$$

etc.

Each of these statements is true. According to the above (incorrect) definition, since each of these statements is true, each of the following statements would also be true:

$$0 \div 0 = 0$$
$$0 \div 0 = 1$$
$$0 \div 0 = 2$$
$$0 \div 0 = 3$$
$$0 \div 0 = 4$$

etc.

This means that the symbol $0 \div 0$ could represent *any* counting number! Because there is no good way to select a *unique* meaning for the symbol $0 \div 0$, we do not assign *any* meaning to this symbol.

To sum up, it is not possible to find a unique counting number q such that $n \div 0 = q$, since if $n \neq 0$, there is no such q at all and if $n = 0$, then q could be any counting number at all. To avoid this difficulty we incorporate into the definition of division the restriction that the divisor must be different from zero.

The definition of division tells us that the equations

$$n = m \times q$$

and

$$n \div m = q$$

express precisely the same relation between the three counting numbers n, m, and q (m different from zero). In light of this, it is not in fact necessary to define the division process at all. Every question about division can be rephrased as a question about multiplication, and in this sense division is, logically speaking, an unnecessary operation. However, since such questions as "What number multiplied by 5 is equal to 20?" arise with great frequency, it is convenient to define the division process.

It is particularly important to notice the similarity between the definition of subtraction in terms of addition and the definition of division in terms of multiplication. If in the definition of subtraction we replace the words "addition" and "subtraction" by (respectively) "multiplication" and "division," we almost obtain the definition of division. (We have to insert the restriction that the divisor cannot be zero.) This similarity between subtraction and division can be used to advantage. For example, because of this similarity we should expect that division will have the same properties as does subtraction. Also, we should expect that the theorems we have seen concerning subtraction will have analogs for division.

PROPERTIES OF DIVISION

We shall not discuss the properties of division in detail. Some of them are left to the reader to justify.

1. DIVISION OF COUNTING NUMBERS DOES NOT POSSESS THE CLOSURE PROPERTY. It is not always possible to perform the division of counting numbers process. For example, the symbol $6 \div 5$ is meaningless since there is no counting number q such that $6 = 5 \times q$. On the other hand *if* the symbol $n \div m$ is meaningful, then it represents a unique counting number. This is what is meant by saying that division of counting numbers is *well-defined*. To say that division of counting numbers is well-defined means that *if* it is possible to divide one counting number by another, then the result of this division is a unique counting number. We can phrase this important property more conveniently as follows: *To say that division of counting numbers is well-defined means that if n, m, a, and b are counting numbers such that n = a and m = b, then the symbols n ÷ a and m ÷ b are either both meaningless or are both meaningful in which case they are equal.* In other words, changing the names of the dividend and divisor does not change the result of the division process.

2. DIVISION OF COUNTING NUMBERS IS NOT COMMUTATIVE. The counting numbers 2 and 4 provide a counterexample to the commutivity of division; that is, $2 \div 4 \neq 4 \div 2$.

3. DIVISION OF COUNTING NUMBERS IS NOT ASSOCIATIVE. There are counting numbers n, m, and p such that $(n \div m) \div p \neq n \div (m \div p)$. For example, consider 8, 4, and 2. We compute:

$$(8 \div 4) \div 2 = 2 \div 2 = 1$$

but

$$8 \div (4 \div 2) = 8 \div 2 = 4$$

4. ONE IS AN IDENTITY FOR DIVISION OF COUNTING NUMBERS. Thus no matter which counting number n represents, $n \div 1 = n$.

5. DIVISION OF COUNTING NUMBERS POSSESSES THE CANCELLATION PROPERTY. Thus if n, m, and p are counting numbers such that

$$n \div p = m \div p$$

then

$$n = m$$

The following example shows how this property can be used in solving equations.

EXAMPLE.   Solve the equation $n \div 3 = 7$.
   Solution: Since $7 = 21 \div 3$ we may write

$$n \div 3 = 21 \div 3$$

(Why?) Then the cancellation property of division tells us that

$$n = 21$$

Exercises

1. Explain why $5 \div 2$ is meaningless.
2. Find counterexamples to the closure, commutivity, and associativity of division of counting numbers.
3. How do the properties of division compare with the properties of subtraction?
4. Find three different triples of counting numbers such that $n \div (m \div p) = (n \div m) \div p$.
5. Supply justifications for the following proof that one is the divisive identity.

   Theorem $n \div 1 = n$ *for all counting numbers* n.
   The Proof:

(1)	n is a counting number	(1)	?
(2)	$1 \times n = n$	(2)	?
(3)	$n = 1 \times n$	(3)	?
(4)	$n \div 1 = n$	(4)	?

   ‡‡

6. The following theorem states that division of counting numbers possesses the cancellation property. Supply justifications for each step of this proof.

   Theorem *If* $n \div p = m \div p$, *then* $n = m$.
   The Proof:

(1)	$n \div p = m \div p$	(1)	?
(2)	$n \div p = y$ and $m \div p = y$, where y is a counting number	(2)	?
(3)	$n = p \times y$ and $m = p \times y$	(3)	?
(4)	$n = m$	(4)	?

   ‡‡

7. Solve these equations by using the cancellation property of division. Justify each step.
   (a) $n \div 2 = 14$. (*Suggestion:* Write $14 = 28 \div 2$.)
   (b) $n \div 3 = 14 - 2$.
   (c) $3n \div 4 = 12$.

THE IMPORTANCE OF DIVISION IN ARITHMETIC

Recall Theorems 10 and 11 (p. 61) which demonstrated the importance of subtraction in arithmetic. The analogs of these theorems for division (stated below) display the importance of division in arithmetic.

Theorem 16 *If* n *and* m *represent counting numbers and* m *is not zero, then* $(n \div m) \times m = n$.

Theorem 17 *If* n *and* m *represent counting numbers such that* $n \div m$ *is meaningful, then* $(n \div m) \times m = n$.

These theorems show that, in a manner of speaking, division has the effect of "undoing" the effect of multiplication and vice versa. Their proofs are included in the exercises.

Theorems 16 and 17 are useful in solving equations, as the next two examples demonstrate.

EXAMPLE 1.   Solve the equation $3n = 18$.

Solution: We already know one way to solve this equation. We can write $18 = 3 \times 6$ and then cancel the 3's. The more conventional way to work the problem is to divide both sides of the equation by 3:

(1) $3n = 18$	(1) Given equation
(2) $(3n) \div 3 = 18 \div 3$	(2) Well-definedness of division
(3) $n = 18 \div 3$	(3) This results from applying Theorem 16 to the left side of equation (2)*
(4) $n = 6$	(4) $18 \div 3 = 6$ since $18 = 3 \times 6$

EXAMPLE 2.   Solve the equation $n \div 4 = 3$.

Solution: This equation can be solved by using the cancellation property of division, writing $3 = 12 \div 4$ and then cancelling the 4's. It can also be solved by multiplying both sides of the equation by 4:

(1) $n \div 4 = 3$	(1) Given equation
(2) $(n \div 4) \times 4 = 3 \times 4$	(2) Well-definedness of multiplication
(3) $n = 3 \times 4$	(3) Applying Theorem 17 to the left side of the equation (2)
(4) $n = 12$	(4) Performing multiplication

Exercises

1. Solve the following equations in the manner of Example 1. Give a reason for each step.
   (a) $5n = 75$.   (b) $2n = 88$.   (c) $3n + 2 = 17$.
2. Solve the following equations in the manner of Example 2 above. Give a reason for each step.
   (a) $n \div 2 = 5$.   (b) $n \div 7 = 0$.   (c) $2n \div 4 = 3$.
3. Supply justifications for this proof of Theorem 16.

   The Proof:

(1) n and m represent counting numbers	(1) ?
(2) $n \times m = m \times n$	(2) ?
(3) $(n \times m) \div m = n$	(3) From (2) by using ?

❡

* Actually the theorem tells us that $(n \times 3) \div 3 = n$, but it is easy to see that since multiplication is commutative $3n = n \times 3$ and so the theorem can be used.

4. Supply justification for this proof of Theorem 17.

   The Proof:

   (1) n, m and $n \div m$ represent counting numbers   (1) ?

   (2) $n \div m = q$, where q is some counting number   (2) $n \div m$ represents a counting number

   (3) $n = m \times q$ (3) From (2) by using ?

   (4) $m \times q = m \times (n \div m)$ (4) From (2) by using ?

   (5) $n = m \times (n \div m)$ (5) From (3) and (4) by using ?

   (6) $m \times (n \div m) = n$ (6) From (5) by using ?

   (7) $(n \div m) \times m = n$ (7) From (6) by using ?

✄

5. Solve the following equations in any way that you like. Give reasons for each step of the solution.

   (a) $n \div 3 = 2$.

   (b) $(2n) \div 3 = 4$.

   (c) $(2n \div 3) + 4 = 8$.

   (d) $(n + 2) \div 6 = 5$.

   (e) $(n - 2) \div 4 = 1$.

   (f) $(n - 2) \div 4 = 0$.

DISTRIBUTIVITY THEOREMS

We have seen that multiplication is related to both addition and subtraction by distributivity relationships. The same is true of division.

Theorem 18   *If n, m, and p represent counting numbers such that p divides both n and m, then p divides the sum of n and m. Moreover, $(n + m) \div p = (n \div p) + (m \div p)$.*

Hypothesis: p divides both n and m.

Conclusion: (I) p divides $n + m$.

      (II) $(n + m) \div p = (n \div p) + (m \div p)$.

The Proof:

(1) There are counting numbers x and y such that $n \div p = x$ and $m \div p = y$ (1) Hypothesis

(2) $n = px$ and $m = py$ (2) From (1) by using ?

(2) $n + m = px + py$ (3) From (2) by using ?

(4) $px + py = p(x + y)$ (4) Axiom (Which?)

(5) $n + m = p(x + y)$ (5) From (3) and (4) by using ?

Conclusion (I) follows from statement (5) by using the definition of "divides."

(6) $(n + m) \div p = x + y$ (6) From (5) by using ?

(7) $(n + m) \div p =$ (7)   From (1) and (6)
     $(n \div p) + (m \div p)$ by using ?

Statement (7) is the second part of the conclusion.

⁑

Theorem 19 *If n, m, and p represent counting numbers such that p divides both n and m, and if n − m is meaningful, then p divides the difference of n and m. Moreover, $(n - m) \div p = (n \div p) - (m \div p)$.*

The proof of this theorem is contained in Exercise (3) below.

Exercises

1. $(8 \div 2) - (6 \div 2) = ? \div 2.$
2. $(9 \div 3) + (? \div 3) = 15 \div 3.$
3. Here is the proof of Theorem 19. Supply justifications for each step.
    Hypothesis: (i) p divides both n and m.
                   (ii) $n - m$ is meaningful.
    Conclusion: (I) p divides $n - m$.
                   (II) $(n - m) \div p = (n \div p) - (m \div p)$.

    The Proof:

    (1)   There are counting numbers   (1)   Hypothesis (i)
          x and y such that
          $n \div p = x$ and $m \div p = y$
    (2) $n = px$ and $m = py$ (2)   From (1) by using ?
    (3) $n - m = px - py$ (3)   From Hypothesis (ii) and (2)
                                                    by using ?
    (4) $p(x - y) = px - py$ (4)   Subtraction and multiplication
                                                    share this distributive property
    (5) $n - m = p(x - y)$ (5)   From (3) and (4) by using ?

    Conclusion (I) follows from statement (5). (How?)

    (6) $(n - m) \div p = x - y$ (6)   From (5) by using ?
    (7) $(n - m) \div p =$ (7)   From (6) and (1) by using ?
          $(n \div p) - (m \div p)$

    Conclusion (II) is statement (7).

⁑

SOME OTHER THEOREMS

In our discussion of subtraction we examined four theorems (Theorems 12, 13, 14, and 15 on p. 63) involving both subtraction and addition of counting numbers. Because division is related to multiplication in much the same way that subtraction is related to addition, we can translate these theorems into theorems about division by replacing addition by multiplication and subtraction by division. These theorems then become

Theorem 20 $(n \div m) \times p = (n \times p) \div m.$

Theorem 21 $(n \div m) \div p = (n \div p) \div m.$

Theorem 22 $n \div (m \times p) = (n \div m) \div p.$

Theorem 23 $n \div (m \div p) = (n \div m) \times p.$

A proof for each of these theorems may be constructed by referring to the proof of the corresponding theorem for subtraction and addition and by replacing addition and subtraction wherever they occur in those proofs by, respectively, multiplication and division.

Here is the proof of Theorem 20. This proof was obtained from the proof of Theorem 12 by making the appropriate changes as described above. The reader should carefully compare this proof with that of Theorem 12 and see what changes have been made.

Proof of Theorem 20: Since it is assumed that $n \div m$ is meaningful, we may begin by putting $n \div m = x$, where x is a counting number.

(1)	$n \div m = x$	(1) Remark above
(2)	$n = m \times x$	(2) From (1) by using the definition of division
(3)	$n \times p = (m \times x) \times p$	(3) From (2) by using well-definedness of multiplication
(4)	$n \times p = (x \times p) \times m$	(4) From (3) by using Exercise 3, p. 56
(5)	$(n \times p) \div m =$ $[(x \times p) \times m] \div m$	(5) From (4) by using the well-definedness of division
(6)	$[(x \times p) \times m] \div m = x \times p$	(6) Theorem 16 (which is the analog of Theorem 10)
(7)	$x \times p = (n \div m) \times p$	(7) From (1) by using well-definedness of multiplication
(8)	$(n \times p) \div m = (n \div m) \times p$	(8) From (5), (6), (7) by using transitivity of equality
(9)	$(n \div m) \times p = (n \times p) \div m$	(9) From (8) by using symmetry of equality

Exercises

1. Using the proof of Theorem 13 (Exercise 1, p. 64), find a proof for Theorem 21. (*Suggestion:* Replace subtraction and addition in the proof of Theorem 13 by division and multiplication.)

2. Using the proof of Theorem 14 (Exercise 2, p. 64), construct a proof of Theorem 22.

3. Using the proof of Theorem 15 (Exercise 3, p. 64), construct a proof of Theorem 23.

4. Translate the following theorem into a theorem about subtraction and addition.

   Theorem   *If n, m, and p represent counting numbers such that p divides m, then p divides nm. Moreover, $nm \div p = n(m \div p)$.*

In this section we have defined subtraction and division of counting numbers. We have examined the properties of these processes and have stated and proved a few theorems about them. Our reason for presenting these proofs was to help the reader to gain some understanding of the nature of a mathematical proof. For the rest of this text we shall not prove many theorems—only those which are of central importance.

We are now finished with our preliminary study of the system of counting numbers. The next section deals with the general concept of an operation, and then we shall begin the development of the other important systems of numbers.

Review Questions

1. How is division of counting numbers defined?
2. Division is to multiplication as subtraction is to _____.
3. When will the symbol $n \div m$ be meaningless?
4. What is meant by a *divisor* of a number?
5. Why is it impossible to divide by zero?
6. What are the properties of division of counting numbers? How do these properties compare with those of multiplication?
7. Give an example of an equation solved by using the cancellation property of division.
8. Give an example of an equation solved by using the well-definedness property of division.
9. What are the two theorems which display the importance of division in arithmetic?
10. Addition, subtraction, multiplication, and division share certain properties which are called distributive properties. What are these? Which of them are axioms and which are theorems?

BINARY OPERATIONS AND THEIR PROPERTIES

Addition and multiplication of counting numbers are examples of what are called *binary operations*. In this section we shall discuss the general concept of a binary operation and some of the properties ascribable to binary operations.

Binary Operations

BINARY OPERATIONS ON THE COUNTING NUMBERS

Both addition and multiplication of counting numbers are processes by means of which given any two counting numbers we are able to find a unique third counting number. We earlier expressed this by saying that these processes possess the *closure property*. Such processes are called *binary operations on the collection of counting numbers*. By a binary operation on the counting numbers we mean a rule or instruction which tells how to assign a unique counting number to every pair of counting numbers regardless of the order in which these two counting numbers are given. Addition of counting numbers is a binary operation since it assigns a unique counting number (the *sum*) to every pair of counting numbers regardless of the order in which the counting numbers are given. Subtraction of counting numbers is not a binary operation because this process does not, for example, assign any counting number (that is, any *difference*) to the counting numbers 4 and 6 given in that order. We express this by saying that the symbol $4 - 6$ does not name a counting number.

There are many other binary operations on the counting numbers than addition and multiplication of counting numbers. We discuss two of these in the examples which follow.

EXAMPLE 1.   We define a binary operation on the counting numbers by giving a *rule* or *instruction* for finding the result of the binary operation applied to two counting numbers *n* and *m*. The instruction for performing the binary operation of this example is

> If *n* and *m* are counting numbers, then the result of performing the binary operation upon *n* and *m* is the largest counting number less than 11 which divides both *n* and *m*.

Let us represent this binary operation by the symbol * (just as addition is represented by + and multiplication by ×). Then $6 * 8 = 2$ since 2 is the largest counting number less than 11 which divides both 6 and 8. $7 * 9 = 1$. $15 * 20 = 5$. $100 * 20 = 10$. This process is a binary operation on the counting numbers, since the process can be applied to any pair of counting numbers and the result of the process is always a unique counting number. Thus the symbol $n * m$ represents exactly one counting number no matter which counting numbers the numerals *n* and *m* represent.

EXAMPLE 2.   Define a process, symbolized by *, on counting numbers according to this instruction:

> If *n* and *m* are counting numbers, then the result of the process applied to *n* and *m*, denoted by $n * m$, is the counting number $n + 2m$.

For example,

$$2 * 5 = 2 + 2(5) = 2 + 10 = 12$$
$$3 * 7 = 3 + 2(7) = 3 + 14 = 17$$
$$0 * 8 = 0 + 2(8) = 0 + 16 = 16$$
$$8 * 0 = 8 + 2(0) = 8 + 0 = 8$$
$$3 * 1 = 3 + 2(1) = 3 + 2 = 5$$
$$1 * 3 = 1 + 2(3) = 1 + 6 = 7$$

It is probably clear to the reader that this operation can always be performed and that the result of performing the operation is always a unique counting number. Even so, let us verify this.

1.   Let *n* and *m* represent any two counting numbers.
2.   Then since multiplication of counting numbers is a binary operation, the symbol $2m$ represents a unique counting number.
3.   Since *n* and $2m$ each represents a counting number, and since addition of counting numbers is a binary operation, we conclude that the symbol $n + 2m$, or $n * m$,

represents a unique counting number regardless of which counting numbers n and m represent.

Consequently this process is a binary operation on the counting numbers.

We ought to observe that the binary operation of Example 2 depends upon the order in which the two counting numbers to be operated upon are given. In general it is true that $n * m$ and $m * n$ are different counting numbers. For instance, $3 * 1 = 5$, while $1 * 3 = 7$.

Exercises

1. Let $*$ represent the process defined on the counting numbers by the instruction: "$n * m$ is the average of n and m"; that is,

$$n * m = (n + m) \div 2$$

Is this process a binary operation? Explain.

2. Let $*$ represent the process defined on the counting numbers according to the instruction: "$n * m$ is the least nonzero counting number divisible by both n and m." Is this process a binary operation? Explain. (*Suggestion:* What if n is zero?)

3. Let $*$ represent the process defined on the counting numbers according to the instruction given symbolically by the equation $n * m = nm - (n + m)$. Is this a binary operation? Explain.

4. Let $*$ represent the process defined on the counting numbers according to the instruction: "$n * m$ is the larger of n and m if $n \neq m$ and is equal to n if $n = m$." (We express this process symbolically as $n * m = \max [n, m]$.) Is this a binary operation? Explain.

BINARY OPERATIONS ON NONMATHEMATICAL OBJECTS

We have thus far mentioned only binary operations which are defined relative to the collection of counting numbers. In fact we may define binary operations on any collection of objects. In order for a process defined on a collection of objects to be a binary operation, it must possess the closure property. That is, if we denote the process by the symbol $*$, then the symbol $n * m$ must represent a unique object of the collection no matter which objects of the collection the symbols n and m represent. To demonstrate this idea let us examine two binary operations defined on collections of objects different from the counting numbers.

EXAMPLE 1. A BINARY OPERATION ON THE COLLECTION OF COLORS.*   Let us imagine the collection of all colors as being represented by a collection of paints, one paint for each color. Now given two colors it is possible to mix equal portions of the colors to produce a third color. This process of mixing colors is a *binary operation on the collection of all colors.* For example, the binary operation acts upon the colors blue and

---

* The word *color* is poorly defined in the language. We intend to ignore shades, hues, etc., when using the word in this example. For example, different shades of green will be regarded as the same color—green.

yellow to produce green, acts upon black and white to produce gray, and acts upon red and blue to produce purple. If we represent the mixing operation by the symbol ∗, then we can state the effect of this binary operation on these colors by writing

$$\text{Blue} * \text{yellow} = \text{green}$$
$$\text{Black} * \text{white} = \text{gray}$$
$$\text{Red} * \text{blue} = \text{purple}$$

This mixing process is a binary operation because any two colors can be mixed and because the result of mixing two colors is a unique color. Thus $n * m$ represents a unique color no matter which colors the symbols n and m represent.

EXAMPLE 2. A BINARY OPERATION ON THE COLLECTION OF ALL PLAYING CARDS. Define a binary operation on the collection of all playing cards according to the following instruction:

If n and m are playing cards, then the result of operating upon these two cards will be the playing card which has the suit of n and the rank of m.

For example, if we symbolize this operation by ∗, then

$$(10 \spadesuit) * (K \spadesuit) = (K \spadesuit)$$
$$(A \spadesuit) * (8 \heartsuit) = (8 \spadesuit)$$
$$(2 \heartsuit) * (6 \clubsuit) = (6 \heartsuit)$$

We are correct in referring to this process as a binary operation on playing cards because the process can always be performed and because the result of performing the process upon a pair of playing cards is a unique playing card.

Exercises

1. Define binary operations on the following collections of objects. Explain why your process is a binary operation.
    (a) The collection of all even counting numbers.
    (b) The collection of all digits.
    (c) The collection of all letters of the alphabet.
2. With respect to the collections of Exercise 1 define processes which fail to be binary operations because they may not always be performed.
3. With respect to the collections of Exercise 1 define processes which fail to be binary operations because while they may always be performed, the result of performing the process is not always a unique object of the collection.

THE DOMAIN OF DEFINITION OF A BINARY OPERATION

It is not possible to think of a binary operation without also thinking of the objects upon which the binary operation operates. Recall that throughout this chapter we have referred to "addition of counting numbers" and "multiplication of counting numbers." Whenever we used the term "addition" without specific reference to the collection of objects, it was clear from context that we meant addition *of counting numbers*. When discussing a binary operation it is necessary to mention

1. The objects upon which the binary operation operates.
2. The instruction which tells how the binary operation is to be performed.

The collection of objects upon which the binary operation operates will be called the *domain of definition* of the binary operation. To see the importance of always mentioning the domain of definition consider the following examples.

EXAMPLE 1.   Consider the process called *addition of even counting numbers*. As the name of the process implies, the process is defined on the collection of all even counting numbers and the instruction for performing the process is, "Add the given counting numbers." If we denote the process by the symbol $\oplus$, then if n and m are even counting numbers the instruction for performing the process can be given symbolically by the equation

$$n \oplus m = n + m$$

For example, $4 \oplus 6 = 10$ and $14 \oplus 18 = 32$.   This process is a binary operation because no matter which even counting numbers the symbols n and m represent, the symbol $n \oplus m$ represents exactly one even counting number.

EXAMPLE 2.   Consider the process called *addition of odd counting numbers*. The domain of definition of this process is the collection of all odd counting numbers and the instruction for performing the process is "Add the given numbers." Denoting the process by the symbol $\boxplus$ this instruction can be rendered in symbols by the equation

$$n \boxplus m = n + m$$

The important thing here is that *this process can never be performed* because the sum of two odd counting numbers is never an odd counting number! To say the same thing another way, no matter which odd counting numbers the symbols n and m represent, $n \boxplus m$ never represents an odd counting number. This process therefore does not possess the closure property and so is not a binary operation.

Comparing the processes of Examples 1 and 2 we see the necessity of always mentioning the domain of definition of a binary operation. It is not enough to say simply "addition," for there are different kinds of addition. If "addition" were thought to mean addition of counting numbers or addition of even counting numbers, then "addition" would refer to a binary operation. On the other hand, if "addition" were interpreted to mean addition of odd counting numbers, then not only would "addition" not be a binary operation, it would be a process which could never even be performed. The point is that unless it is clear from context, the domain of definition should always be specifically mentioned.

Exercises

1. In this problem the symbol

            + means addition of counting numbers
            $\oplus$ means addition of even counting numbers
            $\boxplus$ means addition of odd counting numbers

Which of the following symbols are meaningful? If a symbol is meaningful, state its meaning by identifying the number the symbol represents.

(a) $2 + 3, 2 \oplus 3, 2 \boxplus 3$.

(b) $4 + 8, 4 \oplus 8, 4 \boxplus 8$.

(c) $7 + 3, 7 \oplus 3, 7 \boxplus 3$.

(d) $1 + 0, 1 \oplus 0, 1 \boxplus 0$.

(e) $2 + 0, 2 \oplus 0, 2 \boxplus 0$.

(f) $2x + 2y, 2x + 2y, 2x \boxplus 2y$.

(g) $(2x + 1) + 2y, (2x + 1) \oplus 2y, (2x + 1) \boxplus 2y$.

(h) $(2x + 1) + (2y + 1), (2x + 1) \oplus (2y + 1), (2x + 1) \boxplus (2y + 1)$.

2.   Below is a list of processes defined on various sets of numbers. From the way we have named the processes it is clear what the set of numbers is upon which the process is to be performed. Which of these processes are binary operations? Explain.

(a) Multiplication of even counting numbers.

(b) Multiplication of odd counting numbers.

(c) Multiplication of digits.

(d) Division of even counting numbers.

(e) Subtraction of odd counting numbers.

(f) Addition of *trips* (by a *trip* we mean a number which is a multiple of 3: 0, 3, 6, 9, 12, and so on).

(g) Multiplication of trips.

(h) Subtraction of trips.

(i) Addition of *perfect squares* (a perfect square is a number which is equal to some number multiplied by itself, e.g., $1 = (1)(1)$, $4 = (2)(2)$, $9 = (3)(3)$, and so on).

(j) The *averaging process* on counting numbers (defined by using the instruction $n * m = (n + m) \div 2$).

(k) The averaging process on even counting numbers.

The Well-Definedness Property

Let the symbol $*$ represent a binary operation on some (unspecified) collection of objects. To say that this binary operation possesses the *well-definedness property* means that the effect of operating upon a pair of objects is in no way dependent upon the names assigned to the objects. This can more conveniently be expressed as follows: If $*$ represents a binary operation and if $n = m$ and $a = b$, then $n * a = m * b$.

Every binary operation possesses the well-definedness property for well-definedness is a logical consequence of the fact that the result of applying a binary operation to a pair of objects is a *unique* object. It is the uniqueness of the produced object which ensures the well-definedness of the binary operation. But even some processes, such as subtraction and division of counting numbers, which are not binary operations possess the property that changing the names of the objects being operated upon does not change the effect of the process. More precisely, if $*$ represents a process (such as subtraction or division of counting numbers), this process is said to possess the well-definedness property if whenever $n = m$ and $a = b$, either $n * a$ and $m * b$ are both meaningless or $n * a$ and $m * b$ are both meaningful and are equal.

It is perhaps difficult to see the entire significance of the well-definedness property until one has had the opportunity to examine some processes which are not well-defined. The following example is highly artificial but demonstrates rather dramatically how a process can depend on the names given to the objects to which the process is applied.

EXAMPLE. This process is defined on the collection of all counting numbers and will be denoted by the symbol $*$. The instruction for performing the process is long but not complicated. If n and m represent counting numbers, then perform the following three steps to determine the counting number $n * m$ which is the result of the process:

1. Write out the proper names of the counting numbers n and m.
2. Look at the first letters of these proper names and select the one which appears furthest along in the alphabet. (For example, T appears further along in the alphabet than F.)
3. Determine the position of this letter in the alphabet (first letter, second letter, fifteenth letter, and so on.) If this letter is the pth letter of the alphabet, then put $n * m = p$.

For example, let us compute $2 * 5$. We do it in three steps:

1. Write out the proper names for these numbers.

two and five

2. Look at the first letters of these proper names

T and F

and select the one furthest along in the alphabet.

T

3. Determine the position of the letter T in the alphabet.

T is the twentieth letter

Therefore the result of this process applied to 2 and 5 (in that order) is 20; i.e., $2 * 5 = 20$. Now instead of working this problem using the English language, use German. In German two is *zwei* and 5 is *fünf*. Then we consider the letters Z and F. The letter Z appears further along in the alphabet and is the 26th letter. Hence $2 * 5 = 26$. Now perform this process in French. Two is *deux* and five is *cinq*. Since D is the fourth letter of the alphabet, $2 * 5 = 4$. We conclude that in New York $2 * 5 = 20$, in Berlin $2 * 5 = 26$, and in Paris $2 * 5 = 4$. Here is an obvious example of a process which is not well-defined. Changing the names of the numbers to which the process is applied changes not only the *name* of the counting number which is the result of the process, but the resulting *number* itself. We might go back to the instruction for performing this process and change it to read in part: (1) Write out the *English language* proper names of the counting numbers *n* and *m*. Then (assuming there is only one proper name for each number in the English language—a debatable assumption) the revised instruction would define a well-defined process. But the instruction as it stands defines a process inadequately.

Except for a few special instances (which happily are of no concern to us) processes which are not well-defined are not of mathematical interest. We shall find therefore that all our processes have this important property. Of course, all binary operations have the property automatically, but there are a number of processes which are not binary operations involved in mathematics and all of these have the well-definedness property. The best that a process can be is a binary operation but if it cannot be that, then at least it can have the well-definedness property.

Exercises

1. Find a process defined on the collection of all people which is not well-defined. Explain why your process is not well-defined.
2. Find a process on the collection of all even counting numbers which is not well-defined. Explain why your process is not well-defined.
3. Define a process (symbolized by ∗) on the collection of all counting numbers as follows: If *n* and *m* are counting numbers, then write each of these numbers as the sum of two other numbers, $n = a + b$ and $m = c + d$, and form the number $ac + bd$. This number is the result of performing the process upon *n* and *m*; that is, $n * m = ac + bd$. For example, to find $4 * 7$ write $4 = 2 + 2$ and $7 = 3 + 4$. Since $(2)(3) + (2)(4) = 14$, $4 * 7 = 14$. Explain why this process is not well-defined.

The Commutative and Associative Properties

The properties of commutativity and associativity are meaningful only for binary operations. To say that a binary operation ∗ possesses *the commutative property* means that the symbols $n * m$ and $m * n$ represent the same object no matter which objects the symbols *n* and *m* represent. Thus, a binary operation is commutative if $n * m = m * n$ for all *n* and *m* in the domain of definition. To say that a binary operation ∗ possesses *the associative property* means that the symbols $(n * m) * p$ and $n * (m * p)$ represent the same object, no matter which objects the symbols *n*, *m*, and *p* represent. Thus a binary operation ∗ is associative if $(n * m) * p = n * (m * p)$ for all *n*, *m*, and *p* in the domain of definition.

The associativity of a binary operation may be thought of as meaning that the symbol $n * m * p$ is unambiguous. That is, it does not make any difference which of the two operations involved in $n * m * p$ is performed first.

Exercises

1. Determine which of the following binary operations are commutative and which are associative.
   (a) The binary operation of Example 1, p. 75.
   (b) The binary operation of Example 2, p. 75.
   (c) The binary operation of Exercise 4, p. 76.
   (d) The binary operation on colors defined in Example 1, p. 76.
   (e) The binary operation on playing cards defined in Example 2, p. 77.

The Identity Property

The property of possessing an identity is generally attributed only to binary operations but the concept is meaningful for any well-defined process. If $*$ denotes such a process defined on a certain collection of . . . objects, then we say that the object i is an *identity* for this process if $n * i = n$ no matter which object of the collection the symbol n represents.

Most of the processes studied in elementary arithmetic either possess no identity at all or possess exactly one identity. But there are binary operations which possess more than one identity. For example, the binary operation on the counting numbers defined by the instruction $n * m = n$ possesses infinitely many different identities. In fact, every counting number is an identity for this binary operation because no matter which counting number i represents, $n * i = n$ for every counting number n.

Exercises

1. Which of the following binary operations possess an identity? What is it?
   (a) The binary operation of Example 1, p. 75.
   (b) The binary operation of Example 2, p. 75.
   (c) The binary operation of Exercise 4, p. 76.
   (d) The binary operation on colors in Example 1, p. 76.
   (e) The binary operation on playing cards in Example 2, p. 77.
2. Which of the following processes possess an identity? What is it?
   (a) The process of Exercise 1, p. 76.
   (b) The process of Exercise 2, p. 76.
   (c) The process of Exercise 3, p. 76.
3. The identity we have defined is frequently called the *right identity*. That is, i is called a *right identity* if $n * i = n$ for all n. The object i is called a *left identity* if $i * n = n$ for all n.
   (a) Find an example of a process which has a right identity but no left identities.
   (b) Find an example of a process which has a left identity but no right identities.
   (c) Suppose $*$ represents a commutative binary operation. What about the right and left identities of such an operation?

The Cancellation Property

Like the identity property the cancellation property is usually attributed only to binary operations but the property is meaningful for processes which are only well-defined. If $*$ represents such a process, then to say that process $*$ possesses the cancellation property means that whenever one has three objects n, m, and p such that $n * p$ and $m * p$ are equal, then he may conclude that n and m are themselves equal. That is, the well-defined process $*$ possesses the cancellation property if $n * p = m * p$ implies $n = m$.

Exercises

1. Which of the following binary operations possess the cancellation property?
    (a) The binary operation of Example 1, p. 75.
    (b) The binary operation of Example 2, p. 75.
    (c) The binary operation of Exercise 4, p. 75.
    (d) The binary operation on colors in Example 1, p. 76.
    (e) The binary operation on playing cards in Example 2, p. 77.
2. Which of the following processes possess the cancellation property?
    (a) The process of Exercise 1, p. 76.
    (b) The process of Exercise 2, p. 76.
    (c) The process of Exercise 3, p. 76.
3. The property we have called the cancellation property is frequently called the *right cancellation property*. How would the *left cancellation property* be defined? (*Suggestion:* Compare with Exercise 3, p. 82.)

CHAPTER 3

Elementary Set Theory

Set theory is a moderately old part of modern mathematics, dating from the end of the nineteenth century. This branch of mathematics was born of the need to put mathematical discussions of the "infinite" on a firm basis of logical rigor. Today every major branch of mathematics involves set-theoretic notions in very fundamental ways. Nevertheless our treatment of mathematics will not involve many set-theoretic ideas. However, many of the concepts of set theory are of independent interest and so in this chapter we shall introduce the reader to some of the more elementary aspects of this subject.

SETS

The Concept of Set

Throughout the second chapter we used the phrase "collection of counting numbers." What is a collection? A well-known dictionary gives the following definition:

Collection: A set of objects

But then it also gives:

Set: A number of things forming a complete collection

These definitions involve us with a circular definition of the term collection. They tell us that collection and set are synonymous, but they do not define collection and they do not define set. The concept of a collection is difficult to define in terms of more fundamental concepts. For this reason the concept of collection will be left as an undefined concept in this text.*

---

* Georg Cantor (1845–1918), the mathematician credited with the establishment of set theory as a mathematical subject, wrote that a *set* or *collection* was "a bringing together into a whole of definite well-established objects of our perception or thought. . . ." This statement, however, can in no sense be called a mathematical definition of the term *set*. For what does it mean to "bring together into a whole" and what are "well-established objects of our perception or thought"? This description of a set is therefore not useful in mathematics, although it may have some usefulness *outside* of mathematics.

There are many synonyms for *collection,* the following being just a few: *set, batch, aggregate, family, class,* and *group.* We shall most often use the term *set,* not only because it is shorter and more convenient to say and write but because traditionally the name of the body of ideas that we are about to study is called *set theory.*

Examples of sets are (1) the set of all students in your mathematics class; (2) the set of all words appearing in this text; (3) the set of all people who are mathematicians; (4) the set of all counting numbers which are greater than four and less than ten. We shall denote sets by capital Latin letters: $A, B, C, D, \ldots$.

Sets contain *elements.** The reader is an *element* of the *set* of students in his mathematics class. The word Latin is an *element* of the *set* of all words in this text. We denote elements of sets by small Latin letters: $a, b, c, d, \ldots$. To symbolically express the fact that the element a is an element of the set S we write

$$a \in S$$

The symbol "$\in$" should be read as "is an element of" or "belongs to." If S denotes the set of all counting numbers greater than four and less than ten, then 6 is an element of this set and so we write $6 \in S$. However, 34 is not an element of this set and so we write

$$34 \notin S$$

The symbol $\notin$ should be read as "is not an element of" or "does not belong to."

EXAMPLE 1.   If A represents the set of all people who have been President of the United States, then

$$\text{U. S. Grant} \in A$$

$$\text{Thomas Jefferson} \in A$$

but

$$\text{Jefferson Davis} \notin A$$

EXAMPLE 2.   If S denotes the set of all counting numbers greater than four and less than ten, then $5 \in S, 6 \in S, 7 \in S, 8 \in S$, and $9 \in S$. But $4 \notin S, 10 \notin S$, and $156 \notin S$.

THE EMPTY SET

There is a distinguished set which is given a special name. This set is called the *empty set.*

Definition of the Empty Set   *The empty set is the set which does not contain any elements.*

To demonstrate how the empty set occurs suppose that a college class were asked the following question, "Would all the students who would like a quiz today please raise their hands?" The students who raise their hands comprise a set.

* Synonyms for *element* are *object* or *member.*

If the reader were to raise his hand, then he would be an element of this set. However, it is unlikely that anyone would raise his hand. Let us suppose therefore that no one does. In ordinary language we would say that no students raised their hands, and this would be true. Phrasing our answer in terms of the concept of *set*, we might want to say that the set of students who raised their hands was somehow nonexistent, but this is false! The set of students who raised their hands does exist; it is the *empty set*. We do not say that a set does not exist simply because it has no elements. The set does exist, and it is the empty set. We shall use the symbol ∅ to symbolize the empty set.

EXAMPLES.   The empty set is the set of all counting numbers less than zero. It is the set of all even counting numbers greater than 6 and less than 8.

Describing Sets

THE TABULATION METHOD

Consider the set of all counting numbers which are greater than four and less than ten. We have just described a certain set, and by means of this verbal description the reader is able to tell exactly which counting numbers are elements of this set. We symbolically describe this set by the symbol

$$\{5, 6, 7, 8, 9\}$$

This symbolic description of the set involves *tabulating* (i.e., *listing*) the elements of the set and placing braces (the symbols { and }) around this tabulation. This method for describing sets will be called the *tabulation method*. Here are some examples.

EXAMPLE 1.   The set of all letters of the alphabet:

$$\{a, b, c, d, e, f, g, h, i, j, k, l, m, n, o, p, q, r, s, t, u, v, w, x, y, z\}$$

EXAMPLE 2.   The set of all digits: $\{0, 1, 2, 3, 4, 5, 6, 7, 8, 9\}$.

EXAMPLE 3.   The set of all counting numbers which are greater than 12: $\{13, 14, 15, 16, 17, 18, \ldots\}$.

The last example differs from the first two in that it is impossible to actually tabulate all the elements of the set. In such cases the ellipsis symbol "..." is employed to instruct the reader to continue (or imagine to continue) the tabulation in the manner indicated by the elements of the set which have actually been written down. Thus in Example 3 it should be clear from the numbers actually written down that *every* counting number greater than twelve is an element of this set.

EXAMPLE 4.   Using the tabulation method the set of all even counting numbers is described as: $\{0, 2, 4, 6, 8, 10, 12, 14, \ldots\}$.

EXAMPLE 5.   Consider the set of all counting numbers less than 10000. To tabulate all the elements of this set would be a tedious job. Instead we abbreviate the tabulation and write $\{0, 1, 2, 3, 4, 5, \ldots, 9999\}$. The dots instruct the reader to continue tabulating in the manner indicated by the first few elements, and the symbol "9999" instructs the reader to stop when he gets to 9999.

Let us remark now (and verify later) that when a set is being described by the tabulation method, it does not make any difference in what order the elements are written down nor does it make any difference if an element is written down more than once.

Exercises

1.   Write each of the following sets in tabulated form.
    (a)   The set of all your siblings.
    (b)   The set of all courses in which you are currently enrolled.
    (c)   The set of all counting numbers which divide 50.
    (d)   The set of all odd counting numbers which divide 50.
    (e)   The set of all counting numbers which are divisible by 5.
    (f)   The set of all counting numbers which leave a remainder of 1 when divided by 4.
    (g)   The set of all counting numbers which can be subtracted from 7.
    (h)   The set of all counting numbers which divide 7.
    (i)   The set of all counting numbers which divide 13.
    (j)   The set of all even counting numbers which are less than or equal to 12.
2.   Tabulate the elements of the set of all even counting numbers less than 1 million. Tabulate the elements of the set of all odd counting numbers less than 1 million. (*Remark:* You are certainly *not* going to write out every one of these numbers!)

The tabulation method is often the easiest and most convenient way to symbolically describe a set. However, in many instances this method is quite inconvenient and in others it cannot be used at all.

EXAMPLE 1.   The set of all students in the United States whose last names begin with the letter M would be very difficult to describe using the tabulation method.

EXAMPLE 2.   The set of all planets in the universe which support life similar to ours cannot be described by the tabulation method.   This is because we are unable to identify the elements (if any) of this set.

So it is not always feasible to tabulate a set. But observe that each of the two sets above was described verbally with no difficulty at all. There is a second method for symbolically describing sets which is in essence simply a method for "translating" these verbal descriptions into symbolic descriptions.

THE DESCRIPTIVE METHOD

In any discussion involving sets there is some particular set, called the *universal set*, or, more simply, the *universe*, which contains all the elements of all the sets under discussion. As an example, consider the registrar at a certain university. His job is to concern himself with the various classes offered at his school and with the students registered in those classes. The individual classes are sets whose elements are the students enrolled in them. Thus the registrar deals with sets. A universal set in this situation would be some set which contains all the elements of all the sets with which the registrar deals. In this situation there is one most natural choice for the universal set, namely, the set of all students at the university. This set has the required property: Every element of every set under discussion is contained in it. However, it would also be acceptable to take as the universal set the set of all university students in the United States. This less natural choice of a universal set is perfectly acceptable from the mathematical point of view. The point is that the universal set must contain all the elements with which we might be dealing; whether or not it contains any additional elements is not important.

As another example, as far as the head of the men's physical education department is concerned the most reasonable universe is probably the set of all male students. His universe could also be taken to be the set of all living male animals between the ages of 10 and 100 years.

Here are some sets described verbally. Observe that in each case this description consists of the identification of the universal set from which the elements of the set in question are drawn and then the statement of a property that an element of the universal set must possess in order to be an element of the particular set being described.

EXAMPLE 1. THE SET OF ALL STUDENTS IN THE UNITED STATES WHOSE LAST NAMES BEGIN WITH THE LETTER M.   This verbal description involves first identifying the universe from which the elements of the given set are drawn. This universe is the set of all students in the United States. The second half of the verbal description is a statement of the property that an element of the universal set must have in order to be an element of this particular set. The property is that an element of the universal set must have a last name which begins with the letter M.

EXAMPLE 2. THE SET OF ALL WORDS IN THIS TEXT WHICH HAVE MORE THAN SEVEN LETTERS.   Involved in this verbal description is the identification of the universal set (the set of all words in this text) and the statement of the property that elements of the universal set must possess in order to be elements of this particular set (an element of the universal set must have more than seven letters).

Now we are ready to demonstrate how to describe a set using the descriptive method. The idea is to identify the universal set from which the elements of the given set are drawn and to identify the property that an element of the universal set must possess in order to be an element of the given set.

Consider the set $\{0, 1, 2, 3, 4, 5\}$. In describing this set it is not unreasonable to take as a universal set the set of all counting numbers, which we shall denote by C. To complete the description of this set we must find a property possessed by the elements of this set but not by any other elements of the universal set.

Such a property will distinguish between the elements of this set and the other elements of the universe. We may take this property to be the property of being less than 6. Thus if x is an element of the universal set C, then x is an element of this set if and only if $x < 6$. The symbolic description of the set is

$$\{x \in C : x < 6\}$$

The braces surrounding the entire symbol convey the information that we are looking at the symbol for a set. To the left of the colon is the identification of the universal set. The colon separates the two halves of the symbol and is read as "with the property that" or "such that." To the right of the colon is the statement of the property that an element of the universal set must possess in order to be in this set. The symbol above is read as *"The set of all elements x in C such that (or with the property that) x is less than six."* The general form of this symbol is shown in Fig. 7.

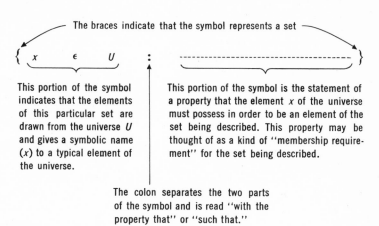

Figure 7   The general form of the descriptive method.

Here are some examples of sets described in both descriptive and tabulated form:

EXAMPLE 1.   The set {Grant, Garfield} may be written as

$$\{x \in P : x\text{'s last name begins with the letter } G\}$$

where P denotes the set of all men who have been presidents of the United States. The universe is the set P.

EXAMPLE 2.   The set {1, 2, 3} is described as

$$\{x \in C : x > 0 \text{ and } x < 4\}$$

where C denotes the set of all counting numbers.

EXAMPLE 3.   The set of all even counting numbers is described as

$$\{x \in C : x \text{ is even}\}$$

where C denotes the set of all counting numbers. There are many ways to phrase the statement which tells which elements of the universe are in this set. For example, the sentence "x is even" could be replaced by any one of the sentences, "x is not odd," "x is divisible by 2," or "$x = 2y$ for some $y \in C$."

Exercises

1. Describe each of the following sets by using the descriptive method. (Be sure to choose a universe.)
    (a) $\{0, 1, 2, 3, 4\}$.
    (b) $\{0, 2, 4, 6, 8\}$.
    (c) $\{2, 4, 6, 8\}$.
    (d) $\{3, 6, 9, 12, 15, 18, 21, 24, 27, 30, 33, \ldots\}$.
    (e) $\{1, 2, 3, 5, 7, 11, 13, 17, 19, 23, 29, 31, 37, 41, 43, \ldots\}$.
    (f) The set of all students at your school who have red hair.
2. Tabulate the elements of each of the following sets. The universe C is the set of all counting numbers.
    (a) $\{x \in C : x < 7 \text{ and } x > 5\}$.
    (b) $\{x \in C : x > 0\}$.
    (c) $\{x \in C : x > 4 \text{ and } x \text{ is odd}\}$.
    (d) $\{x \in C : x + 1 = 5\}$.
    (e) $\{x \in C : x + 3 = 6 \text{ or } x - 2 = 10\}$.
    (f) $\{x \in C : x \in S \text{ and also } x \in T\}$, where S is the set $\{0, 1, 2, 3, 4\}$ and T is the set $\{0, 1, 5, 8\}$.
    (g) $\{x \in C : x \in S \text{ or } x \in T\}$, where S is the set $\{1, 2, 3, 4, 5\}$ and T is the set $\{0, 1, 2, 3, 4\}$.
3. Tabulate the elements of the set $\{x \in U : x \geq 3 \text{ and } x \leq 14\}$ if the universe U is the set of all
    (a) counting numbers.
    (b) odd counting numbers.
    (c) counting numbers which are divisible by 5.
    (d) counting numbers which are greater than 20.
    (These results demonstrate the need to specify the universe when using the descriptive method.)

Review Questions

1. What is the empty set?
2. Discuss the way a set is described using the tabulation method.
3. What does the term *universe* or *universal set* mean?
4. Discuss the way a set is described using the descriptive method.
5. Discuss the relative advantages and disadvantages of the tabulation method over the descriptive method of describing sets.

RELATIONS ON SETS

The Relation of Subset

Consider the sets

$$\{1, 2, 3\} \qquad \text{and} \qquad \{1, 2, 3, 4, 5, 6\}$$

How do these sets compare? Perhaps most obvious is that each element of the first set is also an element of the second:

$$1 \in \{1, 2, 3, 4, 5, 6\}$$
$$2 \in \{1, 2, 3, 4, 5, 6\}$$
$$3 \in \{1, 2, 3, 4, 5, 6\}$$

To express this particular relationship between these sets we say that the set $\{1, 2, 3\}$ is a *subset* of the set $\{1, 2, 3, 4, 5, 6\}$.

Definition of the Subset Relation *Let A and B be sets. If every element of A is also an element of B, then we say that A is a subset of B. In symbols, $A \subseteq B$.*

Here are some examples of pairs of sets which may be compared using the relation of subset.

EXAMPLE 1. In the universe of all people the set G of all U.S. Army generals is a subset of the set M of all men: $G \subseteq M$. Otherwise expressed, G is related to M by the subset relation. Is it true that M is related to G by the subset relation? That is, is it true that $M \subseteq G$?

EXAMPLE 2. In the universe of counting numbers,

$$\{1, 2, 3, 4\} \subseteq \{1, 2, 3, 4, 5, 6, 7, \ldots\}$$
$$\{0, 2, 4, 6, 8, 10, 12, \ldots\} \subseteq \{0, 1, 2, 3, 4, 5, 6, \ldots\}$$
$$\{1, 2, 3, 4, 5\} \subseteq \{1, 2, 3, 4, 5\}$$
$$\{1\} \subseteq \{1, 2\}$$
but
$$\{1, 2, 3\} \nsubseteq \{1, 2\}$$

EXAMPLE 3. An important property of the empty set is that *the empty set is a subset of every set*. Let A be any set: We claim that $\varnothing \subseteq A$. In order to prove that $\varnothing \subseteq A$ it is necessary to prove that if x is an element of $\varnothing$, then $x \in A$. But this is patently true since $\varnothing$ contains no elements.

EXAMPLE 4. Let A be any set. Then $A \subseteq A$. This is true because it is true that every element of A is an element of A. Hence *every set is a subset of itself*. (What does this say about the subset relation?)

EXAMPLE 5. Suppose $A \subseteq B$ and $B \subseteq C$. Then $A \subseteq C$. This is not difficult to prove. (This is, of course, the transitivity property of the subset relation.)

Statements	Justifications
(1) If $x \in A$, then $x \in B$	(1) $A \subseteq B$
(2) If $x \in B$, then $x \in C$	(2) $B \subseteq C$

(3) If $x \in A$, then $x \in C$

(3) Follows from (1) and (2) together

(4) $A \subseteq C$

(4) Follows from (3) using definition of subset

From Examples 4, 5, and 1 we see that the subset relation is reflexive and transitive, but that it is not symmetric.

The Relation of Proper Subset

Definition of the Proper Subset Relation *If A and B are sets, then we say that A is a proper subset of B if $A \subseteq B$ and B contains at least one element that is not contained in A. In symbols, if A is a proper subset of B, we write $A \subset B$.*

Thus $\{7, 8, 9, 14\}$ is a proper subset of $\{5, 6, 7, 8,\ 9, 10, 14, 15\}$, and we write $\{7, 8, 9, 14\} \subset \{5, 6, 7, 8, 9, 10, 14, 15\}$. Here are some more examples.

EXAMPLE 1. $\{2, 4, 6, 8\} \subset \{0, 2, 4, 6, 8, 10, 12, \ldots\}$.

EXAMPLE 2. $\{1\} \subset \{1, 2, 4\}$.

EXAMPLE 3. $\{0, 2, 4, 6, 8, 10, 12, \ldots\} \subset \{0, 1, 2, 3, 4, 5, 6, \ldots\}$.

EXAMPLE 4. $\{1, 2, 3, 4, 5, 6\} \subset \{7, 6, 5, 4, 3, 2, 1\}$. However, $\{7, 6, 5, 4, 3, 2, 1\} \not\subset$ $\{7, 6, 5, 4, 3, 2, 1\}$ since the set on the right does not contain any elements which are not in the set on the left.

EXAMPLE 5. $\{2, 3, 4, 5, 8, 9, 11\} \not\subset \{4, 5, 6, 7, 8, 15, 23\}$. Which part of the definition of proper subset is not satisfied in this example?

EXAMPLE 6. $\varnothing$ is a proper subset of every set except itself.

The second part of Example 4 shows that the relation of proper subset is not reflexive. The sets $\varnothing$ and $\{1, 2\}$ provide a counterexample to symmetry; for while it is true that $\varnothing \subset \{1, 2\}$, it is false that $\{1, 2\} \subset \varnothing$. We leave it as an exercise to show that the relation is transitive.

Exercises

1. Consider the following sets:

$$A = \{1, 2, 3, 4, 5\} \qquad F = \{4\}$$
$$B = \{6, 7, 8\} \qquad G = \{8, 6, 7\}$$
$$C = \{2, 4\} \qquad H = \{0, 1, 2\}$$
$$D = \{4, 6\} \qquad I = \{7, 8\}$$
$$E = \{1\} \qquad J = \{8\}$$
$$K = \varnothing$$

(a) Find all pairs of sets which are related by the subset relation, e.g., $E \subseteq A$ and $A \subseteq A$.

(b) Which of the sets found in part (a) are also related by the proper subset relation?

2. (a)   Find two proper subsets of $\{0, 1\}$.
    (b)   Find three proper subsets of $\{0, 1, 2\}$.
3. In the universe of counting numbers, find counterexamples to the symmetry of the subset relation. Do the same for the relation of proper subset.
4. If A is a proper subset of B, is A a subset of B? If A is a subset of B, is A a proper subset of B? Explain and give counterexamples when appropriate.
5. Show that the proper subset relation is transitive; that is, show that if $A \subset B$ and $B \subset C$, then $A \subset C$.

The Relation of Set Equality

What ought it to mean to say that two sets are *equal*? Using the idea of subset we can give a very precise definition of the relation of equality of sets.

Definition of the Relation of Set Equality   *If A and B are sets, then we say that A is equal to B if*

$$A \subseteq B$$

and

$$B \subseteq A$$

In symbols, if A is equal to B we write A = B.

EXAMPLE 1. $\{1, 2, 3\} = \{3, 1, 2\}$. These sets are equal because each set is a subset of the other. This example illustrates the fact that *the order in which the elements of a set are tabulated is immaterial.*

EXAMPLE 2.   Consider the sets of counting numbers $\{1, 2\}$ and $\{2, 1, 2, 2, 1\}$. These sets are equal because each element of $\{1, 2\}$ is an element of $\{2, 1, 2, 2, 1\}$,

$$1 \in \{2, 1, 2, 2, 1\}$$
$$2 \in \{2, 1, 2, 2, 1\}$$

and each element of $\{2, 1, 2, 2, 1\}$ is an element of $\{1, 2\}$,

$$2 \in \{1, 2\}$$
$$1 \in \{1, 2\}$$
$$2 \in \{1, 2\}$$
$$2 \in \{1, 2\}$$
$$1 \in \{1, 2\}$$

This example illustrates the fact that *in tabulating a set repetitions of the elements are immaterial.* Because it makes the description of a set unnecessarily complicated to repeat elements in the tabulation, we shall agree that repetitions are not allowed when the elements of sets are tabulated.

The relation of set equality is an equivalence relation on sets. We leave it to the reader to verify this statement.

The three relations of *subset, proper subset,* and *equality* are related as the following two theorems show.

Theorem   *Let A and B be sets. Then $A \subseteq B$ if and only if either $A \subset B$ or $A = B$.*

Theorem   *Let A and B be sets. Then $A \subset B$ if and only if $A \subseteq B$ but $A \neq B$.*

Exercises

1. The following sets are in the universe of counting numbers and therefore contain repetitions. Simplify the tabulation of these sets by removing the repetitions.
    (a) $\{0, 1, 1, 2, 1 + 1, 4, 8 \div 2, 3 - 1\}$
    (b) $\{0, 1, 2, 1, 0, 0, 0, 4 \div 2, 1 \times 2\}$
    (c) $\{1, 3, 4, 2, 1, 3, 4\}$
2. (a) Is $\emptyset$ equal to $\{0\}$? Explain.
    (b) Is $\emptyset$ equal to 0? Explain.
    (c) Is $\emptyset$ equal to $\{\emptyset\}$? Explain.
3. Show that the relation of equality of sets is an equivalence relation.
4. List all the subsets of the following sets. Do not forget to include the empty set (which is a subset of every set) and the sets themselves.
    (a) $\{a\}$
    (b) $\{a, b\}$
    (c) $\{a, b, c\}$
    (d) $\{a, b, c, d\}$
5. Based upon your answers to Exercise 4 can you guess the number of subsets of a set containing six elements? Of a set containing seven elements? Of a set containing *n* elements?

The Relation of Disjointness

Definition of the Disjointness Relation   *If A and B are sets which have no elements in common, then A and B are said to be disjoint.*

EXAMPLE 1.   The sets $\{1, 2, 3\}$ and $\{4, 5, 6\}$ are disjoint sets because they have no elements in common. That is, no element of $\{1, 2, 3\}$ is an element of $\{4, 5, 6\}$ and no element of $\{4, 5, 6\}$ is an element of $\{1, 2, 3\}$.

EXAMPLE 2.   *The empty set is disjoint from every set.* Let A be a set. If $\emptyset$ and A had an element in common, then, in particular, that element would belong to $\emptyset$. This is obviously impossible because $\emptyset$ contains no elements.

We now see that (1) the empty set is not only a subset of every set but (2) it is also disjoint from every set. Thus if A is a set, then

1. Every element of the empty set is contained in A.
2. No element of the empty set is contained in A.

Both of these apparently contradictory statements are true. These statements are not really contradictory; they simply appear to be so. They would, however, contradict each other (and hence only one of them could be true) if the empty set contained any elements.

Exercises

1. In the universe of digits, list all sets which are disjoint from $\{0, 1, 2, 3, 4, 5, 6\}$.

2. The disjointness relation is symmetric. Explain.
3. The disjointness relation is not reflexive and not transitive. Give examples which prove these assertions.
4. Suppose A and B are sets such that $A \subseteq B$ and A and B are disjoint. What can you say about the set A?
5. Is it possible for a set to be disjoint from itself? Explain.
6. Are $\{\varnothing\}$ and $\{\varnothing, 1\}$ disjoint. Explain.

Review Questions

1. What are the four relations on sets that we have discussed and how is each defined?
2. If two sets are related by the relation of proper subset, then they are necessarily also related by what other relation?
3. If two sets are related by the relation of equality, then they are necessarily also related by what other relation?
4. In a manner of speaking the subset relation is a combination of what two relations?
5. What are the properties of subset relation? The equality relation? The proper subset relation? The disjointness relation?
6. Make a statement involving the empty set and the relation of subset.
7. Make a statement involving the empty set and the relation of proper subset.
8. The concept of set does not involve any idea of the order in which the elements of the set are described. Explain.
9. Explain why a set is not changed by listing one of its elements more than once.

GRAPHIC REPRESENTATION OF SETS

There are a variety of methods for graphically representing sets. We shall study one of these called the method of *Euler circles*.

We use Euler circles to illustrate graphically the relations between *nonempty* sets.* The universe is represented by a rectangle, the elements of the universe being thought of as points inside the rectangle. To illustrate a nonempty set we draw a circle inside this rectangle. The elements of the set being illustrated are identified with points inside the circle. Thus if A is a nonempty set in the universe U, we draw the diagram in Fig. 8. Next consider a pair of nonempty sets in the

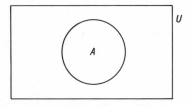

Figure 8 Euler circle diagram illustrating a single set A in the universe U.

---

*The method of Euler circles can be adapted to illustrate relations between the empty set and other sets, but in our discussion of Euler circles we consider only nonempty sets. Incidentally, the name Euler is pronounced like *oiler*.

universe *U*. Figure 9 illustrates these sets if they are disjoint. If one of the sets is a proper subset of the other (say $A \subset B$), then the diagram in Fig. 10 illustrates the sets. If $A = B$, then the diagram in Fig. 11 illustrates the sets. In this diagram the circles representing sets *A* and *B* coincide. If the sets are not disjoint but neither is a subset of the other, they are illustrated by the diagram in Fig. 12.

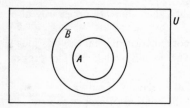

Figure 9 Euler circle diagram illustrating the disjointness relation.

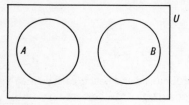

Figure 10 Euler circle diagram illustrating the proper subset relation.

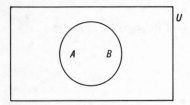

Figure 11 Euler circle diagram illustrating the equality relation.

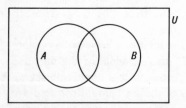

Figure 12 Euler circle diagram illustrating sets not related by equality, subset, proper subset, or disjointness relations.

When using Euler circles it is not possible to illustrate two sets *A* and *B* related by the subset relation with less than two pictures. That is, since to say $A \subseteq B$ means either $A \subset B$ or $A = B$, using Euler circles we need two pictures to illustrate the relationship between *A* and *B* (Fig. 13).

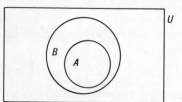   or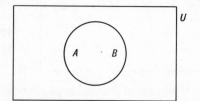

Figure 13   Euler circle diagrams illustrating the subset relation.

Here are some examples of Euler circles used to illustrate relations between sets.

EXAMPLE 1.   If *A*, *B*, and *C* are (nonempty) sets in the universe *U*, and if $A \subset B$ and $B \subset C$, then the diagram which illustrates the relations between these sets is shown in Fig. 14.

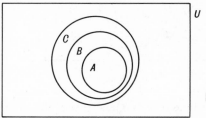

Figure 14

EXAMPLE 2.   If *A*, *B*, *C*, *D*, and *E* are sets in a universe *U* such that $A \subset B$, *B* and *C* are disjoint, $D \subset C$, and $A = E$, then we would draw the diagram shown in Fig. 15 to illustrate the relationships between these five sets.

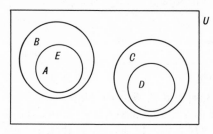

Figure 15

Here are some examples of how specific sets may be illustrated using Euler circles.

EXAMPLE 1.   In the universe of counting numbers, let $A = \{1, 2, 3, 4\}$, $B = \{3, 4, 5, 6, 7\}$, and $C = \{6, 7, 8, 9\}$. These three sets and the relationships between them are illustrated in Fig. 16.

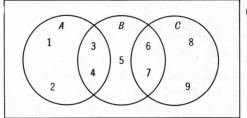

Figure 16

EXAMPLE 2.   In the universe of counting numbers, let $A = \{1, 2\}$, $B = \{1, 2, 3, 4, 5\}$, $C = \{5, 6, 7, 8\}$, and $D = \{9, 10\}$. These sets are illustrated by Euler circles in Fig. 17.

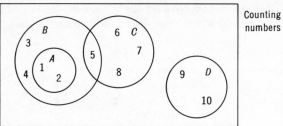

Figure 17

Exercises

1. Draw a diagram to illustrate sets A, B, and C such that A and B are disjoint, B and C are disjoint, but A and C are not disjoint.
2. Draw a diagram illustrating sets A, B, C, and D such that $A \subset B$, $C \subset B$, $D \subset A$, and A and C are disjoint.
3. In the universe of all counting numbers illustrate the sets $A = \{0, 1, 2, 3, 4\}$, $B = \{0, 2, 4, 6, 8, 10, 12, 14, 16\}$, and $C = \{1, 3, 5, 7, 9, 11\}$.
4. In the universe of all counting numbers illustrate the sets $A = \{1\}$, $B = \{1, 2\}$, $C = \{3, 4, 5, 6, 7\}$, $D = \{6, 7\}$, and $E = \{5, 7, 8, 9\}$.

EQUIVALENCE OF SETS

One-to-One Correspondence

   Consider the sets $\{1, 2, 3, 4\}$ and $\{a, b, c, d\}$. How are these sets related? They are disjoint, of course. The two sets are also related in that they contain the same number of elements.* Is there a way to determine that the sets $\{1, 2, 3, 4\}$ and $\{a, b, c, d\}$ have the same number of elements without actually counting the elements of the sets? In Fig. 18 we have constructed a "pairing" of the elements of

$$A = \{1, \quad 2, \quad 3, \quad 4\}$$
$$\updownarrow \quad \updownarrow \quad \updownarrow \quad \updownarrow \quad \text{Figure 18}$$
$$B = \{a, \quad b, \quad c, \quad d\}$$

these sets. The pairing is described by means of arrows. It is clear from the way we have paired the elements of these sets that they have the same number of elements. This particular kind of pairing between the two sets is called a *one-to-one correspondence* between the sets.

Definition of One-to-One Correspondence   *If A and B are sets, then a one-to-one correspondence between set A and set B is a pairing of the elements of A with the elements of B such that:*

* We shall give a definition for "the number of elements" in a finite set on p. 106.

(i)   *Each element of A is paired with exactly one element of B.*
(ii) *Each element of B is paired with exactly one element of A.*

Observe that the pairing shown in Fig. 18 is this kind of pairing. Each number in set *A* is paired with exactly one letter in set *B* and each letter in set *B* is paired with exactly one number in set *A*. Here are more examples of one-to-one correspondences between sets.

EXAMPLE 1.   Is it possible to construct a one-to-one correspondence between the sets $A = \{s, t, u, v, w\}$ and $B = \{a, b, c, d, e\}$? There are quite a few one-to-one correspondences between these two sets. Two such one-to-one correspondences are illustrated in Fig. 19.

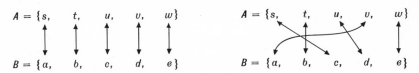

Figure 19

EXAMPLE 2.   Let $A = \{1, 2, 3\}$ and $B = \{a, b, c, d\}$. Consider the pairing illustrated in Fig. 20. Is this a one-to-one correspondence between set *A* and set *B*? No, it is not. Why? While part (ii) of the definition of one-to-one correspondence is satisfied (that is, each element of *B* is paired with exactly one element of *A*) the first part of the definition is not satisfied: It is not true that each element of *A* is paired with *exactly* one element of *B*. The element 1 in set *A* is paired with *two* elements of *B*.

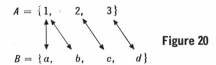

Figure 20

EXAMPLE 3.   Consider the sets $A = \{1, 2, 3\}$ and $B = \{4, 5, 6\}$. There are six distinct one-to-one correspondences between these sets. These correspondences are illustrated in Fig. 21.

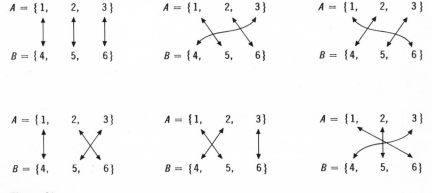

Figure 21

$$A = \{0, \quad 2, \quad 4, \quad 6, \quad 8, \quad 10, \quad 12, \quad 14, \ldots\}$$

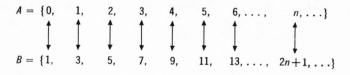

$$B = \{1, \quad 3, \quad 5, \quad 7, \quad 9, \quad 11, \quad 13, \quad 15, \ldots\}$$

Figure 22

EXAMPLE 4.   Figure 22 shows a one-to-one correspondence between the set A of all even counting numbers and the set B of all odd counting numbers. In this example we cannot explicitly show all the pairings because we cannot even explicitly write down all the elements of the two sets. But we can explicitly show enough of the pairings so that the reader will get the idea of how the rest of the elements are to be paired. To which element of set B would the element 46 in set A correspond? (*Answer:* 47) To which element of A is the element 179 in B paired? (*Answer:* 178) We can give a general rule for the pairings like this:

$$n \in A \text{ is paired with } n + 1 \in B$$

This rule for the one-to-one correspondence tells how to pair any element of A with an element of B and vice versa.

EXAMPLE 5.   In Fig. 23 we have illustrated a one-to-one correspondence between the set of all counting numbers and the set of all odd counting numbers. Again, we have not been able to show explicitly how all the elements of the two sets are paired, but

$$A = \{0, \quad 1, \quad 2, \quad 3, \quad 4, \quad 5, \quad 6, \ldots, \quad n, \ldots\}$$

$$B = \{1, \quad 3, \quad 5, \quad 7, \quad 9, \quad 11, \quad 13, \ldots, \quad 2n+1, \ldots\}$$

Figure 23

we have shown a few specific examples and have then tabulated a general element n of the set A and shown that it should be paired with the element $2n + 1$ in set B. For example, given the element $57 \in A$, the element of B with which it is paired is $2(57) + 1$ or 115. Given the element $37 \in B$, the element of A with which it is paired is $(37 - 1)/2$ or 18.

The Relation of Equivalence

The relation of *equivalence of sets* is defined by using the concept of one-to-one correspondence.

Definition of the Relation of Equivalence of Sets   *If A and B are sets, then we say that A is equivalent to B if it is possible to construct a one-to-one correspondence between the sets A and B. In symbols, if A is equivalent to B, then we write $A \sim B$.*

EXAMPLE 1. $\{1, 2, 3\} \sim \{a, b, c\}$. The reader can construct a one-to-one correspondence between these sets to show that they are equivalent. In fact, in Example 3, p. 99, we constructed six such correspondences.

EXAMPLE 2. From Example 5, p. 100, we see that $\{0, 1, 2, 3, 4, 5, 6, \ldots\} \sim$ $\{1, 3, 5, 7, 9, 11, \ldots\}$.

EXAMPLE 3. The set $\{1, 2, 3\}$ is not equivalent to any of its proper subsets. That is, $\{1, 2, 3\} \nsim A$, if A is a proper subset of $\{1, 2, 3\}$. The proper subsets of $\{1, 2, 3\}$ are $\varnothing, \{1\}, \{2\}, \{3\}, \{1, 2\}, \{1, 3\},$ and $\{2, 3\}$. It is not possible to construct a one-to-one correspondence between $\{1, 2, 3\}$ and any of these sets.

In order to understand the relation of equivalence more fully, let us determine which of the properties of a relation are possessed by it.

REFLEXIVITY. Is it true that if A is a set, then $A \sim A$? This is rather obvious. It is always possible to construct a one-to-one correspondence between a set and itself. What is one such one-to-one correspondence?

SYMMETRY. If A and B are sets, and if $A \sim B$, is $B \sim A$? To say that $A \sim B$ means that it is possible to find a one-to-one correspondence between A and B. But this correspondence is also a one-to-one correspondence between B and A. Hence $B \sim A$ and so equivalence of sets is a symmetric relation.

TRANSITIVITY. If A, B, and C are sets, and if $A \sim B$ and $B \sim C$, is it true that $A \sim C$? Let us look at an example. Let A, B, and C be chosen so that $A \sim B$ and $B \sim C$. In Fig. 24 we have illustrated three such sets and the one-to-one correspondences between them. By "connecting together" the two given one-to-one correspondences (as shown in Fig. 25) we can obtain a one-to-one correspondence between sets A and C (as shown in Fig. 26). The reader can easily generalize

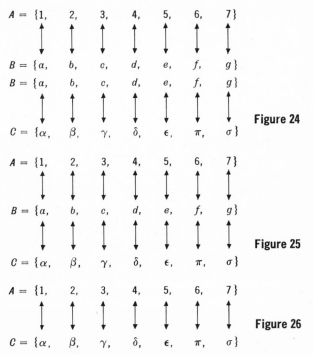

Figure 24

Figure 25

Figure 26

from this example and convince himself that given a one-to-one correspondence between A and B and a one-to-one correspondence between B and C, he can always "connect" the two given one-to-one correspondences and thereby construct a one-to-one correspondence between A and C.

These observations complete the verification that the relation of equivalence of sets is an equivalence relation.

Review Questions

1. What is meant by a one-to-one correspondence between two sets?
2. How many one-to-one correspondences can be constructed between two three element sets?
3. Is it possible for a set to be in one-to-one correspondence with a proper subset of itself? Discuss and give examples.
4. What do we mean when we say that two sets are equivalent?
5. What properties are possessed by the relation of equivalence?

Exercises

1. Show that the following pairs of sets are equivalent.
   (a) $A = \{0, 1, 2, 3, 4, 5, 6\}$ and $B = \{100, 101, 102, 103, 104, 105, 106\}$.
   (b) $A = \{0, 1, 2, 3, 4, 5, \ldots\}$ and $B = \{0, 5, 10, 15, 20, 25, \ldots\}$.
   (c) $B = \{0, 5, 10, 15, 20, \ldots\}$ and $C = \{0, 100, 200, 300, 400, \ldots\}$.
2. Use the one-to-one correspondences you found in parts (b) and (c) of Exercise 1 to construct a one-to-one correspondence between the set A of part (b) and the set C of part (c).
3. (a) Find a one-to-one correspondence between $A = \{6, 7, 8, 9\}$ and $B = \{a, b, c, d\}$ such that $7 \in A$ corresponds to $d \in B$. How many such one-to-one correspondences are there?
   (b) Find a one-to-one correspondence between $B = \{a, b, c, d\}$ and $C = \{x, y, u, v\}$ such that $d \in B$ corresponds to $u \in C$.
   (c) "Connect" the correspondences you found in parts (a) and (b) to obtain a one-to-one correspondence between A and C.
4. Find a proper subset B of the set $A = \{0, 25, 50, 75, 100, \ldots\}$ such that B and A are equivalent. Exhibit your one-to-one correspondence.
5. In what way do the bigamy laws involve the concept of equivalence of sets?
6. We have now defined two equivalence relations on sets. What are they? How are these relations connected?
7. In Fig. 27 we have drawn a line (actually a line extends in both directions without end, so we are looking at only a portion of the line) and have chosen two points

Unit distance

Origin   Unit

Figure 27

on this line which we call the *origin* and the *unit*. The *unit distance* is the distance between these two points. Then we have located more points on the line to the right of the unit, the distance between any two adjacent points being equal to the unit distance as shown in the figure. Thus we are able to locate a special set of points on the line. Denote this set of points by S. Next we label each of the points in set S with a counting number as shown in Fig. 28. The act of labeling the points of set S in this way has the effect of constructing a one-to-one correspondence between the set S of points and the set of counting numbers, the correspondence being given by the rule: A point corresponds to the counting number which labels it. We shall call the set of points located in this way the *counting number line*.

The counting number line is a most convenient way to display the counting numbers graphically. This geometric "picture" of the counting numbers can be used to great advantage when working with counting numbers, for it is possible to "translate" many of the concepts we have already discussed relative to the counting numbers into geometric terms by using the counting number line.

(a) Use the counting number line to explain what it means to say that one counting number is *less than* another. Do the same for the relations of *equality*, *greater than*, *less than or equal to*, and *greater than or equal to*.

(b) The *Law of Trichotomy for Counting Numbers* states that if n and m are counting numbers, then exactly one of these statements is true: $n < m$, $n = m$, $n > m$. Interpret the Law of Trichotomy in terms of the counting number line.

(c) Interpret addition of counting numbers in terms of the counting number line. Solve these equations by using the line:

$$6 + 7 = ? \qquad 6 + ? = 8.$$
$$0 + 4 = ? \qquad ? + 4 = 7.$$

(d) Interpret the closure property, commutative property, zero property, and cancellation property of addition of counting numbers in terms of the counting number line.

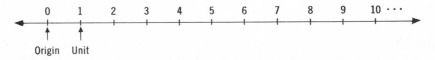

Figure 28   The counting number line.

APPLICATIONS OF EQUIVALENCE

Finite and Infinite Sets

We have seen examples of sets which are equivalent to proper subsets of themselves. For example, we saw that the set of odd counting numbers is equivalent to the set of all counting numbers. Thus the set of counting numbers is equivalent to a proper subset of itself. On the other hand, the set $\{1, 2, 3\}$ is not equivalent to any proper subset of itself. It is possible to classify sets by whether or not they are equivalent to proper subsets of themselves.

Definition of an Infinite Set   *A set is said to be an infinite set if it is equivalent to a proper subset of itself.*

Definition of a Finite Set   *A set is said to be finite if it is not infinite. Thus a set is finite if it is not equivalent to any of its proper subsets.*

The second definition above is not the most convenient description of a finite set from the point of view of elementary set theory. A more convenient description of a finite set is contained in the following alternate definition of finite set.*

Alternate Definition of a Finite Set   *A set is called finite if it is equivalent to one of these sets:*

$$\varnothing$$
$$\{1\}$$
$$\{1, 2\}$$
$$\{1, 2, 3\}$$
$$\{1, 2, 3, 4\}$$
$$\{1, 2, 3, 4, 5\}$$
.
.
.
$$\{1, 2, 3, 4, 5, \ldots, n\}$$
.
.
.

EXAMPLE 1.   The set $\{1, 4, 7, 10, 13, 16, 19, 22, 25, 28, 31, \ldots\}$ is an infinite set because it can be put into one-to-one correspondence with its proper subset $\{4, 7, 10, 13, 16, 19, \ldots\}$. One such one-to-one correspondence is shown in Fig. 29.

EXAMPLE 2.   The set $\{a, b, c, d, e, f\}$ is a finite set since it cannot be put into one-to-one correspondence with any of its proper subsets. But an easier way to prove that this set is finite is to use the alternate definition of finite set and verify that the given set is equivalent to the set $\{1, 2, 3, 4, 5, 6\}$.

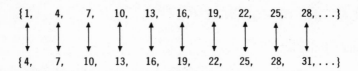

Figure 29

* It is possible to prove that these definitions are logically equivalent.

Exercises

1. Use the definition of infinite set to prove that each of these sets is infinite.
    (a) $\{x \in C : x$ is divisible by $7\}$, where C denotes the set of counting numbers.
    (b) $\{0, 3, 6, 9, 12, 15, 18, \ldots\}$
    (c) $\{1, 3, 6, 10, 15, 21, 28, 36, 45, 55, 66, 78, \ldots\}$
2. Use the first definition of finite set to show that the set $\{a, b, c\}$ is a finite set. (You must show that the given set is not equivalent to any of its proper subsets.)
3. Use the alternate (second) definition of finite set to show that each of these sets is a finite set.
    (a) $\{a, b, c\}$
    (b) $\{0, 2, 4, 6, 8, 10, \ldots, 200\}$
    (c) $\{x \in C : x \geq 20$ and $x < 30\}$, where C denotes the set of all counting numbers.
4. The counting number line (see Exercise 7, p. 102) consists of an infinite set of points. Explain.

The Counting Process and Cardinal Numbers

We have taken advantage of the reader's intuitive understanding of the concepts of (1) *counting the elements* of a finite set and (2) the *number of elements* of a finite set in our discussion of equivalence of sets. But we have not actually said what we mean by "counting" the elements of a finite set nor what we mean by the "number" of elements of a finite set. We can now give rather precise definitions for these concepts.

COUNTING THE ELEMENTS OF A FINITE SET

Let us first examine the process of counting the elements of a finite set. Consider the set $\{a, b, c, d, e\}$. This set is finite since it can be put into one-to-one correspondence with the set $\{1, 2, 3, 4, 5\}$. The "counting process" actually constructs such a one-to-one correspondence. How do we count the elements of $\{a, b, c, d, e\}$? Looking at the element a we say, "one"; looking at b we say, "two"; looking at c we say, "three"; looking at d we say, "four"; and looking at e we say, "five." We stop counting now because we have counted every element of the set. By the act of counting the elements of this set we have actually constructed a one-to-one correspondence between the set of letters and the set $\{1, 2, 3, 4, 5\}$. When we looked at a and said "one" we were in effect pairing the letter a with the counting number 1. Similarly, when we looked at b and said "two" we were in effect pairing b with 2, and so on. The way we counted the elements of the set $\{a, b, c, d, e\}$ established the one-to-one correspondence shown in Fig. 30. More generally, when we "count" the elements of a finite set we are constructing a one-to-one correspondence between that set and one of the sets listed in the alternate definition of a finite set given previously.

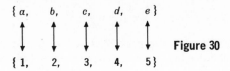

Figure 30

THE CARDINAL NUMBER OF A SET

The number of elements of a finite set is called the *cardinal number* of that set and is defined as follows.

Definition of the Cardinal Number of a Finite Set   *Let A be a finite set. If A is empty, then we say that the cardinal number of set A is zero and write* $c(A) = 0$. *If A is nonempty, then A is equivalent to a set of the form* $\{1, 2, 3, \ldots, n\}$ *and we say that the cardinal number of set A is n and we write* $c(A) = n$.

EXAMPLE 1.   As a result of the counting process we determine that the set $\{t, y, u, i, o, p\}$ is equivalent to the set $\{1, 2, 3, 4, 5, 6\}$. Therefore the cardinal number of $\{t, y, u, i, o, p\}$ is 6. In symbols, $c(\{t, y, u, i, o, p\}) = 6$.

EXAMPLE 2.   The definition tells us that the cardinal number of the empty set is zero. The converse is also true. That is, if a finite set has cardinal number zero, then that set is equal to the empty set. Consequently, $c(A) = 0$ if and only if $A = \varnothing$.

EXAMPLE 3. $c(\{2, 1, 2, 2, 1\}) = c(\{2, 1\}) = 2$.

The concepts of *equivalence* and *cardinal number* are connected as the following theorem shows.

Theorem   *Let A and B be finite sets. If* $c(A) = c(B)$, *then* $A \sim B$. *Conversely, if* $A \sim B$, *then* $c(A) = c(B)$.
The Proof:
Part 1:

(1) $c(A) = c(B) = n$	(1) Hypothesis
(2) (a) $A \sim \{1, 2, 3, \ldots, n\}$	(2) From (1) by using the
(b) $B \sim \{1, 2, 3, \ldots, n\}$	definition of cardinal number
(3) $\{1, 2, 3, \ldots, n\} \sim B$	(3) From (2b) by using symmetry of equivalence
(4) $A \sim B$	(4) From (2a) and (3) by using transitivity of equivalence

Part 2:   Exercise.

We have discussed the concept of cardinal number only as it applies to finite sets, but this concept is also meaningful for infinite sets. Exercise 3 in the following set of exercises introduces the concept of the *cardinal number* of the set of counting numbers.

Exercises

1. Suppose A and B are finite sets such that A is equivalent to a proper subset C of B. How do the counting numbers $c(A)$, $c(C)$, and $c(B)$ compare?
2. Give a proof of part (2) of the theorem which immediately precedes these exercises.
3. The concept of cardinal number is meaningful for infinite sets also. As one example of this, we say that a set A has cardinal number $\aleph_0$ (read "aleph-sub-nought") if A is equivalent to the set of all counting numbers. Give ten examples of sets which have cardinality $\aleph_0$. Such sets are called *countably infinite*. Infinite sets which are not equivalent to the set of all counting numbers are called *uncountably infinite*. We have not yet seen one of these sets and shall have to wait until Chapter 9 before we do.
4. The counting number line (see Exercise 7, p. 102) consists of a countably infinite set of points. Explain.
5. The counting process as described in the text applies only to finite sets. Explain why it is not possible to count the elements of an infinite set. In particular, why is it not possible to count the elements of the set of all counting numbers?

Review Questions

1. What is an infinite set?
2. We defined finite set in two ways. What are they?
3. The process of counting the elements of a finite set involves the idea of a one-to-one correspondence. Discuss this.
4. What do we mean by the cardinal number of a finite set?
5. State a theorem which relates the concepts of cardinal number and equivalence of sets.

OPERATIONS ON SETS

We have discussed the concept of set and the notation for describing sets. We have also discussed some of the important relations on sets. We conclude our study of set theory with a discussion of two of the principal operations on sets.

The Operation of Union

Definition of the Operation of Union   *If A and B are sets in a universe U, then the union of A and B, denoted by $A \cup B$, is the set $\{x \in U : x \in A \text{ or } x \in B\}$.*

Here are some examples of this operation.

EXAMPLE 1. $\{1, 2, 3\} \cup \{4, 5, 6\} = \{1, 2, 3, 4, 5, 6\}$. Each of the elements 1, 2, 3, 4, 5, and 6 is either in $\{1, 2, 3\}$ or in $\{4, 5, 6\}$.

EXAMPLE 2. $\{1, 2\} \cup \{1, 2, 3\} = \{1, 2, 3\}$.

EXAMPLE 3. $\{1, 2, 3, 4, 5\} \cup \{3, 4, 5, 6, 7, 8, 9\} = \{1, 2, 3, 4, 5, 6, 7, 8, 9\}$.   Observe that we do not repeat the elements 3, 4, and 5 in the tabulation of the union.

EXAMPLE 4. $\{0, 2, 4, 6, 8, \ldots\} \cup \{1, 3, 5, 7, \ldots\} = \{0, 1, 2, 3, 4, 5, 6, \ldots\}$.

EXAMPLE 5.   If A is any set, than $A \cup \varnothing = A$ and $\varnothing \cup A = A$.

EXAMPLE 6.   If A is any set, then $A \cup A = A$.

The operation of union may be illustrated graphically by means of Euler circles. Figure 31 consists of four diagrams which illustrate the union of two sets A and B depending on how the sets are related. In each diagram the shaded region represents the union of the sets A and B. Example 1 above is illustrated by Fig. 31a, Example 3 by Fig. 31b, and Example 2 by Fig. 31d.

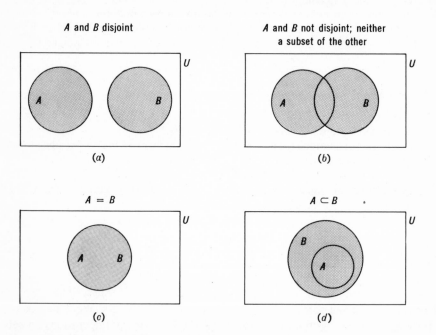

Figure 31   Euler circle diagrams illustrating the operation of union.

The Operation of Intersection

Definition of the Operation of Intersection   *If A and B are sets in the universe U, then the intersection of A and B, denoted by $A \cap B$, is the set $\{x \in U : x \in A$ and $x \in B\}$.*

Thus given two sets we obtain their intersection by constructing a new set consisting of all the elements in *both* of the given sets. This is really a very familiar

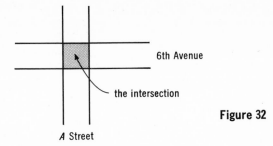

6th Avenue

the intersection

Figure 32

A Street

idea. Is not the intersection of two streets just that portion of the earth which lies in both streets (see Fig. 32)?

EXAMPLE 1. $\{1, 2, 3\} \cap \{3, 4, 5\} = \{3\}$.

EXAMPLE 2. $\{0, 1, 2, 3, 4, 5, 6, \ldots\} \cap \{2\} = \{2\}$.

EXAMPLE 3. $\{2, 3, 4\} \cap \{7, 8, 9\} = \varnothing$.

EXAMPLE 4. If A is any set, then $\varnothing \cap A = \varnothing$ and $A \cap \varnothing = \varnothing$.

In Fig. 33 we have illustrated this operation in terms of Euler circles. In each diagram the shaded region represents the intersection of the sets A and B. Observe that in Fig. 33a no region has been shaded since no elements are common to both sets in this case. Thus we see that if two sets are disjoint, then their inter-

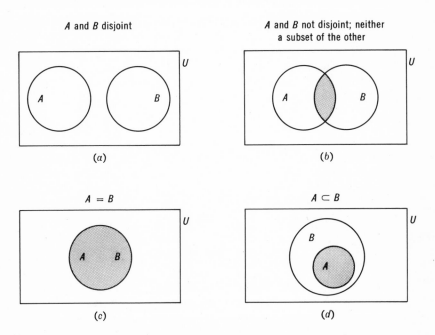

Figure 33 Euler circle diagrams illustrating the operation of intersection.

section is the empty set. Conversely, if two sets have an empty intersection, then they are disjoint. We can combine these two statements as follows.

Theorem   *If A and B are sets, then A and B are disjoint if and only if $A \cap B = \emptyset$.*

Review Questions

1. Define the operations of union and intersection of sets.
2. Illustrate the operations of union and intersection by using Euler circles.
3. Relate the concepts of disjointness and intersection.
4. If A and B are sets, how are A and B related to $A \cup B$? To $A \cap B$?

Exercises

1. Tabulate $A \cup B$ and $A \cap B$ for these pairs of sets:
   (a) $A = \{0, 1, 2, 3, 6\}$ and $B = \{0, 2, 3, 4, 5\}$.
   (b) $A = \emptyset$ and $B = \{0, 1, 2\}$.
   (c) $A = \{0, 1, 2, 3, 4, 5, \ldots\}$ and $B = \{16, 17, 18\}$.
   (d) $A = \{0, 2, 4, 6, 8, \ldots\}$ and $B = \{1, 3, 5, 7\}$.
   (e) $A = \{1, 3, 5, 7, 9, 11, \ldots\}$ and $B = \{0, 1, 2, 3, 4, 5, \ldots\}$.
   (f) $A = \{0, 1, 2, 3, \ldots, 20\}$ and $B = \{15, 16, 17, 18, 19, 20\}$.
   (g) $A = \{100, 101, 102, 103, 104, \ldots\}$ and $B = \{21, 22, 23, 24, 25, \ldots\}$.
2. Use the sets $A = \{1, 2, 3\}$, $B = \{2, 3, 4, 5\}$, and $C = \{2, 4, 7, 8\}$ and tabulate the following sets:
   (a) $(A \cup B) \cup C$.   (d) $A \cap (B \cap C)$.
   (b) $A \cup (B \cup C)$.   (e) $A \cap (B \cup C)$.
   (c) $(A \cap B) \cap C$.   (f) $(A \cap B) \cup (A \cap C)$.
3. Figure 34 is a diagram in which certain sets are represented by means of Euler circles. Use different colored markings (or separate diagrams) to identify the regions which represent the following sets:
   (a) $A \cup B$.   (f) $A \cap G$.
   (b) $A \cap B$.   (g) $B \cup G$.
   (c) $A \cap C$.   (h) $(C \cup E) \cup D$.
   (d) $C \cup A$.   (i) $(F \cap D) \cup E$.
   (e) $C \cup F$.   (j) $(F \cup B) \cap A$.

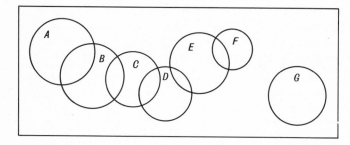

Figure 34

4. (a) If A and B are sets and if $A \cup B = A$, then how are the sets A and B related?

(b) If A and B are disjoint sets and if $A \cup B = A$, then what do you know about the set B?

(c) If A and B are sets and if $A \cap B = B$, then how do A and B compare?

(d) If A and B are disjoint sets and if $A \cap B = B$, then what do you know about B?

(e) Is it possible to find two sets A and B such that A and B are disjoint but nevertheless B is a subset of A? Explain.

(f) If U is the universe and A is a set in that universe, then what can you say about $U \cup A$? About $U \cap A$?

5. If the cardinal number of A is 7 and the cardinal number of B is 6, then

(a) Do you necessarily know the cardinal number of $A \cup B$? Of $A \cap B$?

(b) Can you say anything about the cardinal number of $A \cup B$?

(c) Can you say anything about the cardinal number of $A \cap B$?

(d) If you know that A and B are disjoint, then do you know the cardinal number of $A \cup B$? Of $A \cap B$?

6. All the sets in this problem are finite.

(a) If A is a subset of B, how are the cardinal numbers $c(A)$ and $c(B)$ related?

(b) If A is a proper subset of B, how are $c(A)$ and $c(B)$ related?

(c) If A and B are sets and if $c(A \cup B) = c(A) + c(B)$, how are A and B related?

(d) If $c(A \cup B) = c(A)$, then how are A and B related?

(e) If $c(A \cap B) = 0$, how are A and B related?

(f) If $c(A \cap B) = c(A)$, how are A and B related?

(g) If $c(A \cap B) < c(A)$, how are A and B related?

(h) Is it possible to find sets A and B such that $c(A \cup B) < c(A)$?

(i) Is it possible to find sets A and B such that $c(A \cap B) > c(A)$?

(j) Let A and B be arbitrary sets. How do the cardinal numbers $c(A \cup B)$ and $c(A) + c(B) - c(A \cap B)$ compare? Explain fully.

7. (a) Suppose A and B are sets such that $A \cup B = A \cap B$. How are A and B related?

(b) Is it possible to find sets A and B such that $A \cup B \subset A \cap B$?

(c) Is it possible to find sets A and B such that $A \cap B \subset A \cup B$?

8. Does the operation of union possess the commutative property? That is, is it true that the sets $A \cup B$ and $B \cup A$ are equal no matter which sets A and B represent. Answer the same question for the operation of intersection.

9. Is the operation of union associative? Is the operation of intersection associative?

10. Is there an identity for the operation of union? That is, is there a set I such that $A \cup I = A$ no matter which set A represents? Is there an identity for intersection?

11. Find examples of sets A, B, and C such that $A \cup B = C \cup B$ but $A \neq C$. What does the exhibition of such an example tell you about the operation of union?

12. Does the operation of intersection possess the cancellation property? Justify your answer.

CHAPTER 4

Elementary Number Theory

This chapter is a continuation of the study of the system of counting numbers begun in Chapter 2. We shall discuss those aspects of the system of counting numbers which are prerequisite to our study of the system of fractions in Chapter 5. Three of the four principal topics of this chapter are directly related to the study of fractions. The last part of the chapter contains a proof of the Infinitude of Primes Theorem and a discussion of the indirect method of proof used to prove this theorem.

THE LONG DIVISION ALGORITHM AND THEOREM

The Division Algorithm Theorem

Consider the counting numbers 20 and 3. Is it possible to find two counting numbers q and r such that the statement

$$20 = (3)(q) + r$$

is true? Surely, in fact, there are many such pairs of numbers:

$$20 = (3)(0) + 20 \qquad 20 = (3)(4) + 8$$
$$20 = (3)(1) + 17 \qquad 20 = (3)(5) + 5$$
$$20 = (3)(2) + 14 \qquad 20 = (3)(6) + 2$$
$$20 = (3)(3) + 11$$

Of the seven different pairs of numbers q and r for which the equation $20 = (3)(q) + r$ is true there is exactly one pair for which the number r is less than 3, namely the pair $q = 6$ and $r = 2$. All of this is rather obvious and is an example of the following theorem.

The Division Algorithm Theorem *If n and m are counting numbers with m not equal to zero, then there exist (possibly many pairs of) numbers q and r such that*

$$n = (m)(q) + r$$

Furthermore, there is exactly one such pair of numbers with r less than m.

The Division Algorithm Theorem is an example of a kind of theorem called an *existence theorem*. The theorem asserts the *existence* of certain numbers. We have studied other such theorems (can the reader identify some of these?), and we shall study more of them in coming chapters. Existence theorems are very important because we do not like to spend effort studying something until we know that it exists.

The Long Division Process

Because of the Division Algorithm Theorem we are able to define a new process on the counting numbers. Suppose n and m are counting numbers and that m is not equal to zero. Then we know that there exists another pair of numbers q and r such that $n = mq + r$ and r is less than m. Thus given the pair of counting numbers n and m, we are able to assert the existence of another pair of counting numbers q and r. We have here a process which acts upon certain pairs of counting numbers (n and m) and produces other pairs of counting numbers (q and r). We call this process the *long division process*. This process is substantially different from the other processes we have studied because the result of performing the process is a *pair* of counting numbers rather than a single counting number. For example, when the long division process is applied to the counting numbers $n = 34$ and $m = 9$, the result is the pair of counting numbers $q = 3$ and $r = 7$. When the process is applied to the counting numbers $n = 18$ and $m = 9$, the result is the pair of counting numbers $q = 2$ and $r = 0$. The result of the process applied to $n = 15$ and $m = 7$ is the pair of counting numbers $q = 2$ and $r = 1$. The long division process applied to $n = 4$ and $m = 6$ is the pair $q = 0$ and $r = 4$. The only time the process cannot be applied is when m is equal to zero. (Why can't the process be applied in this case?)

THE DIFFERENCE BETWEEN THE PROCESS OF DIVISION OF COUNTING NUMBERS AND THE LONG DIVISION PROCESS

It is in a sense unfortunate that the name of the long division process includes the word *division*, for the process called division of counting numbers as defined in Chapter 2 and the process of long division as discussed above are very different processes. The long division process produces *two* counting numbers, while the process of division of counting numbers produces *one* counting number.

Even though these two processes are different, they are related. If the remainder obtained as a result of the long division process is equal to zero, then it is possible to perform the process of division of counting numbers. Conversely, if it is possible to perform the process of division of counting numbers, then the remainder obtained by means of the process of long division is zero. We can express all of this in a theorem.

Theorem *If n and m are counting numbers and if m is different from zero, then n ÷ m is meaningful if and only if the process of long division produces a zero remainder.*

We leave the proof of this theorem to the reader.

EXAMPLE. Is the symbol 15 ÷ 6 meaningful? No, it is not; when 15 is long divided by 6 a remainder of 3 is obtained. The theorem then implies that the symbol 16 ÷ 5 has no meaning. That is, 15 is not divisible by 6.

Finally, let us remark upon the ambiguity in such expressions as, "Divide 11567 by 341." If by the word divide we are referring to the process of division of counting numbers as defined in Chapter 2, then it is not possible to divide 11567 by 341. However, if the word divide refers to the process called long division, then it is possible to "divide" 11567 by 341 and a pair of numbers are obtained as the result of the process. To avoid any possible confusion we shall continue to use the word divide to refer to the process called division of counting numbers. When referring to the process called long division we shall use the term long divide.

Exercises

1. Find all possible pairs of counting numbers q and r such that $n = m(q) + r$ when
   (a) $n = 111$ and $m = 28$.
   (b) $n = 96$ and $m = 18$.
   (c) $n = 124$ and $m = 11$.
   (d) $n = 5$ and $m = 17$.
   (e) $n = 7$ and $m = 0$.
2. Can you think of counting numbers n and m such that there is exactly one pair of counting numbers q and r such that $n = (m)(q) + r$? Can you generalize your answer and say precisely when the numbers q and r will be unique?
3. What is the result of applying the long division process to the following pairs of counting numbers:
   (a) $n = 116$ and $m = 116$.
   (b) $n = 111$ and $m = 28$.
   (c) $n = 96$ and $m = 18$.
   (d) $n = 124$ and $m = 11$.
   (e) $n = 5$ and $m = 17$.
4. In the statement of the Division Algorithm Theorem it is hypothesized that the counting number m should be different from zero. Why?
5. Why can't the long division process be applied when m is equal to zero?
6. Prove the theorem stated in the text relating the process of division to the process of long division.

The Long Division Algorithm

If the divisor and the dividend are relatively small counting numbers then it is easy to determine the result of the long division process simply by inspection.

But if the numbers n and m are large, then it is not easy to find the numbers q and r by inspection. In these cases we need some sort of computational device by means of which we can find the numbers q and r. One computational device for finding the pair of numbers resulting from the long division process is the familiar *long division algorithm*.* For example, if $n = 11567$ and $m = 341$, then the long division algorithm takes the familiar form

$$
\begin{array}{r}
33 \\
341\overline{)11567} \\
1023 \\
\hline
1337 \\
1023 \\
\hline
314
\end{array}
$$

and so we see that $q = 33$ and $r = 314$. The long division algorithm is specifically constructed to give us the numbers which are the result of the long division process acting upon $n = 11567$ and $m = 341$. In fact, the reader will no doubt recall that one way to check the above application of the long division algorithm is to multiply 341 by 33 and then add 314. The result should be 11567. Thus

$$11567 = (341)(33) + 314$$

In substance the long division algorithm is a subtractive device. When applied to the counting numbers $n = 11567$ and $m = 341$ this algorithm answers the question, "How many times can we subtract 341 from 11567 and what is remaining after the subtractions have all been performed?" In fact the long division algorithm is not really needed to answer this question. The simple-minded way to answer the question is to start subtracting:

$$
\begin{array}{l}
11567 \\
-341 \quad \longleftarrow \text{First subtraction} \\
\hline
11226 \\
-341 \quad \longleftarrow \text{Second subtraction} \\
\hline
10885 \\
-341 \quad \longleftarrow \text{Third subtraction} \\
\hline
\end{array}
$$

$$\vdots \qquad \vdots$$

---

* The word *algorithm* (as used in this text) means any particular method of computing, as, for example, the ways that numerals are placed on the paper in order to add, multiply, subtract, or long divide them. An algorithm is a computational device, containing only a finite number of steps, for performing a particular computation.

This algorithm is more commonly called the *division algorithm;* but since we are distinguishing between "division" and "long division" we shall call it the *long division algorithm.*

1337

$\underline{-341}$ ◄─────── Thirty-first subtraction

996

$\underline{-341}$ ◄─────── Thirty-second subtraction

655

$\underline{-341}$ ◄─────── Thirty-third subtraction

314 ◄─────── No more 341's can be
subtracted because this
remainder is less than 341

Thus we can subtract 341 from 11567 a total of 33 times and the remainder after having done this is 314. That is,

$$11567 - (341)(33) = 314$$

or

$$11567 = (341)(33) + 314$$

This last equation shows us that the result of performing the long division process on 11567 and 341 is the pair $q = 33$ and $r = 314$. But this simple-minded subtraction device is time-consuming and tedious. It can be shortened in a number of ways, as by subtracting more than one 341 at a time. For example,

11567

$\underline{-3410}$ ◄─────── Subtracting ten 341's

8157

$\underline{-3410}$ ◄─────── Subtracting ten more 341's, a total
of twenty 341's

4747

$\underline{-3410}$ ◄─────── Subtracting ten more 341's, a total
of thirty 341's

1337

$\underline{-341}$ ◄─────── Subtracting the thirty-first 341

996

$\underline{-341}$ ◄─────── Subtracting the thirty-second 341

655

$\underline{-341}$ ◄─────── Subtracting the thirty-third 341

314 ◄─────── No more 341's can be subtracted
because the remainder is less
than 341

Putting this computation into a form which more closely resembles the familiar long division algorithm, we write

$$\left.\begin{array}{r}1\\1\\1\\10\\10\\10\end{array}\right\} 10 + 10 + 10 + 1 + 1 + 1 = 33$$

$$\begin{array}{r}341\overline{)11567}\\ \underline{3410}\\ 8157\\ \underline{3410}\\ 4747\\ \underline{3410}\\ 1337\\ \underline{341}\\ 996\\ \underline{341}\\ 655\\ \underline{341}\\ 314\end{array}$$

The familiar long division algorithm finds the numbers 33 and 314 in only two steps. The device above involved six steps and the simple-minded procedure involved thirty-three steps. The long division algorithm is simply a more efficient way to perform these many subtractions.

We have seen that the long division algorithm is a computational tool specifically designed to provide the pair of numbers which are the result of applying the long division process to a given pair of counting numbers. Given counting numbers n and m (m different from zero) the Division Algorithm Theorem tells us that numbers q and r exist such that

$$n = (m)(q) + r$$

and

$$r < m$$

and the long division algorithm is the computational device by means of which we actually find these numbers.

Review Questions

1. State the Division Algorithm Theorem. What kind of a theorem is it? Why is it called that?

2. What is the effect of the long division process upon a pair of nonzero counting numbers?
3. How is the long division algorithm used in arithmetic?
4. How does the long division process relate to the process of division of counting numbers?
5. How does the long division process relate to the Division Algorithm Theorem?
6. How does the Division Algorithm Theorem relate to the long division algorithm?
7. Describe some of the differences between division of counting numbers and the process of long division.
8. When the long division process is applied to a pair of nonzero counting numbers there is produced another pair of counting numbers which satisfy two conditions. What are these conditions?
9. In what way is the term *divide* ambiguous? How can this ambiguity be avoided?

EXPONENTS

Suppose n is the product of three factors, each of which is equal to 2: $n = 2 \cdot 2 \cdot 2$. Since such products occur frequently in arithmetic, mathematicians have invented a notation to simplify the writing of them. If n and m are *nonzero* counting numbers, then the symbol n^m is used to abbreviate the product

$$\underbrace{n \cdot n \cdot n \cdots n}_{m \text{ factors}}$$

In the symbol n^m, m is called the *exponent* and we say that n *is raised to the mth power*. The number n is called the *base*. For example,

$$3^1 = 3$$
$$2^5 = 2 \cdot 2 \cdot 2 \cdot 2 \cdot 2$$
$$4^3 = 4 \cdot 4 \cdot 4$$
$$10^2 = 10 \cdot 10$$

Exponents are particularly useful when the base number is ten. Examine the following list:

$$10^1 = 10$$
$$10^2 = 10 \cdot 10 = 100$$
$$10^3 = 10 \cdot 10 \cdot 10 = 1000$$
$$10^4 = 10 \cdot 10 \cdot 10 \cdot 10 = 10000$$
$$10^5 = 10 \cdot 10 \cdot 10 \cdot 10 \cdot 10 = 100000$$

From these examples it appears that if n represents a counting number greater than zero, then

$$10^n = \underbrace{10000 \cdots 000}_{n \text{ zeros}}$$

Thus the distance to the sun, which is approximately 93 million miles, can be written $93 \times 1,000,000$ or as 93×10^6 miles. The number $100,000,000,000,000,-000,000,000,000,000$ can conveniently be written as 10^{29}.

The symbol n^m has an obvious meaning when both n and m are nonzero. But what meaning ought we to assign to this symbol if one of n and m is zero? Let us consider the various possibilities.

1. The exponent is zero and the base number is not zero.

It is convenient to assign the meaning 1 to any symbol of the form n^0, where n is different from zero. Our reason for doing this will be made clear very shortly.

2. The base number is zero and the exponent is not zero.

We assign the meaning of zero to any symbol of the form 0^m, where m is different from zero. It is not difficult to understand why we do this, for it is reasonable to interpret the symbol 0^m as an abbreviation of the product

$$\underbrace{0 \cdot 0 \cdot 0 \cdots 0}_{m \text{ factors}}$$

and this product is equal to zero.

3. Both the base number and the exponent are zero.

Consider the symbol 0^0. What value might we reasonably want to assign to this symbol? One person might argue that since 0^0 is a counting number raised to the 0th power, by (1) above, 0^0 ought to be equal to 1. However, another person could just as well argue that since 0^0 is 0 raised to an exponent, this symbol should represent 0 by virtue of (2) above. There being no particular reason to choose one of these values over the other, we shall avoid the difficulty altogether by not assigning any meaning to this symbol.*

There are certain theorems concerning exponents which will be used frequently in the work that follows, so let us consider these theorems now.

Theorem 1 *If n is a counting number and if p and q are nonzero counting numbers, then*

$$n^p \cdot n^q = n^{p+q}$$

The Proof: $n^p \cdot n^q$ is an abbreviation of the product

$$\underbrace{(n \cdot n \cdot n \cdots n)}_{p \text{ factors}}\underbrace{(n \cdot n \cdot n \cdots n)}_{q \text{ factors}}$$

---

*Trying to define the symbol 0^0 leads to logical complications. We shall adopt the point of view that the symbol 0^0, like the symbol $0 \div 0$, is a nonsense symbol to which no meaning can be attached.

By virtue of the associative property of multiplication this product can be regarded simply as the product of $p + q$ factors; i.e., this product can also be abbreviated by n^{p+q}. Hence $n^p \cdot n^q = n^{p+q}$.

EXAMPLES. $3^5 \cdot 3^7 = 3^{5+7} = 3^{12}$

$12^6 \cdot 12 = 12^6 \cdot 12^1 = 12^7$

Theorem 2   *If n and m are counting numbers and if p is a nonzero counting number, then*

$$(nm)^p = n^p \cdot m^p$$

The Proof: The symbol $(nm)^p$ is an abbreviation for the product

$$\underbrace{(nm)(nm)(nm) \cdots (nm)}_{p \text{ factors}}$$

Using the commutativity and associativity of multiplication, this product can be rewritten in the form

$$\underbrace{(n \cdot n \cdot n \cdots n)}_{p \text{ factors}}\underbrace{(m \cdot m \cdot m \cdots m)}_{p \text{ factors}}$$

and this product is abbreviated by the symbol $n^p \cdot m^p$. Hence both $(nm)^p$ and $n^p \cdot m^p$ are abbreviations for the same product. Therefore $(nm)^p = n^p \cdot m^p$.

EXAMPLES. $2^3 \cdot 3^3 = (2 \cdot 3)^3 = 6^3$

$4^7 \cdot 5^7 = (4 \cdot 5)^7 = 20^7$

$(36)^2 = (3 \cdot 12)^2 = 3^2 \cdot 12^2$

Theorem 3   *If n is a counting number and if p and q are nonzero counting numbers, then*

$$(n^p)^q = n^{pq}$$

The Proof: The symbol $(n^p)^q$ is an abbreviation for the product

$$\underbrace{(n^p)(n^p)(n^p) \cdots (n^p)}_{q \text{ factors}}$$

Since n^p means $n \cdot n \cdot n \cdots n$ (p factors), this product can be rewritten in the form

$$\underbrace{\underbrace{(n \cdot n \cdot n \cdots n)}_{p \text{ factors}}\underbrace{(n \cdot n \cdot n \cdots n)}_{p \text{ factors}}\underbrace{(n \cdot n \cdot n \cdots n)}_{p \text{ factors}} \cdots \underbrace{(n \cdot n \cdot n \cdots n)}_{p \text{ factors}}}_{q \text{ factors}}$$

and this (because of the associative property of multiplication) is the product of pq factors each of which is n. Hence the symbol n^{pq} is also an abbreviation for this product. Since $(n^p)^q$ and n^{pq} are abbreviations for the same product, they are equal.

EXAMPLES. $(3^2)^4 = 3^{2 \cdot 4} = 3^8$
$(6^2)^0 = 6^{2 \cdot 0} = 6^0 = 1$
$(12^7)^7 = 12^{7 \cdot 7} = 12^{49}$

The last theorem is similar to Theorem 1 except that it deals with division instead of multiplication.

Theorem 4 *If n is a counting number and if p and q are nonzero counting numbers such that* $q \geq p$, *then*

$$n^q \div n^p = n^{q-p}$$

The Proof: By virtue of Theorem 1 the statement

$$n^q = n^p \cdot n^{q-p}$$

is true. Then using the definition of division we can conclude that the statement

$$n^q \div n^p = n^{q-p}$$

is true as well. But this is exactly the statement we were to prove.

EXAMPLES. $4^3 \div 4^2 = 4^{3-2} = 4$
$(2^3 \cdot 2^5) \div 16 = 2^{3+5} \div 2^4 = 2^8 \div 2^4 = 2^{8-4} = 2^4$

The concept of exponent is a very useful one and it is by means of these theorems that we work with exponents. It is because of these theorems that we defined n^0 $(n \neq 0)$ to be 1. For consider the product of 5^3 and 5^0. In view of Theorem 1 it is natural to want to write

$$5^3 \cdot 5^0 = 5^{3+0} = 5^3$$

But this equation will be true only if $5^0 = 1$. In view of Theorem 4 it is natural to want the equation

$$5^3 \div 5^0 = 5^{3-0} = 5^3$$

to be true. But the equation can be true only if $5^0 = 1$. These considerations (and others that we have not discussed) make it appear desirable that n^0 $(n \neq 0)$ should be equal to 1. Hence we define it to be so.

Review Questions

1. State the four theorems given in the text which deal with exponents.
2. Outline proofs of these four theorems.
3. Explain why we decided that it would be a good idea to define the symbol 5^0 to be equal to 1. Do the same for the symbol 3^0.
4. What is the meaning of 0^7?
5. What meaning did we assign to the symbol 0^0?

Exercises

1. Determine the missing number.
   (a) $2^3 \cdot 5^3 = 10^?$.
   (b) $3^4 \cdot 5^? = 15^4$.
   (c) $(2^2)^2 = ?$
   (d) $(n^p)^2 = ?$
   (e) $(3^6)^? = 3^{24}$.
   (f) $a^2 \cdot a^2 = a^3 \cdot a^?$.
   (g) $(2 \cdot 3)^4 = 16 \cdot 9^?$.
   (h) $4^5 = 16 \cdot 16 \cdot ?$
   (i) $125 = 5^?$.
   (j) $2 \cdot 3^2 = ?$
   (k) $(2 \cdot 3)^2 = ?$
   (l) $2^2 \cdot 3^3 = 6^2 \cdot ?$
   (m) $(2 + 3)^2 = ?$
   (n) $2^2 + 3^2 = ?$
   (o) $2^2 \cdot 3^3 = 36 \cdot ?$
   (p) $(4^?)^2 = (4 \cdot 4)^3$
   (q) $(n^s)^t = (n^t)^?$.
   (r) $2^5 \div 2^? = 8$.
   (s) $2^? \div 2^6 = 1$.
   (t) $2(2^6 \div 2^4) = ?$
   (u) $(2^2 \cdot 3^2) \div (2 \cdot 3) = ?$
   (v) $(2^3 \cdot 3^3 \cdot 5^2) \div (2^2 \cdot 3 \cdot 5) = ?$

2. Supply counterexamples showing it is false that if n, m, and p are counting numbers, then $(n + m)^p = n^p + m^p$.

3. The well-known equation $E = mc^2$ involves the second power of a number. Does the equation say that $E = mcmc$ or that $E = mcc$? What is the difference between the symbols $2 \cdot 3^2$ and $(2 \cdot 3)^2$?

4. The following theorem is similar to Theorem 2 except that it involves division instead of multiplication.

   Theorem   *If n and m are counting numbers such that m divides n, and if p is a non-zero counting number, then*

   $$n^p \div m^p = (n \div m)^p$$

   Show by direct calculation that the theorem is true when

   (a) $n = 10$, $m = 5$, and $p = 3$.
   (b) $n = 80$, $m = 16$, and $p = 2$.
   (c) $n = 8$, $m = 4$, and $p = 4$.

FACTORIZATIONS OF COUNTING NUMBERS

VOCABULARY

Suppose that a counting number n is the product of two other counting numbers a and b: $n = ab$. We already know that a and b are called *factors* of the product n. A synonym for factor is *divisor*. Hence both a and b are divisors of the number n. We also say that n is *divisable* by a and by b. The product n is called a *multiple* of a and of b.

As an illustration of these terms observe that

$$18 = 2 \cdot 9 = 2 \cdot 3 \cdot 3 = 3 \cdot 6 = 18 \cdot 1$$

Therefore,

(a) 18 is the *product* of

$$\left.\begin{cases} 2 \text{ and } 9 \\ 6 \text{ and } 3 \\ 18 \text{ and } 1 \\ 2, 3, \text{ and } 3 \end{cases}\right\}.$$

(b) 18 is a *multiple* of 1, 2, 3, 6, 9, and 18.
(c) 1, 2, 3, 6, 9, and 18 are *factors* of 18.
(d) 1, 2, 3, 6, 9, and 18 are *divisors* of 18.
(e) 18 is *divisible* by 1, 2, 3, 6, 9, and 18.

Exercises

1. What is a synonym for *factor*?
2. *n* is divisible by *a* if and only if *a* is a _____ of *n*. *n* is a multiple of *a* if and only if *a* is a _____ of *n*. If *n* is divisible by *a*, then *a* is a _____ of *n*. If the product of *a* and *b* is *n*, then each of *a* and *b* is a _____ of *n*.
3. Describe the set of all divisors of 10. Describe the set of all multiples of 10. Describe the set of all factors of 10. Describe the set of all counting numbers which are divisible by 10.
4. 1 is a _____ of every number. Every number is _____ by 1.
5. Is 0 a multiple of 2? Of 3? Of *n*? If *n* is a counting number, what is the least multiple of *n*? What is the least nonzero multiple of *n*? Is there a greatest multiple of *n*?
6. If *n* is a counting number, is 0 a divisor of *n*? What is the least number which is a divisor of *n*? Is there a greatest divisor of *n*?
7. A counting number greater than 1 is called a *perfect* number if it is equal to the sum of its divisors different from itself. Thus the counting number 6 is a perfect number because the divisors of 6 different from 6 itself are 1, 2, and 3, and since $1 + 2 + 3 = 6$.
   (a) Search among the *even* counting numbers less than 30 to find other perfect numbers.
   (b) It is known that if there are any *odd* perfect numbers, then they are very large and cannot be found by simple experimentation. Verify that no odd counting number less than thirty is a perfect number.

Prime Numbers

Clearly if *n* is a nonzero counting number, then *n* is divisible by the counting numbers 1 and *n*. Some numbers are divisible *only* by themselves and by 1, while others have more than just these two factors. For example, 5 is divisible only by itself and by 1, but 6 is divisible by 1, 2, 3, and 6 itself. We classify counting numbers greater than 1 by the factors the numbers possess.

Definition of a Prime Number *If n is a counting number greater than 1, then n is called a prime number (or, more simply, a prime) if n is divisible only by itself and 1.*

Definition of a Composite Number   *If n is a counting number greater than* 1 *and is not a prime, then n is called a composite number.*

Thus every counting number greater than 1 is either prime or composite. The numbers 0 and 1 are not included in this classification.

The prime numbers have been studied in depth and much is known about them. For example, it can be proven (and we shall do so in the last section of this chapter) that the set of all prime numbers is an infinite set. However, only finitely many primes are actually known. The prime numbers between 1 and 1000 are listed in Fig. 35.

2	101	211	307	401	503	601	701	809	907
3	103	223	311	409	509	607	709	811	911
5	107	227	313	419	521	613	719	821	919
7	109	229	317	421	523	617	727	823	929
11	113	233	331	431	541	619	733	827	937
13	127	239	337	433	547	631	739	829	941
17	131	241	347	439	557	641	743	839	947
19	137	251	349	443	563	643	751	853	953
23	139	257	353	449	569	647	757	857	967
29	149	263	359	457	571	653	761	859	971
31	151	269	367	461	577	659	769	863	977
37	157	271	373	463	587	661	773	877	983
41	163	277	379	467	593	673	787	881	991
43	167	281	383	479	599	677	797	883	997
47	173	283	389	487		683		887	
53	179	293	397	491		691			
59	181			499					
61	191								
67	193								
71	197								
73	199								
79									
83									
89									
97									

Figure 35   List of prime numbers between 1 and 1000.

The largest known prime number is the counting number $2^{11213} - 1$. The proof that this number is a prime is very long and was accomplished only by means of a high-speed computer. There is no simple yet effective procedure for determining whether a large number is prime.

Prime Factorizations

When a counting number is written as a product of factors, we call this product a *factorization* of that number. Thus $10 \cdot 18$ is a factorization of 180. So is $9 \cdot 20$. In general, there are many factorizations of a counting number. A factorization of a counting number which is a product of prime numbers is called a *prime factorization* of that number.

Neither of the two factorizations of 180 above are prime factorizations, since in the first case 10 is not a prime number and in the second 9 is not a prime. However, the factorization $2 \cdot 2 \cdot 3 \cdot 3 \cdot 5$, or, more compactly, $2^2 \cdot 3^2 \cdot 5$, is a prime factorization of 180 since each of the numbers 2, 3, and 5 is a prime number.

EXAMPLES.   The reader can verify by multiplying the factors together that each of the following products is a factorization of the corresponding counting number.

Counting Number	Factorizations
115	$1 \cdot 115$, $5 \cdot 23$
220	$220 \cdot 1$, $2 \cdot 110$, $10 \cdot 11 \cdot 2$, $2 \cdot 2 \cdot 5 \cdot 11$, $44 \cdot 5$
65	$5 \cdot 13$, $65 \cdot 1$, $13 \cdot 5$, $1 \cdot 65$
1004	$2 \cdot 502$, $4 \cdot 251$, $2 \cdot 2 \cdot 251$, $1 \cdot 1004$
5	$5 \cdot 1$
7	$7 \cdot 1$

Perhaps it is already evident to the reader that while there may be many factorizations of a given counting number, there is only one *prime factorization* for each number.

The Unique Factorization Theorem*   *Every counting number greater than 1 can be written as a product of prime numbers. Thus if n is a counting number ($n > 1$), we can write*

$$n = p_1 p_2 p_3 \cdots p_m$$

where each of the symbols $p_1, p_2, p_3, \ldots, p_m$ represents a prime number. Moreover, except for the order in which these prime numbers appear in the product this factorization is unique.

For example, we saw that $180 = 2^2 \cdot 3^2 \cdot 5$. The theorem tells us that there is no prime factorization of 180 which does not involve precisely the factors 2, 2, 3, 3, and 5. It is true that $180 = 5 \cdot 3 \cdot 2^2 \cdot 3$, but this is the same factorization as the one above—only the order of writing down the prime factors is different.

---

* The Unique Factorization Theorem is also called the Fundamental Theorem of Arithmetic. This name conveys the importance of the theorem.   The Division Algorithm Theorem occupies a place of almost equal importance in arithmetic, and these two theorems together are the backbone of arithmetic.

Here are some examples of how we find prime factorizations of numbers.

EXAMPLE 1.   Let us find the prime factorization of 63. Unless it is immediately evident what the prime factors of a counting number are, the best procedure is to factor the number in any way at all. Let us factor 63 as $7 \cdot 9$. Now examine each of these factors. If each of them is a prime number, then we have found the prime factorization. If any of the factors are composite numbers then these factors must in turn be factored. Repeat this process until all the factors are prime numbers.

We have so far obtained the factorization $7 \cdot 9$. But 9 is not a prime. Hence we continue by factoring 9 as $3 \cdot 3$. We now have factored 63 as $7 \cdot 3 \cdot 3$. This is the prime factorization of 63, since each of these three factors is a prime number. We generally write the prime factors in increasing order of size from left to right and use exponents to make the factorizations easier to read. Hence we usually write $63 = 3^2 \cdot 7$.

EXAMPLE 2.   To find the prime factorization of 1863 we might begin by observing that 1863 is divisible by 9, so that we can write $1863 = 9 \cdot 207$. Since $9 = 3^2$, this gives us $1863 = 3^2 \cdot 207$. Now 207 is also divisible by 9; $207 = 9 \cdot 23$. Since 23 is a prime, the prime factorization of 1863 is $3^2 \cdot 3^2 \cdot 23$ or $3^4 \cdot 23$.

EXAMPLE 3.   What is the prime factorization of 294?
   Solution: Since 294 is divisible by 2, $294 = 2 \cdot 147$. Now 147 is divisible by 3, $147 = 3 \cdot 49$. Finally, $49 = 7^2$. Combining these observations, we find that the prime factorization of 294 is $2 \cdot 3 \cdot 7^2$.

EXAMPLE 4.   Find the prime factorization of 263.
   Solution: We might begin by trying to divide 263 by various small numbers such as 2, 3, 4, 5, 6, 7, and so on. But 263 is not divisible by any of these numbers. Then we might try some larger numbers, and again we would fail to find any factors. Eventually we might look at the table of primes given earlier to see if perhaps this number is a prime. It is. Hence the prime factorization of 263 is simply 263.

EXAMPLE 5.   The prime factorization of 2541 is $3 \cdot 7 \cdot 11^2$.

Exercises

1. Find the prime factorizations of the following numbers.
    (a) 42.   (e) 200.
    (b) 462.   (f) 163.
    (c) 8820.   (g) 212.
    (d) 1776.   (h) 646.
2. Count from 2 to 50 using prime factorizations to name the numbers: 2, 3, 2^2, 5, $2 \cdot 3$, etc.
3. Consider the prime factorization $2^3 \cdot 5^2$. We may rewrite this factorization so as to involve the prime 7 by using zero exponents: $2^3 \cdot 5^2 = 2^3 \cdot 5^2 \cdot 7^0$. Explain why the true statement $2^3 \cdot 5^2 = 2^3 \cdot 5^2 \cdot 7^0$ is *not* a counterexample to the Unique Factorization Theorem.
4. The following divisibility tests can be helpful when trying to find the prime factorization of a number.

    A counting number is divisible by 2 if its last digit is divisible by 2.

A counting number is divisible by 4 if the number formed from its last two digits is divisible by 4.

A counting number is divisible by 8 if the number formed from its last three digits is divisible by 8.

A counting number is divisible by 3 if the sum of its digits is divisible by 3.

A counting number is divisible by 9 if the sum of its digits is divisible by 9.

A counting number is divisible by 5 if its last digit is either 5 or 0.

A counting number is divisible by 10 if its last digit is 0.

(a) Test each of these counting numbers for divisibility by 2, 3, 4, 5, 8, 9, and 10 by using these tests.

  (i) 96.   (iii) 766268109451128.
  (ii) 31475869105.   (iv) 4545451003.

(b) Find the prime factorizations of these numbers.

  (i) 3240.   (ii) 209952.   (iii) 820125.

Multiplication of Counting Numbers by Using Prime Factorizations

Suppose that two counting numbers are represented by their prime factorizations. For example, consider the counting numbers $2 \cdot 3^2 \cdot 11$ and $2^4 \cdot 3^2$. The product of these numbers is very easily computed. Using the associative and commutative properties of multiplication of counting numbers, we can write

$$(2 \cdot 3^2 \cdot 11)(2^4 \cdot 3^2) = (2 \cdot 2^4)(3^2 \cdot 3^2)(11)$$

Now using Theorem 1, p. 119, we can write

$$(2 \cdot 2^4)(3^2 \cdot 3^2)(11) = 2^5 \cdot 3^4 \cdot 11$$

Thus the product of these counting numbers is $2^5 \cdot 3^4 \cdot 11$.

This example demonstrates that the product of counting numbers is found by adding the exponents of like prime factors. Here are some more examples.

EXAMPLE 1. $(2 \cdot 3^2 \cdot 5^2 \cdot 7^4 \cdot 13^2)(3 \cdot 5^3 \cdot 11^2 \cdot 13) = ?$

Solution: Using the associative and commutative properties of multiplication we can rewrite this product in the form

$$(2)(3^2 \cdot 3)(5^2 \cdot 5^3)(7^4)(11^2)(13^2 \cdot 13)$$

which, by using Theorem 1, p. 119, can be rewritten in the form

$$2 \cdot 3^3 \cdot 5^5 \cdot 7^4 \cdot 11^2 \cdot 13^3$$

EXAMPLE 2. $(125)(294) = (5^3)(2 \cdot 3 \cdot 7^2) = 2 \cdot 3 \cdot 5^3 \cdot 7^2$

It is rather easy to identify the multiples of a given counting number using prime factorizations. Consider the counting number $2^3 \cdot 3^5 \cdot 7^4$. What must be true about the prime factorization of a nonzero multiple of this number? Suppose n is such a multiple. Then since

$$n = (2^3 \cdot 3^5 \cdot 7^4)(\text{some nonzero counting number})$$

it follows that the prime factorization of n must involve the primes 2, 3, and 7 raised to at least the powers 3, 5, and 4, respectively. That is, any nonzero multiple of $2^3 \cdot 3^5 \cdot 7^4$ has the form

$$2^a \cdot 3^b \cdot 7^c \cdot \text{(other prime powers)}$$

where a, b, and c are counting numbers such that $a \geq 3$, $b \geq 5$, and $c \geq 4$.

EXAMPLE. Any nonzero multiple of $2^3 \cdot 5^6$ must have the form

$$2^a \cdot 5^b \cdot \text{(other prime powers)}$$

where a and b are counting numbers such that $a \geq 3$ and $b \geq 6$.

Exercises

1. Find the products by using prime factorizations. Leave these products written as prime factorizations.
    (a) $(2^2 \cdot 3 \cdot 5^2 \cdot 7^4)(2 \cdot 3^2 \cdot 7^2 \cdot 11)$.
    (b) $(2^2 \cdot 5^3 \cdot 11^2)(13^3)(3^4 \cdot 7^5)(2^2 \cdot 5)$.
    (c) $(2^5)(3^5)(5^{10})(7^{10})(2^2 \cdot 3^5)(2 \cdot 3 \cdot 5^2 \cdot 7)$.
    (d) $198 \cdot 144$.
    (e) $212 \cdot 100 \cdot 64$.
    (f) $8800 \cdot 188$.
2. If $n = 2^3 \cdot 3 \cdot 5^2 \cdot 7$, then what is the prime factorization of
    (a) n^2.   (c) n^4.
    (b) n^3.   (d) n^m, where m is a nonzero counting number.
3. (a) What can be said about the prime factorization of n^2 if it is known that n is divisible by 2?
    (b) What can be said about the prime factorization of n if it is known that n^2 is divisible by 2?
    (c) What can be said about the prime factorization of n^2 if it is known that n^2 is divisible by 4? By 8?
4. Fill in the missing exponents so that the first number will be a multiple of the second.
    (a) $2^4 \cdot 3^? \cdot 5^4 \cdot 7^?$ and $2 \cdot 3^2 \cdot 5 \cdot 7^3$.
    (b) $2^6 \cdot 3^? \cdot 5^? \cdot 7^?$ and $2^3 \cdot 3 \cdot 5^2 \cdot 7^5$.
    (c) $2^{100} \cdot 3^?$ and $2^{88} \cdot 3^{48}$.
5. What can be said about the prime factorization of a nonzero multiple of 198? Of 144?

Division of Counting Numbers by Using Prime Factorizations

FINDING DIVISORS OF A COUNTING NUMBER

Consider the counting number $2^3 \cdot 3^2 \cdot 5^4$. What are the divisors of this number? If n is a divisor, then this number is a multiple of n. It follows from this and our previous remarks about multiples that the prime factorization of n cannot involve any prime factors other than 2, 3, and 5 (although it may not involve all of these) and these prime factors can be raised to at most the powers 3, 2, and 4, respectively. Thus the prime factorization of n has the form

$$n = 2^a \cdot 3^b \cdot 5^c$$

where a, b, and c are counting numbers such that $a \leq 3$, $b \leq 2$, and $c \leq 4$. Each of the following numbers is a divisor of $2^3 \cdot 3^2 \cdot 5^4$:

$$2^0 \cdot 3^1 \cdot 5^0, \quad 2^1 \cdot 3^1 \cdot 5^1, \quad 2^2 \cdot 3^2 \cdot 5^0, \quad 2^0 \cdot 3^2 \cdot 5^3, \quad 2^2 \cdot 3^0 \cdot 5^4$$

Here are some more examples of finding divisors of a given number.

EXAMPLE 1. The divisors of $2^3 \cdot 3^2 \cdot 5^3 \cdot 7^5$ all have the general form $2^a \cdot 3^b \cdot 5^c \cdot 7^d$, where a, b, c, and d are counting numbers such that $a \leq 3$, $b \leq 2$, $c \leq 3$, and $d \leq 5$.

EXAMPLE 2. Find all of the divisors of $2 \cdot 3^2 \cdot 5$.
Solution: We know that every divisor of $2 \cdot 3^2 \cdot 5$ has the general form

$$2^a \cdot 3^b \cdot 5^c$$

where $a \leq 1$, $b \leq 2$, and $c \leq 1$. Hence the divisors of $2 \cdot 3^2 \cdot 5$ are precisely the counting numbers $2^0 \cdot 3^0 \cdot 5^0, 2^0 \cdot 3^0 \cdot 5^1, 2^0 \cdot 3^1 \cdot 5^0, 2^0 \cdot 3^2 \cdot 5^0, 2^0 \cdot 3^1 \cdot 5^1, 2^0 \cdot 3^2 \cdot 5^1, 2^1 \cdot 3^0 \cdot 5^0,$ $2^1 \cdot 3^0 \cdot 5^1, 2^1 \cdot 3^1 \cdot 5^0, 2^1 \cdot 3^2 \cdot 5^0, 2^1 \cdot 3^1 \cdot 5^1,$ and $2^1 \cdot 3^2 \cdot 5^1$.

These examples demonstrate that if n and m are counting numbers such that m divides n, then the primes which occur in the prime factorization of m all occur in the prime factorization of n and the powers to which these primes occur in the prime factorization of m are less than or equal to the powers to which these primes occur in the prime factorization of n.

EXAMPLE 3. Does either of the numbers $2^3 \cdot 3^5 \cdot 7^3 \cdot 11^2$ and $3^6 \cdot 7^2 \cdot 11$ divide the other? No. The first does not divide the second because 2 is not a factor of the second. The second does not divide the first because 3 occurs to the sixth power in the second number and occurs only to the fifth power in the first.

EXAMPLE 4. For which exponents n does $2^3 \cdot 3^n \cdot 5$ divide $2^4 \cdot 3^7 \cdot 5^2$? The exponent n may be any one of the numbers 0, 1, 2, 3, 4, 5, 6, or 7 and the first number will divide the second. If n is any other number, then the first number will not divide the second.

Exercises

1. Fill in the missing exponents in such a way that the first number will be a divisor of the second number.
   (a) $2^a \cdot 3^b \cdot 5$ and $2^2 \cdot 3 \cdot 5^3$.
   (b) $2^3 \cdot 3^5 \cdot 5^a \cdot 7^2$ and $2^3 \cdot 3^6 \cdot 5 \cdot 7^3$.
   (c) $2 \cdot 3 \cdot 5^a$ and $2^2 \cdot 3$.
   (d) $2^2 \cdot 3^2 \cdot 5 \cdot 7^a$ and 1980.
2. Fill in the missing exponents so that the first number will not be a divisor of the second number.
   (a) $2^2 \cdot 3^2 \cdot 5^a \cdot 11^b$ and $2^3 \cdot 3^5 \cdot 5^2 \cdot 11^2$.
   (b) $2 \cdot 7^a$ and 1980.

3. Suppose m divides n and n is the number given. What does the prime factorization of m look like?
    (a) $2 \cdot 3 \cdot 5$.
    (b) $2^2 \cdot 3^2 \cdot 5^2$.
    (c) $2^2 \cdot 3^5 \cdot 5^3 \cdot 7^{10}$.
4. Tabulate the set of all divisors of the numbers given. Use prime factorizations to do this.
    (a) $3 \cdot 5^2$.
    (b) $2^2 \cdot 3 \cdot 5$.
    (c) $3 \cdot 5 \cdot 7^3$.
    (d) $3 \cdot 5^2 \cdot 7^2$.
5. In general the prime factorization of a counting number has the form

$$p_1{}^{n_1} \cdot p_2{}^{n_2} \cdot p_3{}^{n_3} \cdot p_4{}^{n_4} \cdots p_k{}^{n_k}$$

where the numbers $p_1, \ldots, p_k$ are primes and the numbers $n_1, \ldots, n_k$ are the exponents. It is a result of a branch of mathematics called combinatorial analysis that there are precisely

$$(n_1 + 1)(n_2 + 1) \cdots (n_k + 1)$$

divisors of such a number.
    (a) In Exercise 4a there are (according to the above stated result) $(1 + 1)(2 + 1)$ or 6 divisors of $3 \cdot 5^2$. Does this agree with your answer to that exercise?
    (b) How many divisors of the number in Exercise 4b ought you to have found? In Exercises 4c and 4d?
    (c) How many divisors of $2^3 \cdot 3^2 \cdot 5^4$ are there?
    (d) We claimed to have found all the divisors of $2 \cdot 3^2 \cdot 5$ in Example 2 preceding these exercises. Were we correct?

PERFORMING DIVISION BY USING PRIME FACTORIZATIONS

Suppose we want to divide $2^3 \cdot 3^5 \cdot 5^3$ by $2^2 \cdot 3^2 \cdot 5$. (We know that this division is possible because the second number is a divisor of the first.) Let us write

$$2^3 \cdot 3^5 \cdot 5^3 \div 2^2 \cdot 3^2 \cdot 5 = q$$

The definition of division then implies that

$$2^3 \cdot 3^5 \cdot 5^3 = (2^2 \cdot 3^2 \cdot 5)(q)$$

Hence q is a divisor of $2^3 \cdot 3^5 \cdot 5^3$, and consequently we may conclude that q has the general form $2^a \cdot 3^b \cdot 5^c$ where a, b, and c are counting numbers. Thus

$$2^3 \cdot 3^5 \cdot 5^3 = (2^2 \cdot 3^2 \cdot 5)(2^a \cdot 3^b \cdot 5^c)$$

Since we already know how to multiply counting numbers using prime factorizations, we may conclude that

$$2^3 \cdot 3^5 \cdot 5^3 = 2^{2+a} \cdot 3^{2+b} \cdot 5^{1+c}$$

It then follows (because of the uniqueness of prime factorizations) that

$$3 = 2 + a, \quad 5 = 2 + b, \quad \text{and} \quad 3 = 1 + c$$

These equations may be solved for a, b, and c and we obtain

$$a = 3 - 2, \quad b = 5 - 2, \quad \text{and} \quad c = 3 - 1$$

Thus the quotient q is equal to $2^{3-2} \cdot 3^{5-2} \cdot 5^{3-1}$ or $2 \cdot 3^3 \cdot 5^2$.
   We have seen that

$$2^3 \cdot 3^5 \cdot 5^3 \div 2^2 \cdot 3^2 \cdot 5 = 2^{3-2} \cdot 3^{5-2} \cdot 5^{3-1}$$

This example demonstrates the way division is performed by using prime factorizations. As we have seen multiplication of prime factorizations was accomplished by adding the exponents of like prime factors and we now see that division is performed by subtracting the exponents of like prime factors. That is, the quotient is found by subtracting the exponents of each of the prime factors of the divisor from the corresponding exponents of the dividend. Here are some more examples.

EXAMPLE 1. $2^3 \cdot 3^5 \cdot 7^3 \cdot 11^4 \div 2 \cdot 3^4 \cdot 7^2 \cdot 11^2 = 2^{3-1} \cdot 3^{5-4} \cdot 7^{3-2} \cdot 11^{4-2}$
$$= 2^2 \cdot 3 \cdot 7 \cdot 11^2$$

EXAMPLE 2. $2 \cdot 3^4 \cdot 5^7 \cdot 7^8 \cdot 11^2 \div 2 \cdot 3^4 \cdot 5^3 \cdot 7 \cdot 11^2 = 2^{1-1} \cdot 3^{4-4} \cdot 5^{7-3} \cdot 7^{8-1} \cdot 11^{2-2}$
$$= 2^0 \cdot 3^0 \cdot 5^4 \cdot 7^7 \cdot 11^0$$
$$= 5^4 \cdot 7^7$$

If the dividend has prime factors which the divisor does not have, then these prime factors may be inserted into the divisor by using zero exponents. Thus, for example,

$$2^2 \cdot 3^5 \cdot 7^3 \cdot 13^8 \div 3^2 \cdot 7 = 2^2 \cdot 3^5 \cdot 7^3 \cdot 13^8 \div 2^0 \cdot 3^2 \cdot 7 \cdot 13^0$$
$$= 2^{2-0} \cdot 3^{5-2} \cdot 7^{3-1} \cdot 13^{8-0}$$
$$= 2^2 \cdot 3^3 \cdot 7^2 \cdot 13^8$$

Exercises

1. Perform these divisions by using prime factorizations.
    (a) $2^3 \cdot 3^2 \cdot 11^4 \cdot 13^6 \div 3^2 \cdot 11^4 \cdot 13^2 = ?$
    (b) $2^5 \cdot 7^3 \cdot 5^2 \div 2^4 \cdot 7^3 \cdot 5 = ?$
    (c) $1188 \div 198 = ?$
    (d) $250 \div 10 = ?$
    (e) $2^3 \cdot 5^2 \cdot 7 \cdot 11^2 \div 2^2 \cdot 5 \cdot 7 = ?$
2. Simplify by using prime factorizations.
    (a) $(2^3 \cdot 3^5 \cdot 7 \cdot 11^2 \div 3^4 \cdot 11)(2 \cdot 5^3 \cdot 7 \cdot 11^9) = ?$
    (b) $(3^4 \cdot 5^3 \cdot 7^2 \cdot 11^7 \div 3^4 \cdot 5 \cdot 7 \cdot 11^5) \div 5 \cdot 7 \cdot 11 = ?$
3. Suppose that $n = 2^a \cdot 3^b \cdot 7^c \cdot 11^d$ and $m = 2^u \cdot 3^v \cdot 7^x \cdot 11^y$. Explain why $n \div m = 2^{a-u} \cdot 3^{b-v} \cdot 7^{c-x} \cdot 11^{d-y}$.

GREATEST COMMON DIVISOR

We are now ready to move on to the first of the important tools that we need in order to study fractions. Our discussion of these tools rests heavily upon our study of prime factorizations.

Suppose n and m are nonzero counting numbers. A number which divides *both* n and m is called a *common divisor* of n and m. Every pair of nonzero counting numbers has at least one common divisor, namely, 1. Some numbers have more than one common divisor. For example, 15 and 21 have the common divisors 1 and 3. The common divisors of 12 and 42 are 1, 2, 3, and 6.

Consider now the set of all common divisors of two nonzero counting numbers n and m. As we observed before, these numbers necessarily have at least one common divisor, the counting number 1. Hence the set of common divisors of n and m is nonempty. But not only is the set of common divisors of n and m nonempty, it is also *finite*. (Why?) Since every nonempty finite set of counting numbers contains a largest element (a fact we have not proven but which is intuitively obvious), every pair of nonzero counting numbers has a *greatest* common divisor. We shall denote this greatest common divisor by GCD. Thus, for example, the GCD of 45 and 30 is 15. The GCD of 15 and 21 is 3 and the GCD of 12 and 25 is 1.

It is not difficult to determine the GCD of small numbers by inspection. However, we need a general procedure for finding GCD's and the concept of prime factorization is very useful in this respect.

Consider the numbers $n = 2^3 \cdot 5^2 \cdot 7 \cdot 11^2$ and $m = 2^2 \cdot 3 \cdot 5 \cdot 7$. The GCD of these numbers is the greatest number which divides them both and consequently if we think of the GCD as written in its prime factorization, the number we seek will involve as many different prime factors as possible and each of these prime factors will be raised to the largest possible power. The only prime numbers which divide both n and m are 2, 5, and 7. This observation tells us that the GCD has the form $2^? \cdot 5^? \cdot 7^?$. It remains to determine the exponents. We consider these exponents one at a time. First, the prime 2 occurs to the third and second powers respectively in n and m. Hence the largest power of 2 which divides *both* numbers is the second power, and consequently the GCD has the form $2^2 \cdot 5^? \cdot 7^?$. Because the largest power of 5 dividing *both* n and m is the first power, the GCD has the form $2^2 \cdot 5^1 \cdot 7^?$. The largest power of 7 dividing *both* n and m is the first power and so we conclude that the GCD of n and m is $2^2 \cdot 5 \cdot 7$.

The process of finding GCD's involves two steps. First, determine the primes which divide *both* numbers and, second, determine the largest power of each of these primes dividing *both* numbers.

EXAMPLE 1.   The GCD of the numbers $2^3 \cdot 3^2 \cdot 5^6 \cdot 7^3 \cdot 11^2$ and $2 \cdot 3^2 \cdot 7^4$ will involve the primes 2, 3, and 7 since these are all of the primes which divide both numbers. So the GCD has the form $2^? \cdot 3^? \cdot 7^?$. The largest power of 2 which divides both numbers is the first; 3^2 is the largest power of 3 dividing both numbers and 7^3 is the largest power of 7 dividing both numbers. Hence the GCD is $2 \cdot 3^2 \cdot 7^3$.

EXAMPLE 2.   The GCD of $3^4 \cdot 5^6 \cdot 13^4$ and $3^7 \cdot 5^2 \cdot 11 \cdot 13^4$ is $3^4 \cdot 5^2 \cdot 13^4$.

The GCD of more than two counting numbers can be found in very much the same way as we find the GCD of two numbers.

EXAMPLE 3.   Find the GCD of the numbers $2^3 \cdot 3^4 \cdot 5^2 \cdot 7$, $2^2 \cdot 3^7 \cdot 5^3 \cdot 7^2$, and $2 \cdot 3 \cdot 5^7 \cdot 7^3 \cdot 11$.

Solution: The primes which divide all three of these numbers are 2, 3, 5, and 7. The largest power of 2 which divides all three numbers is the first and so the GCD looks like

$$2^1 \cdot 3^? \cdot 5^? \cdot 7^?$$

The largest power of 3 dividing all three numbers is the first; the largest power of 5 dividing all three numbers is the second; and the largest power of 7 dividing all three numbers is the first. Hence, the GCD is $2 \cdot 3 \cdot 5^2 \cdot 7$.

EXAMPLE 4.   The GCD of $2 \cdot 3^4 \cdot 5^2 \cdot 7^4$, $2^3 \cdot 3^5 \cdot 7^3 \cdot 13^2$, $3^4 \cdot 7^{11}$, and $3^5 \cdot 7^4 \cdot 13^4$ is $3^4 \cdot 7^3$ since the only primes dividing all four numbers are 3 and 7 and the largest powers of these primes dividing all four numbers are (respectively) the fourth and third powers.

RELATIVELY PRIME COUNTING NUMBERS

Finally, let us introduce an important and useful relation on the collection of all nonzero counting numbers which derives from the concept of greatest common divisor. Given a pair of nonzero counting numbers it may be that their GCD is 1. In this case we say that the counting numbers are *relatively prime to each other* or just that they are *relatively prime*. For example, 35 and 36 are relatively prime since the GCD of these numbers is 1. On the other hand, 36 and 24 are not relatively prime since their GCD is 12 and not 1.

This relation is not reflexive; the reader can easily find counting numbers which are not relatively prime to themselves. (Can he find any that are relatively prime to themselves?) However, the relation is symmetric since if n has no divisors in common with m except 1, then m has no factors in common with n except 1. The reader can find examples which show that the relation is not transitive.

In the next chapter we shall see how this relation is used in the study of fractions.

Review Questions

1.   What is meant by the *greatest common divisor* of a pair of counting numbers?
2.   Let n and m represent nonzero counting numbers. Let S represent the set of prime numbers which occur in the prime factorization of n and let T be the set of prime numbers occurring in the prime factorization of m. In terms of the sets S and T

describe the set of prime numbers occurring in the prime factorization of the GCD of n and m.

3. A prime number occurs to the fifth power in the prime factorization of a number n and to the seventh power in the prime factorization of a number m. To what power will this prime occur in the GCD of n and m?

4. Describe in a general way the procedure for finding the GCD of a finite set of numbers.

5. What does it mean to say that the counting numbers n and m are relatively prime?

6. Which properties are possessed by the relation "is relatively prime to"?

Exercises

1. Find the GCD of the following pairs of counting numbers.
    (a) $3^2 \cdot 5^3 \cdot 11$ and $2 \cdot 3 \cdot 5 \cdot 7$.
    (b) 198 and 144.
    (c) $2^3 \cdot 3^3 \cdot 5^2 \cdot 7^6 \cdot 13^5$ and $3^5 \cdot 5 \cdot 7^{10} \cdot 11^{14}$.
    (d) 660 and 84.

2. Find the GCD of the numbers
    (a) 198, 144, and 68.
    (b) $2^2 \cdot 3 \cdot 5$, $2 \cdot 3^4 \cdot 5^2$, and $2^3 \cdot 5 \cdot 7 \cdot 11$.
    (c) $2^2 \cdot 3 \cdot 5^2 \cdot 7^3$, $2^4 \cdot 3 \cdot 5^2 \cdot 11^2$, $2 \cdot 3^2 \cdot 5^2 \cdot 7^2$, and $2^6 \cdot 3^2 \cdot 11^2$.
    (d) 363, 198, and 18.

3. Why is the set of common divisors of a pair of nonzero counting numbers necessarily a finite set?

4. The process of finding GCD's can be thought of as a binary operation on the collection of all nonzero counting numbers. Denoting the operation by the symbol $*$ we can give the instruction for performing the operation by the equation

$$n * m = \text{GCD of } n \text{ and } m$$

For example,

$$2 * 3 = 1, \quad 14 * 8 = 2, \quad \text{and } 14 * 21 = 7$$

    (a) Does this operation have the closure property?
    (b) Is this operation commutative?
    (c) This operation is associative. Verify that the numbers 198, 144, and 18 associate with respect to this operation.
    (d) This operation does not possess an identity. Explain.
    (e) This operation does not possess the cancellation property. Give an example.

5. Give examples which show that the relation "is relatively prime to" is neither reflexive nor transitive. Use the fact that the GCD operation (see Exercise 4 above) is commutative to prove that this relation is symmetric.

6. **Theorem**   *The GCD of counting numbers n and m is g if and only if the counting numbers $n \div g$ and $m \div g$ are relatively prime.*

    Verify that this theorem is true for the numbers in Exercise 1.

7. Complete the following statement: A counting number greater than 1 is relatively prime to every smaller nonzero counting number if and only if _____.

8. Complete the following statement: If a and b are counting numbers and if p is a prime number which does not divide a and if p divides ab, then _____.

9. Show by example that your answer to Exercise 8 is false if the number p is allowed to be a composite number.

10. **Theorem** *If a counting number n is divisible by the counting numbers a and b, then n is divisible by ab if a and b are relatively prime.*

    (a) Use this theorem and the divisibility tests of Exercise 4, p. 126, to find divisibility tests for 6, 18, 12, 24, and 40.

    (b) Give examples which show that if a and b are not relatively prime, then if n is divisible by both a and b it need not be divisible by the product ab.

LEAST COMMON MULTIPLE

Let n and m represent counting numbers. A number which is a multiple of both n and m is called a *common multiple* of n and m. For example, 24 is a common multiple of 6 and 8. The least nonzero common multiple of n and m is called the *least common multiple* (LCM) of n and m.

The least common multiple of 6 and 4 is 12. Of course, 0 is also a common multiple of 6 and 4 but we have excluded the common multiple 0 in the definition of LCM.

It is not too difficult to find the LCM of two nonzero counting numbers by inspection if the numbers are small. However, we need a general procedure for finding the LCM of two numbers. We are going to formulate such a procedure by using prime factorizations.

As an example of the procedure for finding LCM's consider the counting numbers

$$n = 2^3 \cdot 3^2 \quad \text{and} \quad m = 3^4 \cdot 5^7$$

We seek the least (nonzero) number which is a multiple of both of these. Since this LCM must be divisible by n the prime factorization of the LCM must involve the primes 2 and 3. Since the LCM must be divisible by m it must also involve the prime 5. Hence the LCM has the general form

$$2^a \cdot 3^b \cdot 5^c$$

where a, b, and c are counting numbers. Since the LCM is a multiple of both n and m the exponents must be such that

$$a \geq 3, b \geq 4, \text{ and } c \geq 7$$

Since we are seeking the *least* common multiple we must choose these exponents to be as small as possible. Hence the LCM is

$$2^3 \cdot 3^4 \cdot 5^7$$

Here are some more examples.

EXAMPLE 1. Any common multiple of $2^2 \cdot 3^4 \cdot 5 \cdot 7^2$ and $2^3 \cdot 3^5 \cdot 7$ has the form $2^a \cdot 3^b \cdot 5^c \cdot 7^d$ since each of the primes 2, 3, 5, and 7 must occur in the prime factorization of a common multiple. Since a common multiple is a multiple of $2^2 \cdot 3^4 \cdot 5 \cdot 7^2$

we know that $a \geq 2$, $b \geq 4$, $c \geq 1$, and $d \geq 2$. Since a common multiple is a multiple of $2^3 \cdot 3^5 \cdot 7$, we know that $a \geq 3$, $b \geq 5$, and $d \geq 1$. Since a common multiple is a multiple of both numbers, we know that $a \geq 3$, $b \geq 5$, $c \geq 1$, and $d \geq 2$. The *least* common multiple therefore is $2^3 \cdot 3^5 \cdot 5 \cdot 7^2$.

EXAMPLE 2. The LCM of $2^3 \cdot 3^4 \cdot 5 \cdot 7^5 \cdot 13^2$ and $3^5 \cdot 5^7 \cdot 7^5 \cdot 11^2 \cdot 17^4$ has the form $2^a \cdot 3^b \cdot 5^c \cdot 7^d \cdot 11^e \cdot 13^f \cdot 17^g$. The smallest possible exponents such that the LCM will be divisible by both of the given numbers are $a = 3$, $b = 5$, $c = 7$, $d = 5$, $e = 2$, $f = 2$, and $g = 4$. Thus the LCM is $2^3 \cdot 3^5 \cdot 5^7 \cdot 7^5 \cdot 11^2 \cdot 13^2 \cdot 17^4$.

The least common multiple of more than two counting numbers is found in the same way that the least common multiple of two numbers is found.

EXAMPLE. Find the LCM of $2^3 \cdot 7^5$, $3^4 \cdot 5^2 \cdot 7^4$, $2 \cdot 5 \cdot 7 \cdot 11^3$, and $3^4 \cdot 11^5 \cdot 13$.

Solution: The LCM must involve each of the prime factors of each of these numbers and therefore has the form

$$2^a \cdot 3^b \cdot 5^c \cdot 7^d \cdot 11^e \cdot 13^f$$

Selecting the smallest possible exponents so that the LCM will be divisible by each of the four given numbers, we see that the LCM of these four numbers is $2^3 \cdot 3^4 \cdot 5^2 \cdot 7^5 \cdot 11^5 \cdot 13$.

Review Questions

1. What is meant by the *least common multiple* of a pair of counting numbers? Why do we not study the *greatest common multiple*?
2. Let n and m represent nonzero counting numbers. Let S denote the set of all prime numbers which occur in the prime factorization of n, and let T denote the set of all prime numbers which occur in the prime factorization of m. In terms of the sets S and T describe the set of prime numbers occurring in the prime factorization of the LCM of n and m.
3. A prime number occurs to the fifth power in the prime factorization of n and to the seventh power in the prime factorization of m. To what power will this prime occur in the LCM of n and m?
4. Describe in a general way the procedure for finding the LCM of a finite set of counting numbers.

Exercises

1. Find the LCM of the following numbers.
   (a) $2^2 \cdot 3^3 \cdot 13^4$ and $3^2 \cdot 5^3 \cdot 7^2 \cdot 11^7 \cdot 13$.
   (b) 198 and 64.
   (c) 25 and 64.
   (d) $2^2 \cdot 5 \cdot 7 \cdot 11 \cdot 13^2$ and $2^4 \cdot 5^2 \cdot 7^2 \cdot 11^3 \cdot 13^4$.
   (e) 660 and 144.
2. Find the LCM of the following numbers.
   (a) $2^2 \cdot 3$, $2 \cdot 3 \cdot 5^2$, $3^2 \cdot 7 \cdot 11$, and $2 \cdot 3 \cdot 5 \cdot 13$.
   (b) 198, 144, and 660.
   (c) $2 \cdot 5^2$, $7^2 \cdot 13$, $3 \cdot 5$, and $3^2 \cdot 5^2 \cdot 7$.
   (d) 225, 35, and 84.

3. Explain why the set of all common multiples of a pair of nonzero counting numbers is necessarily infinite.
4. The process of finding LCM's is a *binary operation* on the collection of all *nonzero* counting numbers. Denoting this operation by $*$, the instruction for performing this operation is $n * m = $ LCM of n and m. For example, $2 * 3 = 6, 15 * 30 = 60$, and $4 * 5 = 20$.
   (a) Does this operation have the closure property?
   (b) Is this operation commutative?
   (c) Is there an identity for this operation?
   (d) Does this operation possess the cancellation property?
   (e) Is the binary operation associative?
5. Suppose n and m are counting numbers.
   (a) If the LCM of n and m is nm, how are n and m related?
   (b) If n and m are relatively prime, then what is their LCM?
   (c) Based upon your answers to parts (a) and (b), state a theorem.
6. Suppose n and m are counting numbers, g is their GCD, and d is their LCM.
   (a) Write an equation involving the four numbers n, m, g, and d. (If necessary, experiment with some numbers to discover the relationship between these numbers.)
   (b) You are given that the GCD of two numbers is $3 \cdot 5$ and their LCM is $2^2 \cdot 3^2 \cdot 5^2 \cdot 7$. One of the numbers is $3^2 \cdot 5 \cdot 7$. What is the other? (*Suggestion:* Use your answer to part (a).)
   (c) The product of two numbers is $2^3 \cdot 3^5 \cdot 5^6 \cdot 7^5$ and their GCD is $3^2 \cdot 5^2 \cdot 7^2$. What is their LCM?
7. Find the LCM of 147 and 72. Then find counting numbers s and t such that $(147)(s) = $ LCM and $(72)(t) = $ LCM. How are these numbers s and t related?
8. Work Exercise 7 for each of the pairs of numbers 100 and 75, $2^3 \cdot 5 \cdot 7^2$ and $2 \cdot 3 \cdot 5^2 \cdot 7$, and 1260 and 2772.

THE INDIRECT METHOD OF PROOF

We have yet to prove that the set of all prime numbers is an infinite set. There are many different ways to prove this interesting theorem, but the easiest involves a type of proof called the *indirect method of proof*.

In Chapter 2 a number of theorems were proved by using a method of proof called the *direct method* and were of a rather straightforward nature. Beginning with a statement which was assumed to be true (the hypothesis), a valid sequence of statements was found which led directly from this assumption to the desired conclusion. Frequently, the direct method is best for proving a given theorem; however, there are many theorems whose proofs by direct method are very difficult. The theorem mentioned above is one of these.

There is a second method called *proof by indirect method*. Using this method of proof we do not prove directly that the conclusion is true; instead we prove that the conclusion is true by proving that the conclusion cannot be false. We do this by *assuming that the conclusion is false* and then drawing conclusions from this assumption. Eventually we shall draw a conclusion which is in contradiction to something we already know to be true. As soon as this contradiction is obtained, we know that one of two things went wrong:

1. Our argument is invalid, or
2. Our initial assumption is incorrect.

If our argument is valid, it must be that the assumption made at the beginning is incorrect: that is, the assumption, "the conclusion is false," is incorrect. But this means that the conclusion is true. This is precisely what we wanted to prove in the first place.

The method of indirect proof is not as uncommon as it may appear. As a matter of fact we have used this kind of argument already. Consider our argument on p. 45 proving that the cancellation property for multiplication of counting numbers must exclude 0. We argued as follows:

(1) We can cancel 0	(1) Assumption
(2) $7 \times 0 = 8 \times 0$	(2) Both 7×0 and 8×0 equal 0
(3) $7 = 8$	(3) According to (1) we can cancel the 0's in (2)

We may stop now for we have obtained the contradiction we desired. Statement (3) is an obvious contradiction to something we already know (namely, that $7 \neq 8$). We know therefore that we did something wrong. Either our argument is invalid or our initial assumption, statement (1), is incorrect. After carefully examining our argument we see that it is valid. Hence it must be that the initial assumption is incorrect. But if this assumption is incorrect, then it must be true that we cannot cancel 0. This is exactly what we wanted to prove.

We also used this kind of argument on p. 66 to show that 7 cannot be divided by 0. Here is that argument. We want to prove that $7 \div 0$ is meaningless so we begin by assuming that it is meaningful.

(1) $7 \div 0$ is meaningful	(1) This is our initial assumption
(2) $7 \div 0 = q$, for some counting number q	(2) This is nothing more than a restatement of statement (1)
(3) $7 = 0 \times q$	(3) Follows from (2) by using the definition of division
(4) $7 = 0$	(4) Follows from (3) since $0 \times q = 0$

Statement (4) is obviously a contradiction to the known fact that $7 \neq 0$. Hence if our argument is valid, then our initial assumption must be incorrect. The argument is valid. Therefore our initial assumption is incorrect and consequently we may conclude that $7 \div 0$ is not meaningful. This is precisely what we wanted to prove.

We are now ready to prove that the set of all prime numbers is an infinite set by the method of indirect proof.

Theorem   *If S denotes the set of all prime numbers, then S is an infinite set.*
Hypothesis: S denotes the set of all prime numbers.
Conclusion: S is an infinite set.
The Proof: As with all indirect proofs we begin by assuming that the hypothesis is true and that the conclusion is false.

(1)   S denotes the set of all prime numbers and S is a finite set.

(1)   Remark above and the fact that if a set is not infinite, then it is finite.

(2)   S contains a largest element which we shall denote by p.

(2)   Every finite set of counting numbers contains a largest element.

(3)   Let m denote the product of all the prime numbers

(3)   Since by (1) there are only finitely many primes and since multiplication has the closure property, the product of all the primes is a counting number.

(4)   Let $n = m + 1$

(4)   Addition has closure, and so $m + 1$ is a counting number

(5) n is divisible by some prime, say q

(5)   Every counting number greater than 1 (and n is greater than 1) is divisible by at least one prime number

(6) $n = q \cdot a$ where a is some counting number

(6)   This is simply another way of saying that n is divisible by q

(7) $m = q \cdot b$ where b is some counting number

(7)   This is simply another way of saying that m is divisble by q (since m is the product of all primes including the prime q)

(8) $qa = qb + 1$

(8)   From (6) and (7) since $n = m + 1$

(9) $qa - qb = 1$

(9)   From (8) by using the definition of subtraction

(10) $q(a - b) = 1$

(10)   From (9) by using the distributive property shared by subtraction and multiplication

(11) q divides 1

(11)   From (10)

We have finally obtained what we wanted—a contradiction to something we already know. We already know that 1 is not divisible by any prime number. This contradiction could not have been obtained unless either our argument is invalid or our initial assumption is incorrect. Careful re-examination convinces us that our argument is valid. The only thing left to conclude therefore is that the initial assumption that S was a finite set is incorrect. Hence S is not finite; that is, S is an infinite set. This is precisely the conclusion we wanted and consequently the proof is complete.

Exercises

1. We needed to know in step (5) of the above proof that the counting number n was greater than 1. Explain why n is greater than 1.
2. Explain why every counting number greater than 1 is divisible by at least one prime number. (This is step (5) of the proof.)
3. Prove the following theorem.

    Theorem   *If $n = a + b$ and if p divides n and divides a, then p divides b also.*

    (*Remark:* The proof of this theorem is actually included in the proof of the Infinitude of Primes Theorem given in the text. The method of proof that should be used is the direct method.)

CHAPTER 5

The System of Fractions

The system of counting numbers is very useful, but it has certain serious deficiencies. One of these is that the operation of division can not always be performed. Phrasing this in another way, one of the deficiencies of the system of counting numbers is that equations of the form $a = bx$, where a and b are counting numbers and b is different from zero, do not always have solutions. Because of this we are motivated to invent a new system of numbers in which it is always possible to divide by nonzero numbers. The result of our attempts in this direction is the *system of fractions*. The organization of our study of the system of fractions is very similar to the organization of our study of the system of counting numbers. We begin by defining and studying the fractions which are the objects of the new system. Then we study the important relations and operations which can be defined on the set of fractions.

THE NEW NUMBERS: THE FRACTIONS

The fact that division of counting numbers can be performed only when the dividend is a multiple of the divisor has many unpleasant consequences, both in mathematics and in our everyday lives. The reader can easily think of problem situations encountered recently which would have been difficult or even impossible to solve if the only numbers available were the counting numbers but which had relatively easy solutions if he was able to employ numbers resulting from the division of one counting number by another. These new numbers may be called *fractions*, *fractional numbers*, or *nonnegative rational numbers*. We shall use the first of these and call the new numbers fractions.

There are a variety of ways we might formulate a definition of a fraction but most of them eventually come down to this: A fraction is a number which when multiplied by some counting number results in another counting number. Thus the fraction 2/3 when multiplied by 3 results in 2. In fact, the fraction 2/3 is distinguished from all other numbers in that it and it alone has the property that when multiplied by 3 the result is 2. The fraction 4/5 is that unique number which when multiplied by 5 results in 4. This means exactly the same thing as to say that the fraction 4/5 is the solution of the equation $4 = 5x$. Similarly 2/3 is the solution of the equation $2 = 3x$.

These observations motivate our definition of a fraction.

Definition of Fraction   *By a fraction we shall mean the unique solution of an equation of the form*

$$a = bx$$

where a and b are counting numbers and b is not zero. The fraction which is the solution of this equation is denoted by the symbol a/b. The counting number a is called the numerator and b is called the denominator of the fraction.

EXAMPLES.   The fraction represented by the symbol 6/7 is the number which is the solution of the equation $6 = 7x$. That is, $6 = 7(6/7)$. The solution of the equation $45 = 89x$ is a fraction and is symbolized by 45/89. The fraction denoted by the symbol 0/7 is the number which is the solution of the equation $0 = 7x$.

A COUNTING NUMBER IS A FRACTION

The first observation we must make is that every counting number is a fraction. For example, consider the counting number six. We know already from our study of the system of counting numbers that six is the solution of the equation

$$6 = 1x$$

but on the other hand we have just defined the solution of this equation to be the fraction symbolized by 6/1. Thus the number six can be regarded as a counting number or as a fraction. Generally when we want to emphasize that six is a counting number we will name it by 6 and when we want to emphasize that it is a fraction we will name it by 6/1. At any rate, this number plays a dual role. Now of course the same remarks hold for any counting number in place of six. The reader must develop a certain indifference to whether we call such numbers as six, ten, five, and two counting numbers or fractions.

There are fractions which are not counting numbers. For example, the solution of the equation $2 = 3x$ is a fraction but not a counting number. Hence the set of counting numbers is a *proper* subset of the set of fractions.

Review Questions

1.   What is a fraction?
2.   Explain why the set of counting numbers is a proper subset of the set of fractions.

Exercises

1.   Let n and m be counting numbers and let $\div$ denote division of counting numbers. Is the symbol $n \div m$ meaningful if the symbol n/m is meaningful? Suppose the

symbols $n \div m$ and n/m are both meaningful. How are the numbers they represent related?

2. Is there a fraction named by 6/0? By 0/0? By 0/6? What do you know about the symbols a and b if you know that the symbol a/b represents a fraction?

RELATIONS ON THE SET OF FRACTIONS

We would like to invent relations on the set of fractions which will correspond to the relations we have already defined for counting numbers. In particular, our experience with the system of counting numbers leads us to believe that it would prove useful if we could invent a relation corresponding in some way to the relation of equality of counting numbers.

Equality of Fractions

FINDING THE DEFINITION

Recognizing that we ought to define a relation on the set of all fractions to be called *equality of fractions*, how ought we to define this relation? That is, if n and m are fractions, what meaning ought we to assign to the statement, "The fraction n is equal to the fraction m"? Let us see how we can arrive at a definition of such a relation.

Let n and m represent fractions. According to the definition of fraction there are counting numbers a, b, c, and d such that

$$a = b(n) \quad \text{and} \quad c = d(m)$$

Based upon our experience with the system of counting numbers, it seems reasonable that we should be able to multiply both sides of the first equation by d and both sides of the second equation by b to obtain the equations

$$da = db(n) \quad \text{and} \quad bc = bd(m)$$

These last two equations can be used to show us how we might define equality of fractions.

Suppose we knew what it meant to write $n = m$. Then would not the following argument be reasonable?

1. If $n = m$, then it ought to follow that $db(n) = bd(m)$.
2. If $db(n) = bd(m)$, then it ought to follow from the equations $da = db(n)$ and $bc = bd(m)$ that $da = bc$.
3. Hence if $n = m$, then it ought to follow that $da = bc$.

On the other hand suppose that we knew that $da = bc$. Then would not this argument appear plausible?

1. If $da = bc$, then it ought to follow from the equations $da = db(n)$ and $bc = bd(m)$ that $db(n) = bd(m)$.

2. If $db(n) = bd(m)$, then it ought to follow that $n = m$.
3. Hence if $da = bc$, then it ought to follow that $n = m$.

Thus we have seen that it is reasonable to say

$$n = m \text{ if and only if } da = bc$$

These remarks motivate our definition of equality of fractions. Because of what we have seen above we have reason to believe that a good way to define equality of fractions is as follows.

Definition of Equality of Fractions   *If a/b and c/d are fractions, then to say that a/b equals c/d, in symbols $a/b = c/d$, means that $da = bc$.*

EXAMPLES.   The fractions represented by the symbols 2/4 and 1/2 are equal according to this definition because $(2)(2) = (4)(1)$. The fractions represented by 3/7 and 9/21 are equal because $(21)(3) = 63 = (7)(9)$.

We should observe that when using this definition to determine whether or not two fractions are related by equality of fractions, it is necessary to be able to determine whether or not two counting numbers are related by equality of counting numbers. Thus the concept of equality of fractions is built upon the concept of equality of counting numbers.

TESTING THE DEFINITION

We have stated a definition for the concept of equality of fractions and have explained what motivated our formulation of the definition. But before we irrevocably accept this definition we ought to examine it to make sure that it gives us the kind of relation we really want. To decide on the appropriateness of the definition we must have in mind certain criteria:

1.   IS EQUALITY OF FRACTIONS AN EQUIVALENCE RELATION?   The other two relations of equality that we have studied (equality of counting numbers and equality of sets) were equivalence relations and consequently it would seem natural that the relation of equality of fractions should also be an equivalence relation. The verification that equality of fractions possesses the reflexive, symmetric, and transitive properties is contained in Exercise 1.

2.   DO EQUALITY OF FRACTIONS AND EQUALITY OF COUNTING NUMBERS AGREE ON THE COUNTING NUMBERS?   Since every counting number is also a fraction we have a choice: We can think of counting numbers as counting numbers or we can think of them as fractions. Now it is certainly reasonable to expect that if our definition of equality of fractions is any good, then when we think of a pair of counting numbers as counting numbers they should be equal if and only if they are equal when we think of them as fractions. We can rephrase this idea by introducing some symbolism. Let $\mathcal{C}$ denote the relation of equality of counting numbers and let $\mathcal{F}$ denote the relation of equality of fractions. Then let n and m be counting numbers. Since n and m are counting numbers, either

$n \mathrel{\mathfrak{C}} m$ or $n \mathrel{\not\mathfrak{C}} m$. But n and m are also fractions, and so n and m are either related by the relation $\mathfrak{F}$ or are not related by this relation: $n \mathrel{\mathfrak{F}} m$ or $n \mathrel{\not\mathfrak{F}} m$. When we say that the relations $\mathfrak{C}$ and $\mathfrak{F}$ *agree on the counting numbers*, we mean that

$$n \mathrel{\mathfrak{C}} m \text{ if and only if } n \mathrel{\mathfrak{F}} m$$

EXAMPLE. Explain in two ways why the fractions 6/1 and 7/1 are not equal.

Solution: One way is to apply the definition of equality of fractions: Since $(1)(6) \neq (1)(7)$ we conclude that $6/1 \neq 7/1$. Another way is first to note that equality of fractions and equality of counting numbers agree on the counting numbers and then to observe that because of this since the counting numbers 6 and 7 are not equal, the fractions 6/1 and 7/1 cannot be equal.

Review Questions

1. State the definition of equality of fractions.
2. Equality of fractions is defined in terms of what relation on counting numbers?
3. What does it mean to say that equality of fractions and equality of counting numbers agree on the counting numbers?
4. What kind of a relation is equality of fractions?

Exercises

1. Supply justifications for the following proofs. In these theorems the symbols a, b, c, d, e, and f represent counting numbers and b, d, and f are nonzero.
   (a) *Equality of fractions is reflexive.* If a/b is a fraction, then $a/b = a/b$.
      (1) $ba = ba$
      (2) $a/b = a/b$
   (b) *Equality of fractions is symmetric.* If a/b and c/d are fractions and if $a/b = c/d$, then $c/d = a/b$.
      (1) $a/b = c/d$
      (2) $da = bc$
      (3) $bc = da$
      (4) $c/d = a/b$
   (c) *Equality of fractions is transitive.* If a/b, c/d, and e/f are fractions and if $a/b = c/d$ and $c/d = e/f$, then $a/b = e/f$.
      (1) $a/b = c/d$ and $c/d = e/f$
      (2) $da = bc$ and $fc = de$
      (3) $fda = fbc$ and $bfc = bde$
      (4) $fda = bde$
      (5) $fa = be$
      (6) $a/b = e/f$
2. What do you know about the numerator of a fraction which is equal to zero? What do you know about its denominator?
3. It does not make any sense to say that the relations of equality of fractions and equality of counting numbers agree on the fractions. Why not?
4. Let a, b, c, and d be nonzero counting numbers such that $ab = cd$. Using this equality, obtain as many pairs of equal fractions as you can.

The Different Names of a Fraction

According to the definition of equality of fractions, the symbols 1/2 and 3/6 represent the same fraction. In fact, the fraction symbolized by 1/2 is the same as the fraction symbolized by 2/4, 3/6, 4/8, 5/10, 67/134, and so on. Thus a fraction has many different names. The following key theorem provides information as to how we can obtain "new" names from "old" names.

The Renaming Theorem *If a/b is a fraction and if m is a nonzero counting number, then $a/b = am/bm$.*
The Proof:

(1) $(bm)(a) = (b)(ma)$	(1) Associativity of multiplication of counting numbers
(2) $(b)(ma) = (b)(am)$	(2) Commutivity of multiplication of counting numbers
(3) $(bm)(a) = (b)(am)$	(3) From (1) and (2) by using ?
(4) $a/b = am/bm$	(4) From (3) by using the definition of equality of fractions

※

The Renaming Theorem may be verbalized as "Numerator (a) and denominator (b) may be multiplied by the same nonzero counting number (m) without changing the fraction." Reading the equation $a/b = am/bm$ from right to left we get the statement, "If the numerator (am) and denominator (bm) have a common factor (m), then both numerator and denominator may be divided by this factor without changing the fraction."

EXAMPLES.
$$\frac{1}{2} = \frac{(1)(67)}{(2)(67)} = \frac{67}{134}$$

$$\frac{14}{21} = \frac{(2)(7)}{(3)(7)} = \frac{2}{3}$$

Exercises

1. Use the Renaming Theorem to rewrite the given fractions so that they have the given counting number as denominator. Use the definition of equality to verify your answers.
   (a) 2/3, 9.   (d) 67/12, 660.
   (b) 4/25, 75.   (e) 75/9, 3.
   (c) 1/10, 540.   (f) 90/42, 21 and 14 and 7.
2. Use the Renaming Theorem to rename the following fractions so that they have the given counting number as numerator. Use the definition of equality of fractions to verify your answers.
   (a) 10/21, 20.   (c) 14/7, 2.
   (b) 32/36, 8.   (d) 90/42, 30 and 45.

3. Write the given pairs of fractions so that they have the given counting number as denominator. Verify your answers by using the definition of equality of fractions.
   (a) 2/3 and 7/8, 48.   (c) 16/9 and 5/15, 45.
   (b) 2/3 and 4/5, 30.   (d) 17/45 and 11/30, 90.
4. This theorem is often useful in solving equations involving fractions.

   Theorem $a/b = n/b$ *if and only if* $a = n$.

   (a) Supply justifications for the following proof of the theorem.

Proof: Part I	*Proof: Part II*
(1) $a/b = n/b$	(1) $a = n$
(2) $ba = bn$	(2) $ba = bn$
(3) $a = n$	(3) $a/b = n/b$

   (b) Use this theorem and the Renaming Theorem to solve the following equations.
   (i) $7/15 = n/3$.   (iv) $42/12 = n/6$.
   (ii) $n/8 = 3/2$.   (v) $21/18 = n/6$.
   (iii) $15/100 = n/5$.   (vi) $0/6 = n/19$.
5. Tabulate the set of all fractions. One way to do this is to arrange the fraction symbols in an array as shown below. This array has infinitely many rows and columns. In the nth row all the numerators are equal to n and in the mth column all the denominators are equal to m. Why is every fraction symbol (except 0) included somewhere in this array? How would you find the fraction symbol a/b in this array? Trace through this array in the manner indicated by the curved and arrowed line.

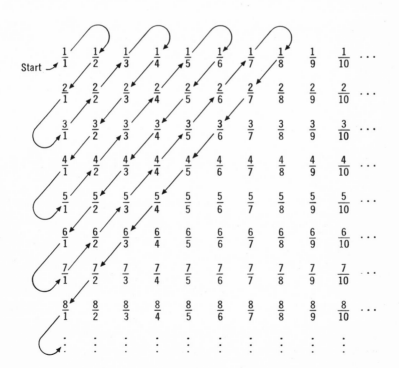

That is, the curved line first hits 1/1, then 1/2, then 2/1, then 3/1, and so on. Now tabulate the set of all fractions as follows. Begin by tabulating 0. Continue the tabulation by writing down the fractions in the order that their symbols are hit by the curved line as it progresses through the array of symbols. If the curved line hits a symbol which represents a fraction already tabulated, then ignore that symbol and pass on to the next symbol. This will ensure that there will be no repetitions in the tabulation. Write out the first forty fractions in this tabulation.

6. Explain why the set of all fractions is equivalent to the set of all counting numbers. (*Suggestion:* Use Exercise 5.)

There are two concepts which are involved in almost every computation involving fractions. Each of these involves renaming fractions in appropriate ways. These are the concepts of *least common denominator* and *writing in lowest terms*.

LEAST COMMON DENOMINATOR

Suppose two fractions are represented by the symbols a/b and c/d. Can we rename these fractions so that they will have the same denominator? One way to do this is to use the Renaming Theorem and observe that

$$\frac{a}{b} = \frac{ad}{bd} \quad \text{and} \quad \frac{c}{d} = \frac{bc}{bd}$$

The denominator bd is called a *common denominator* of the two fractions. However in general the common denominator bd is a number considerably larger than it need be. Let us look at these fractions again. The denominators of these fractions are b and d. Let k be the LCM of b and d. Then as we saw in the preceding chapter there are (nonzero) counting numbers n and m such that

$$k = bn \quad \text{and} \quad k = dm$$

We can now use the Renaming Theorem to write

$$\frac{a}{b} = \frac{an}{bn} = \frac{an}{k} \quad \text{and} \quad \frac{c}{d} = \frac{cm}{dm} = \frac{cm}{k}$$

This time we have written the given fractions so that their denominators are equal and the common denominator which we have used is the *least possible* common denominator.

Definition of Least Common Denominator *The least common denominator (LCD) of two or more fractions is the least common multiple of their denominators.*

While it is not necessary (logically) to use the LCD when renaming fractions so that they will have the same denominators, the LCD is often the most convenient common denominator to use since it is the smallest such number. We shall most frequently make use of the LCD when renaming fractions in this way.

EXAMPLE 1.   The fractions 11/21 and 8/35 may be written in many ways so that they have the same denominator. However, if we want to write them with the *least* common denominator, then we compute the LCM of the denominators 21 and 35. This LCM is 105, and consequently

$$\frac{11}{21} = \frac{(11)(5)}{(21)(5)} = \frac{55}{105}$$

and

$$\frac{8}{35} = \frac{(8)(3)}{(35)(3)} = \frac{24}{105}$$

EXAMPLE 2.   The LCD of the fractions $(2 \cdot 3)/(5^2 \cdot 7 \cdot 11)$ and $1/(3 \cdot 5 \cdot 7^2)$ is the LCM of the two denominators, which is $3 \cdot 5^2 \cdot 7^2 \cdot 11$. Using the Renaming Theorem we obtain

$$\frac{2 \cdot 3}{5^2 \cdot 7 \cdot 11} = \frac{(2 \cdot 3)(3 \cdot 7)}{(5^2 \cdot 7 \cdot 11)(3 \cdot 7)} = \frac{2 \cdot 3^2 \cdot 7}{3 \cdot 5^2 \cdot 7^2 \cdot 11}$$

and

$$\frac{1}{3 \cdot 5 \cdot 7^2} = \frac{(1)(5 \cdot 11)}{(3 \cdot 5 \cdot 7^2)(5 \cdot 11)} = \frac{5 \cdot 11}{3 \cdot 5^2 \cdot 7^2 \cdot 11}$$

The same procedure applies to any number of fractions.

EXAMPLE 3.   To write the fractions 2/15, 3/10, 7/18, and 3/14 with the same least denominator begin by finding the LCM of the four denominators. This is $2 \cdot 3^2 \cdot 5 \cdot 7$. The fractions are then renamed as follows:

$$\frac{2}{15} = \frac{(2)(2 \cdot 3 \cdot 7)}{2 \cdot 3^2 \cdot 5 \cdot 7} \qquad \frac{3}{10} = \frac{(3)(3^2 \cdot 7)}{2 \cdot 3^2 \cdot 5 \cdot 7}$$

$$\frac{7}{18} = \frac{(7)(5 \cdot 7)}{2 \cdot 3^2 \cdot 5 \cdot 7} \qquad \frac{3}{14} = \frac{(3)(3^2 \cdot 5)}{2 \cdot 3^2 \cdot 5 \cdot 7}$$

Exercises

1. Find the LCD of the given fractions and rewrite each fraction with this LCD as its denominator.
    (a)   15/21 and 7/20.
    (b)   3/4 and 5/6.
    (c)   2/3, 4/21 and 9/35.
    (d)   4/15 and 17/35.
    (e) $2/(3^2 \cdot 5^4 \cdot 7)$ and $2/(3^3 \cdot 5 \cdot 7^2 \cdot 11)$.
    (f)   3/15, 5/18, and 3/35.
    (g)   7/100, 4/125, and 5/12.
    (h) $23/(3^2 \cdot 5^4 \cdot 7)$, $31/(5^2 \cdot 7^3 \cdot 11)$, and $51/(7^2 \cdot 3^4)$.

WRITING FRACTIONS IN LOWEST TERMS

In most situations we would not want to refer to the fraction 37/74 by that name, but by the name 1/2. What is there about the name 1/2 which is preferable to the name 37/74? The name 1/2 is simpler because its numerator and denominator are smaller numbers and, in fact, they are the smallest possible. That is, the numerator and denominator are *relatively prime*.

Definition of "Written in Lowest Terms"   *If a fraction is denoted by a symbol a/b where a and b are relatively prime, then we say that the fraction has been written in lowest terms.*

How does one write a fraction in lowest terms? If a/b is the fraction and if g is the GCD of a and b, then we know that the counting numbers $a \div g$ and $b \div g$ are relatively prime (see Exercise 6, p. 134). We also know that

$$\frac{a}{b} = \frac{a \div g}{b \div g}$$

(Why?) Hence given a fraction we write it in lowest terms by dividing both numerator and denominator by their GCD.

EXAMPLE.   To write 15/21 in lowest terms we compute the GCD of 15 and 21 and then use the Renaming Theorem to divide both numerator and denominator by this GCD:

$$\frac{15}{21} = \frac{(5)(3)}{(7)(3)} = \frac{5}{7}$$

The fraction 5/7 is written in lowest terms because 5 and 7 are relatively prime.

We shall follow the convention that when a fraction is presented as the answer to a problem it should be written in lowest terms.

Exercises

1. Write each of these fractions in lowest terms. Explain what you are doing.
   - (a) 18/42.
   - (b) 5/125.
   - (c) 36/18.
   - (d) 126/99.
   - (e) 15/14.
   - (f) 2365/900.
   - (g) $(2^2 \cdot 3 \cdot 5^4 \cdot 7^2 \cdot 11^2)/(2 \cdot 3^2 \cdot 5 \cdot 7 \cdot 13)$.
   - (h) 495/150.
   - (i) 64/576.

Review Questions

1. In the statement of the Renaming Theorem why does the number m have to be nonzero?
2. Let a/b and c/d be fractions and let k be the least common multiple of b and d. Show how to write these fractions with their denominators equal to k.
3. What is the least common denominator of two fractions?
4. What does it mean to say that a fraction is written in lowest terms?
5. How does one write a fraction in lowest terms?
6. Where in the study of fractions do the following number-theoretic concepts become involved?
   - (a) Greatest common divisor.
   - (b) Least common multiple.
   - (c) Relatively prime.

The Four Inequality Relations

The next thing we ought to do is to define the four inequality relations relative to the fractions. We shall define *less than* for fractions and leave the other three relations for the consideration of the reader.

What ought we to mean by saying that one fraction is less than another? The analysis here is similar to the analysis which led to the definition of equality of fractions. Suppose n and m are fractions. To simplify matters let us suppose we have written n and m so that they have the same denominators: $n = a/b$ and $m = c/b$. What ought we to mean by "n is less than m"? We can find an answer to this question by carefully examining the equations

$$a = bn \quad \text{and} \quad c = bm$$

which we obtain by using the definition of fraction. Let us suppose we knew what it meant to write $n < m$. Then would not this argument be reasonable?

1. If $n < m$, then it ought to follow that $bn < bm$.
2. If $bn < bm$, then from the equations $a = bn$ and $c = bm$ it ought to follow that $a < c$.
3. Hence if $n < m$, then it ought to follow that $a < c$.

On the other hand suppose that we knew that $a < c$. Then would not this argument be plausible?

1. If $a < c$, then from the equations $a = bn$ and $c = bm$ it ought to follow that $bn < bm$.
2. If $bn < bm$, then it ought to follow that $n < m$.
3. Hence if $a < c$, then it ought to follow that $n < m$.

Combining these two arguments we see that it is reasonable to say that

$$n < m \text{ if and only if } a < c$$

This is the clue we need to find a definition of *less than* for fractions.

Definition of the Relation of Less Than for Fractions   *If a/b and c/b are fractions, then $a/b < c/b$ if and only if $a < c$.*

Observe that this definition requires that the fractions to be compared be written with the same denominators. This is not a serious complication in view of our discussion of least common denominators. There is a way of telling which of two fractions is the smaller without first having to rename the fractions. This is discussed in Exercise 5.

Thus the definition tells us that to determine whether two fractions are related by *less than* all we really need to do, if the fractions have been written with the same denominator, is to compare the counting numbers which are their numerators. The definition of *less than* for fractions is therefore an extension of the concept of *less than* for counting numbers. We leave it to the reader to verify for himself that *less than* for fractions possesses only the transitive property. The new relation has exactly the same properties as the corresponding relation for counting numbers.

The other three inequality relations are defined similarly.

Definitions   *Let a/b and c/b be fractions. Then we say that $a/b \leq c/b$ if $a \leq c$, $a/b > c/b$ if $a > c$, and $a/b \geq c/b$ if $a \geq c$.*

These inequality relations for fractions possess exactly the same properties as the corresponding relations for counting numbers. We leave the discussion of these properties to the reader.

Exercises

1. How do the following fractions compare?
    (a) 15/32 and 21/32.
    (b) 2/3 and 4/5.
    (c) 2/3, 4/21, and 9/35.
    (d) 4/7, 5/6, 3/4, 1/2, 1/3, and 3/8.
2. Verify that *less than* for fractions possesses only the transitivity property.
3. State the properties possessed by the relations $>$, $\leq$, and $\geq$ for fractions.
4. The *Law of Trichotomy* for fractions is: *If n and m are fractions, then exactly one of these statements is true:*

$$n < m, \quad n = m, \quad n > m$$

   Prove the Law of Trichotomy for fractions by writing n and m so that they have the same denominators and then applying the Law of Trichotomy for counting numbers to the numerators. (See Exercise 7b, p. 103.)
5. This theorem provides a means of telling which of two fractions is the larger without having first to write the fractions so that they have the same denominator:

   Theorem $a/b < c/d$ if and only if $da < bc$.

   (Compare this theorem with the definition of equality of fractions.)
    (a) Use the theorem to show that each of the following statements is true: $3/4 < 7/8$, $1/2 < 2/3$, $78/35 < 12/5$, and $0/5 < 1/9$.
    (b) Prove that if $a/b < c/d$, then $da < bc$. (*Suggestion:* Since $a/b < c/d$ it follows that $da/db < bc/bd$.)
    (c) Prove that if $da < bc$, then $a/b < c/d$.
    (d) Find analogs of this theorem for the relations of $>$, $\leq$, and $\geq$.
6. Since every counting number is a fraction, it is possible to compare counting numbers with each of the relations of less than for counting numbers and less than for fractions. However it does not make any difference which of these relations is used because these relations *agree on the counting numbers*. Explain what it means to say that these two relations agree on the counting numbers.

ADDITION OF FRACTIONS

From our experience with the system of counting numbers it is clear that one of the first operations we ought to define is one we would call *addition of frac-*

tions. This operation should, in some way not yet explicitly stated, relate to the operation of addition of counting numbers, and its properties should be like those of addition of counting numbers. Our job then is to invent this operation.

Let n and m be fractions. It will simplify matters considerably if we assume that n and m have been written so that they have the same denominators: $n = a/b$ and $m = c/b$. Then the following argument if plausible and is the motivation for our definition of addition.

(1) $n = a/b$ and $m = c/b$	(1) We are supposing that the fractions n and m have been written with the same denominators
(2) $a = bn$ and $c = bm$	(2) This follows from (1) by using the definition of fraction
(3) $a + c = bn + bm$	(3) This follows from (2) by using well-definedness of addition of counting numbers
(4) $bn + bm = b(n + m)$	(4) This statement is entirely reasonable in light of our experience
(5) $a + c = b(n + m)$	(5) This follows from (3) and (4) by using transitivity

Now observe that statement (5) says $n + m$ is the solution of the equation

$$a + c = bx$$

But according to the definition of fraction the solution of this equation is the fraction represented by

$$\frac{a + c}{b}$$

Thus it appears that we ought to define the operation of addition of fractions in such a way that the sum of a/b and c/b is $(a + c)/b$.

Definition of Addition of Fractions   *If a/b and c/b are fractions, then $a/b + c/b = (a + c)/b$.*

Note that according to this definition fractions can be added only after they have been renamed so that they have the same denominator. Moreover, the addition of the fractions is accomplished by addition of the counting numbers which are the numerators. Again we observe how the system of fractions is built upon the system of counting numbers: To perform addition of fractions one really performs addition of counting numbers.

EXAMPLE 1.   Add 3/4 and 5/6.
Solution: Since $3/4 = 9/12$ and $5/6 = 10/12$ (12 is the LCD), we get $3/4 + 5/6 = 9/12 + 10/12 = 19/12$. This answer is written in lowest terms.

EXAMPLE 2.   Add 2/3, 4/21, and 9/35.
Solution: The LCD of these fractions is 105. Then $2/3 = 70/105$, $4/21 = 20/105$, and $9/35 = 27/105$. Hence $2/3 + 4/21 + 9/35 = (70 + 20 + 27)/105 = 117/105$.

Since 117/105 is not written in lowest terms we use the Renaming Theorem and write the answer as 29/35.

There is a way of adding fractions without first having to rename them so that they have the same denominators. This is discussed in Exercise 6. This method is easier for very simple problems, but as a general method it involves more work than the one we have used.

THE PROPERTIES OF ADDITION OF FRACTIONS

We can get a very good idea of the appropriateness of our definition by examining addition of fractions for its properties. We are motivated in our search for properties by our knowledge of the properties of addition of counting numbers.

1.   ADDITION OF FRACTIONS IS A BINARY OPERATION.   No matter which fractions the numerals n and m represent, the symbol $n + m$ represents exactly one fraction. There are two things being said here: First, it is possible to add any two fractions, and second, the sum of any two fractions is a unique fraction— that is, there is only one answer to an addition problem involving fractions. It is not difficult to see that any two fractions can be added, for we have already seen that any two fractions can be written with the same denominator, and once the fractions to be added have been written with the same denominator the addition is actually performed by adding the counting numbers which are the numerators of the summands. Since addition of counting numbers possesses the closure property, we know that these numerators can be added and that the result is a counting number. The real question is whether the sum of two fractions is a *unique* number. Why is there a question about this? We have seen that before two fractions can be added they must first be rewritten so that they have the same denominator, and we know that there are many different ways to choose this common denominator. It is therefore conceivable that the result of adding a pair of fractions might in some way depend upon the particular common denominator used. The following theorem states that the result of performing addition does not depend upon the particular common denominator used; that is, the theorem shows that addition of fractions does not depend upon the symbols which represent the summands.

Theorem   *Addition of fractions is well-defined. If a/b, c/d, a'/b', and c'/d' are fractions such that $a/b = a'/b'$ and $c/d = c'/d'$, then $a/b + c/d = a'/b' + c'/d'$. The Proof:*

(1)	$b'a = ba'$ and $d'c = dc'$	(1)	Hypothesis
(2)	$dd'b'a = dd'ba'$ and $bb'd'c = bb'dc'$	(2)	From (1) by using the well-definedness of multiplication of counting numbers

(3) $dd'b'a + bb'd'c = dd'ba' + bb'dc'$ — (3) From (2) by using well-definedness of addition of counting numbers

(4) $b'd'(da + bc) = bd(d'a' + b'c')$ — (4) From (3) by using distributivity

(5) $\dfrac{da + bc}{bd} = \dfrac{d'a' + b'c'}{b'd'}$ — (5) From (4) by using the definition of equality of fractions

(6) $\dfrac{a}{b} + \dfrac{c}{d} = \dfrac{a'}{b'} + \dfrac{c'}{d'}$ — (6) From (5) by using the definition of addition of fractions and the Renaming Theorem

⌗

This theorem shows that the particular symbols representing the fractions to be added do not affect the number which is their sum. Hence the sum of two fractions, computed according to our definition, is a unique fraction. This means that addition of fractions possesses the closure property and thus is a binary operation.

2. THE BINARY OPERATION OF ADDITION OF FRACTIONS IS COMMUTATIVE AND ASSOCIATIVE. We shall prove that the operation is commutative and leave the proof of the associativity to the reader.

Theorem *Addition of fractions is commutative.*
The Proof: To simplify the proof we shall assume that the two fractions to be added have been written with the same denominator.

(1) $\dfrac{a}{b} + \dfrac{c}{b} = \dfrac{a + c}{b}$ — (1) Definition of addition of fractions

(2) $= \dfrac{c + a}{b}$ — (2) Applying commutivity of addition of counting numbers to the numerator

(3) $= \dfrac{c}{b} + \dfrac{a}{b}$ — (3) Definition of addition of fractions

⌗

The reader should observe that the commutative property of addition of *counting numbers* was employed in this proof. In fact step (2) was the key step in the proof. This is another example of how the system of fractions depends upon the system of counting numbers from which it was derived. The discussion of an aspect of the system of fractions depends in most cases on the corresponding aspect of the system of counting numbers.

3. ZERO IS AN IDENTITY FOR ADDITION OF FRACTIONS. No matter which fraction a/b represents, $a/b + 0 = a/b$. We leave the verification of this to the reader.

4.   ADDITION OF FRACTIONS POSSESSES THE CANCELLATION PROPERTY.   If a/b, c/d, and e/f are fractions such that $a/b + e/f = c/d + e/f$, then $a/b = c/d$. We leave the verification of this property to the reader.

5.   THE BINARY OPERATIONS OF ADDITION OF COUNTING NUMBERS AND ADDITION OF FRACTIONS AGREE ON THE COUNTING NUMBERS.   Whether we regard two counting numbers as counting numbers and add them by using the binary operation of addition of counting numbers or whether we regard them as fractions and add them by using the binary operation of addition of fractions makes no difference, we get the same sum. If we represent the binary operation of addition of counting numbers by $\overset{C}{+}$ and the binary operation of addition of fractions by $\overset{F}{+}$, then this can be stated as follows: *If n and m are counting numbers, then* $n \overset{C}{+} m = n \overset{F}{+} m.$

In view of the fact that addition of fractions possesses these properties, we can feel secure that we have in fact defined a good operation.

Review Questions

1.   State the definition of addition of fractions.
2.   What does it mean to say that addition of fractions agrees on the counting numbers with addition of counting numbers?
3.   Addition of fractions is really a two-step process. What are these two steps?
4.   Compare the properties of addition of fractions with those of addition of counting numbers.

Exercises

1.   Perform the following additions. Write the answers in lowest terms. Explain each step.
    (a) $1/3 + 17/39$.   (f) $2/3 + 18/7 + 3/25 + 1/4$.
    (b) $4/15 + 6/12$.   (g) $8/9 + 9/8 + 16/5 + 1/25$.
    (c) $2/41 + 1/2$.   (h) $2/(3^2 \cdot 5) + 7/(2 \cdot 3 \cdot 5)$.
    (d) $16/3 + 3/5$.   (i) $1/5 + 1/6 + 1/7 + 1/8$.
    (e) $15/14 + 16/15$.   (j) $2/99 + 1/72 + 14/21 + 3/54$.
2.   Perform the following additions. The letters represent counting numbers. Explain each step.
    (a) $a/b + cb/d$.   (c) $1/2 + c/b + 2/c$.
    (b) $2/a + a/2$.   (d) $a/b + c/b + b/d$.
3.   Supply justifications for the following proof that addition of fractions is associative.
Theorem   *Addition of fractions is associative.*
The Proof: To make the proof shorter we begin with three fractions which have already been written with the same denominator.

    (1) $\dfrac{a}{b} + \left(\dfrac{c}{b} + \dfrac{d}{b} \right) = \dfrac{a}{b} + \dfrac{c+d}{b}$

(2) $$= \frac{a + (c + d)}{b}$$

(3) $$= \frac{(a + c) + d}{b}$$

(4) $$= \frac{a + c}{b} + \frac{d}{b}$$

(5) $$= \left(\frac{a}{b} + \frac{c}{b}\right) + \frac{d}{b}$$

⌘

4. Prove that zero is an identity for addition of fractions. Upon what property of addition of counting numbers does this result depend?
5. Prove that addition of fractions possesses the cancellation property by proving the following theorem.

   Theorem *If a/b, c/b, and d/b are fractions such that $a/b + d/b = c/b + d/b$, then $a/b = c/b$.*

   (*Suggestion:* Perform addition on each side of $a/b + d/b = c/b + d/b$ and then apply the definition of equality of fractions. At this point you should have an equation which involves only counting numbers. Now apply the cancellation property of addition of counting numbers. Then change back to an equation involving the fractions a/b and c/b.)
6. It is possible to perform addition of fractions without first renaming the summands.

   Theorem *If a/b and c/d are fractions, then* $\frac{a}{b} + \frac{c}{d} = \frac{da + bc}{bd}$.

   Prove this theorem. (*Suggestion:* Begin by renaming a/b and c/d so that each has the denominator bd.)
7. Perform the additions of Exercises 1(a) through 1(e) by using the theorem of Exercise 6.
8. Solve the following equations by using the cancellation property of addition of fractions.

   (a) $n + 1/2 = 2/3$. (c) $2n + 1/3 = 7/3$.
   (b) $n + 4/7 = 11/9$. (d) $n + 2/5 = 3/4 + 1/3$.
9. In searching for an appropriate definition for addition of fractions we might have tried the following definition before we found the one we wanted.

   Definition *If a/b and c/d are fractions, then* $\frac{a}{b} + \frac{c}{d} = \frac{a + c}{b + d}$.

   On the surface this might appear to be an acceptable way to define addition. However, upon closer examination we would find that this process does not have the properties that we feel an operation to be called addition ought to have.

   (a) Show that this process does not agree on the counting numbers with addition of counting numbers.
   (b) Show that this process is not well-defined, that changing the names of the summands may change the sum. Find at least two examples of this.

   Because this process is neither well-defined nor in agreement with addition of counting numbers it would be a most unwise choice for the addition of fractions process. The one we have already selected is a much superior choice.

SUBTRACTION OF FRACTIONS

How should subtraction of fractions be defined? Recalling how subtraction of counting numbers was defined in terms of addition of counting numbers, it seems reasonable that we should at least try to define subtraction of fractions in a similar way.

Definition of Subtraction of Fractions *The process of subtraction of fractions, denoted by* $-$, *is defined as follows: If n and m are fractions then n $-$ m represents that fraction d which satisfies the equation*

$$n = m + d$$

If no such fraction d exists, then m cannot be subtracted from n and the symbol n $-$ m is meaningless.

EXAMPLES. $4/3 - 1/2$ is equal to $5/6$ since $4/3 = 1/2 + 5/6$. $4/3 - 5/3$ is meaningless because there is no fraction d such that $4/3 = 5/3 + d$.

Because of the similarity in the definitions of subtraction of fractions and subtraction of counting numbers we might anticipate that subtraction of fractions will have the same properties as subtraction of counting numbers. This is true (see the exercises), and so subtraction of fractions is *well-defined*, possesses an *identity* (0), and possesses the *cancellation* property. Moreover, subtraction of fractions and subtraction of counting numbers *agree on the counting numbers*. Subtraction of fractions, then, is no better and no worse a process than subtraction of counting numbers, its principal failing being that it is not a binary operation.

The Importance of Subtraction in Arithmetic

In Chapter 2 we saw that the importance and usefulness of subtraction of counting numbers could be displayed by a pair of theorems showing how subtraction is connected to addition. (These are Theorems 10 and 11, p. 61.) Here are the analogs of these theorems for the system of fractions.

Theorem 1 *If n and m represent fractions such that n $-$ m is meaningful, then* $(n - m) + m = n$.
The Proof:

(1) $n - m = d$, where d is some fraction	(1) By hypothesis $n - m$ is meaningful and so represents a fraction
(2) $n = m + d$	(2) From (1) by using the definition of subtraction
(3) $d + m = n$	(3) From (2) by using ?

(4) $(n - m) + m = d + m$

(4) From (1) by using a property of addition of fractions (which?)

(5) $(n - m) + m = n$

(5) From (4) and (3) by using ?

⁂

Theorem 2 *If n and m are fractions, then* $(n + m) - m = n.$

We leave the proof of this theorem to the reader as an exercise.

The Subtraction Theorem

We have seen how the subtraction operation is related to the operation of addition. Indeed the definition of subtraction was chosen in just such a way that this connection would be exceedingly obvious. But the definition does not make it easy to actually perform subtraction. We saw that addition of fractions is performed by using addition of counting numbers. Should there not be some way of subtracting fractions by using subtraction of counting numbers?

The Subtraction Theorem *If* a/b *and* c/b *are fractions and if* $a \geq c$, *then* $a/b - c/b = (a - c)/b.$
The Proof: Let us note that the hypothesis $a \geq c$ is used simply to ensure that it will be possible to subtract c/b from a/b.

(1) $a = (a - c) + c$

(1) By Theorem 11, page 61, and the hypothesis

(2) $\dfrac{a}{b} = \dfrac{(a - c) + c}{b}$

(2) From (1) by ?

(3) $\dfrac{a}{b} = \dfrac{a - c}{b} + \dfrac{c}{b}$

(3) From (2) by using the definition of addition of fractions

(4) $\dfrac{a}{b} = \dfrac{c}{b} + \dfrac{a - c}{b}$

(4) From (3) by ?

(5) $\dfrac{a}{b} - \dfrac{c}{b} = \dfrac{a - c}{b}$

(5) From (4) by using the definition of subtraction

⁂

The Subtraction Theorem provides an effective procedure for subtracting fractions. After the fractions have been renamed so that their denominators are equal, the actual subtraction itself is very easy, involving only the subtraction of one counting number from another. Once again we see evidence of the way the system of fractions is built on top of the system of counting numbers.

EXAMPLE. Subtract 5/7 from 8/9.

Solution: First we change the names of these fractions so that they will have the same denominators: $5/7 = 45/63$ and $8/9 = 56/63$. Then

$$\frac{8}{9} - \frac{5}{7} = \frac{56}{63} - \frac{45}{63} = \frac{56 - 45}{63} = \frac{11}{63}$$

Since 11/63 is written in lowest terms, we are finished.

Review Questions

1. How is subtraction of fractions defined?
2. How are the operations of subtraction of counting numbers and subtraction of fractions similar?
3. What does it mean to say that the operations of subtraction of counting numbers and subtraction of fractions agree on the counting numbers?
4. What are the properties of subtraction of fractions?
5. Under what circumstances will it be possible to subtract c/b from a/b?
6. How are addition and subtraction of fractions connected?
7. How is subtraction of fractions actually performed?

Exercises

1. Perform the following subtractions.
   - (a) $9/11 - 9/14$.
   - (b) $9/10 - 8/15$.
   - (c) $19/36 - 7/18$.
   - (d) $5/7 - 1/3$.
   - (e) $45/122 - 3/24$.
   - (f) $(4/5 - 3/35) + 3/7$.
   - (g) $(16/32 - 5/12) - 1/16$.
   - (h) $(1/88 + 4/7) - 3/55$.
2. Solve the following equations (if possible). Justify each step.
   - (a) $15 = n + 40/6$.
   - (b) $n = 2/3 - 1/5$.
   - (c) $5/6 = 1/2 - n$.
   - (d) $14/6 - 2/3 = n$.
   - (e) $n + 1/2 = 1/3$.
   - (f) $n + 15/16 = 1$.
   - (g) $3/4 - n = 6/8$.
   - (h) $4/n + 1/2 = 5/2$.
   - (i) $3/n + 3 = 9/2$.
   - (j) $n - 1/2 = 5/3$.
3. Perform the following subtractions. The letters represent counting numbers. Explain each step.
   - (a) $a/b - c/d$.
   - (b) $a/bc - d/c$.
   - (c) $a/b - b/a$.
   - (d) $(a/b - c/d) - e/f$.
4. Give examples which show that the operation of subtraction of fractions does not possess
   - (a) the closure property.
   - (b) the commutative property.
   - (c) the associative property.
5. Prove by using the Subtraction Theorem that zero is an identity for subtraction of fractions. Upon what property of subtraction of counting numbers does this result depend?
6. Subtraction of fractions can be performed without first renaming the minuend and subtrahend so that they have the same denominators.

   Theorem *If a/b and c/d are fractions and if it is possible to subtract c/d from a/b, then*

   $$\frac{a}{b} - \frac{c}{d} = \frac{da - bc}{bd}$$

   (Cf. Exercise 6, p. 157.)
   - (a) Prove this theorem. (*Suggestion:* Begin by renaming a/b and c/d so that each has the denominator bd. Then use the Subtraction Theorem.)
   - (b) Work Exercises 1(a) through 1(d) by using this theorem.

7. Prove that subtraction of fractions possesses the cancellation property by using the well-definedness property of addition and Theorem 1, p. 158. (*Suggestion:* The hypothesis of your theorem should be $a/b - c/d = e/f - c/d$ and the conclusion should be $a/b = e/f$.)
8. Prove that subtraction of fractions possesses the cancellation property by using the theorem of Exercise 6. (*Suggestion:* Apply the theorem to both sides of the equation $a/b - c/d = e/f - c/d$. Then apply the definition of equality of fractions. Simplify the resulting equation as much as possible. This should leave you with the equation $af = eb$, from which you may conclude that $a/b = e/f$.)
9. State the well-definedness property of subtraction of fractions.
10. Prove Theorem 2, p. 159. (*Suggestion:* Start with the equation $n + m = m + n$ and apply the definition of subtraction of fractions.)
11. Solve the equations

$$n - 1/5 = 2/3 \quad \text{and} \quad n - 2/3 = 4/7$$

(a) by using the definition of subtraction of fractions.
(b) by using well-definedness of addition of fractions together with Theorem 1, p. 158.
(c) by using the cancellation property of subtraction of fractions.

MULTIPLICATION OF FRACTIONS

How shall we define an operation on fractions which agrees on the counting numbers with the operation of multiplication of counting numbers? Let us suppose that n and m are fractions and write $n = a/b$ and $m = c/d$. Then according to the definition of fraction

$$a = bn \quad \text{and} \quad c = dm$$

Using these two equations it is not unreasonable to write

$$(a)(c) = (bn)(dm)$$

and then to rewrite this equation in the form

$$ac = (bd)(nm)$$

This last equation tells us that nm is the solution of the equation $ac = (bd)(x)$. Consequently it appears that we ought to define multiplication of fractions so that the product of a/b and c/d is ac/bd.

Definition of the Operation of Multiplication of Fractions *If a/b and c/d are fractions, then $a/b \cdot c/d = ac/bd$.*

It should come as no surprise that the new operation for fractions is defined in terms of the old operation for counting numbers, for to multiply fractions we actually multiply the counting numbers which are their numerators and denominators.

EXAMPLES. $\dfrac{2}{3} \cdot \dfrac{5}{7} = \dfrac{2 \cdot 5}{3 \cdot 7} = \dfrac{10}{21}$

$\dfrac{4}{9} \cdot \dfrac{3}{7} = \dfrac{4 \cdot 3}{9 \cdot 7} = \dfrac{(4)(3)}{(3 \cdot 7)(3)} = \dfrac{4}{3 \cdot 7} = \dfrac{4}{21}$

THE PROPERTIES OF MULTIPLICATION OF FRACTIONS

We should test this definition to see if it has given us an operation possessing the properties which we feel an operation to be called multiplication of fractions ought to possess. Here are some of the properties of this operation.

1. MULTIPLICATION OF FRACTIONS IS A BINARY OPERATION. First we must make sure that it is always possible to perform this operation. Let a/b and c/d be fractions. Now since a/b and c/d are fractions, the counting numbers b and d are not zero and consequently the product bd is not zero. (Why?) But if the number bd is not zero, then the symbol ac/bd names a fraction. This shows that it is always possible to perform the multiplication operation. Second, in verifying that multiplication of fractions is a binary operation we must check whether performing this operation upon a pair of fractions always results in exactly one fraction; that is, whether the product of two fractions is unique. This is the well-definedness property of multiplication of fractions.

Theorem *Multiplication of fractions is well-defined. If a/b, c/d, a'/b', and c'/d' are fractions such that $a/b = a'/b'$ and $c/d = c'/d'$, then $(a/b)(c/d) = (a'/b')$ (c'/d').*

We shall not prove this theorem here. The statements of a proof may be found in the exercises. The important thing for the reader to understand is why this theorem is worth mentioning at all. The point is that the definition of multiplication of fractions makes use of the particular names by which the factors to be multiplied have been named—the counting numbers which are the numerators and denominators of these names are involved in the computation of the product. Thus we must consider whether the computation of the product will give the same product when the numerators and denominator of the factors are changed. This is what the well-definedness property is all about.

We conclude therefore that the result of performing multiplication of fractions upon a pair of fractions is a unique fraction in all cases, and consequently multiplication of fractions is a binary operation.

2. MULTIPLICATION OF FRACTIONS IS COMMUTATIVE, ASSOCIATIVE, POSSESSES AN IDENTITY (1), AND POSSESSES THE CANCELLATION PROPERTY. We leave the discussion of these properties to the reader.

3. MULTIPLICATION OF FRACTIONS AGREES ON THE COUNTING NUMBERS WITH MULTIPLICATION OF COUNTING NUMBERS. For example, the product of the numbers six and seven can be found by regarding these numbers as counting numbers and using the binary operation of multiplication of counting numbers, or it can

be found by regarding these numbers as fractions and using the binary operation of multiplication of fractions.

4. MULTIPLICATION OF FRACTIONS SHARES A DISTRIBUTIVE PROPERTY WITH ADDITION OF FRACTIONS. This is a very important property of both multiplication and addition. We saw that the corresponding property in the system of counting numbers was one of the most important aspects of that system. Consequently if the distributive property

$$n(m + p) = nm + np$$

did not hold when n, m, and p represent fractions, then we would have real doubts as to the appropriateness of our definitions of addition and/or multiplication of fractions.

There are many theorems about the binary operation of multiplication of fractions that could be proved now. Of these the only one we want to mention is the following.

Theorem *Suppose that n and m are fractions. Then nm = 0 if and only if n = 0 or m = 0.*

The theorem is the analog for fractions of a theorem for counting numbers. (Refer to Theorem 8, p. 55.) We leave the proof of this theorem as an exercise.

Exercises

1. Find the products.
    (a) $2/5 \cdot 4/9$.
    (b) $5/16 \cdot 3/4$.
    (c) $7/8 \cdot 11/9$.
    (d) $3/2 \cdot 5/11$.
    (e) $(2 \cdot 5^2)/(3^2 \cdot 7) \cdot (3 \cdot 7^3)/(5^2 \cdot 11)$.
    (f) $(2^2 \cdot 13)/(5 \cdot 11) \cdot (5^2 \cdot 7)/(2^3 \cdot 3)$.
    (g) $144/198 \cdot 660/282$.
    (h) $2/3 \cdot 4/5 \cdot 9/15 \cdot 21/8 \cdot 32/128$.
2. Find the solutions of the following equations. Justify each step.
    (a) $(2/3 + 5/3)(7/5) = n$.
    (b) $2/3 + (5/2)(7/5) = n$.
    (c) $(2/3)(4/5) - n = 1/4$.
    (d) $(8/15)(5/2 + 2/3) = n$.
    (e) $2/5 - (1/3)(2/7) = n$.
    (f) $(2/5 - 1/3)(2/7) = n$.
    (g) $(2/3)(n - 1/2) = 5/3$.
    (h) $(1/2)(3/5 - 3n) = 1/5$.
3. Simplify the following expressions and rewrite them in the form n/m where n and m are counting numbers.
    (a) $a/b \cdot b/c$.
    (b) $[(ab)/c][(ac)/b]$.
    (c) $[(ab)/(cd)][(ec)/(bf)][(fdc)/(ace)]$.
    (d) $[(a + b)/c](c/b)(c/a)$.

4. Supply justifications for the following proof of the well-definedness of multiplication of fractions.

Theorem *If a/b, a'/b', c/d, and c'/d' are fractions such that $a/b = a'/b'$ and $c/d = c'/d'$, then $(a/b)(c/d) = (a'/b')(c'/d')$.*
The Proof:
(1) $b'a = ba'$ and $d'c = dc'$
(2) $(b'a)(d'c) = (ba')(dc')$
(3) $(b'd')(ac) = (bd)(a'c')$
(4) $ac/bd = a'c'/b'd'$
(5) $(a/b)(c/d) = (a'/b')(c'/d')$

⁂

Observe that in this proof the well-definedness of multiplication of counting numbers was used to establish the well-definedness of multiplication of fractions. This is another example of the way the system of fractions is built upon the system of counting numbers.

5. The following questions have to do with the properties of multiplication of fractions.
    (a) Prove that multiplication of fractions is commutative; i.e., if a/b and c/d are fractions, prove that $a/b \cdot c/d = c/d \cdot a/b$.
    (b) Prove that multiplication of fractions is associative by considering three fractions a/b, c/d, and e/f and proving that $(a/b \cdot c/d)(e/f) = (a/b)(c/d \cdot e/f)$.
    (c) Verify that 1 is an identity for multiplication.
    (d) Supply the justifications for this proof of the cancellation property of multiplication.

Theorem *If $a/b \cdot c/d = e/f \cdot c/d$, then $a/b = e/f$.*
The Proof:
(1) $a/b \cdot c/d = e/f \cdot c/d$
(2) $ac/bd = ec/fd$
(3) $fdac = bdec$
(4) $fa = be$
(5) $a/b = e/f$

⁂

6. Supply justifications for the following proof that multiplication distributes over addition.

Theorem *If a/b, c/d, and e/f are fractions, then $(a/b)(c/d + e/f) = (a/b)(c/d) + (a/b)(e/f)$.*
The Proof: This proof is somewhat abbreviated.
(1) $(a/b)(c/d + e/f) = (a/b)[(fc + de)/df]$
(2) $(a/b)[(fc + de)/df] = [a(fc + de)]/bdf$
(3) $[a(fc + de)]/bdf = [afc + ade]/bdf$
(4) $[afc + ade]/bdf = afc/bdf + ade/bdf$
(5) $afc/bdf + ade/bdf = ac/bd + ae/bf$
(6) $ac/bd + ae/bf = (a/b)(c/d) + (a/b)(e/f)$
(7) $(a/b)(c/d + e/f) = (a/b)(c/d) + (a/b)(e/f)$

⁂

7. If in the proof of the theorem in Exercise 6 the symbol "$+$" is replaced by the symbol "$-$" we get a proof of the following theorem, which says that multiplication distributes over subtraction.

   Theorem *If a/b, c/d, and e/f are fractions such that $c/d - e/f$ is meaningful, then $(a/b)(c/d - e/f) = (a/b)(c/d) - (a/b)(e/f)$.*

   Write out the proof of this theorem.

8. Prove the theorem on p. 163. (*Suggestion:* Begin by writing $n = a/b$ and $m = c/d$. Then arrange things so that you can apply Theorem 8, p. 55, which is the analog of the present theorem for counting numbers.)

9. Using the distributive property for multiplication and addition of counting numbers, it is possible to think of multiplication of counting numbers as repeated addition. Is there a corresponding idea for fractions?

10. While searching for a definition for an operation to be called multiplication of fractions, we might have tried the following definition:

    If a/b and c/b are fractions (written so that they have the same denominator), then

    $$\frac{a}{b} \cdot \frac{c}{b} = \frac{ac}{b}$$

    This definition might (on the surface at least) appear reasonable because each addition and subtraction of fractions with the same denominators is accomplished by performing the appropriate process upon the numerators. So perhaps multiplication of fractions should also be accomplished by multiplying the numerators. But upon closer examination this definition is seen to be inappropriate because the process it defines does not possess the properties that we feel a process to be called multiplication of fractions ought to possess. In particular:

    (a) *This process is not well-defined.* Find examples which demonstrate this.
    (b) *This process does not agree on the counting numbers with multiplication of counting numbers.* Find at least two examples which demonstrate this. (*Suggestion:* Apply the process to the fractions 12/3 and 9/3.)

    There is not much point in studying this process further. It fails to possess these most important properties and so we can discard it altogether.

Multiplicative Inverse

Consider the equation

$$\frac{2}{3} = \frac{7}{6} \cdot n$$

We can solve this equation by multiplying both sides by the fraction 6/7:

$$\frac{2}{3} \cdot \frac{6}{7} = \left(\frac{7}{6} \cdot n\right)\left(\frac{6}{7}\right) \qquad \text{(Well-definedness)}$$

$$= \left(n \cdot \frac{7}{6}\right)\left(\frac{6}{7}\right) \qquad \text{(Commutivity)}$$

$$= (n)\left(\frac{7}{6}\cdot\frac{6}{7}\right) \qquad \text{(Associativity)}$$

$$= (n)(1) \qquad \text{(Performing multiplication)}$$

$$= n \qquad \text{(Identity)}$$

Hence $n = 2/3 \cdot 6/7 = 4/7$.

The key step in solving this equation was to multiply $7/6$ by $6/7$ to obtain 1. When the product of two fractions is equal to the multiplicative identity 1, the two fractions are said to be *multiplicative inverses* of each other.* For example, $6/7$ and $7/6$ are multiplicative inverses of each other. The fraction $6/7$ is the multiplicative inverse of $7/6$ and $7/6$ is the multiplicative inverse of $6/7$. The multiplicative inverse of 5 is $1/5$ and the multiplicative inverse of $1/5$ is 5.

The concept of multiplicative inverse is a key idea in the system of fractions. The systems of counting numbers and fractions are distinguished from one another in that in the system of counting numbers the only number to possess a multiplicative inverse is one, while in the system of fractions every number except zero possesses a multiplicative identity. This concept is also the principal concept involved in the study of the process of division of fractions, which we shall begin in the next section.

Exercises

1. Find the multiplicative inverses of the following fractions.
    (a) $1/1$.   (d) $1 + 3/2$.
    (b) 6.   (e) $15/7 - 2/3$.
    (c) $7/18$.   (f) $(7/8)(4/5)$.
2. Let S denote the set of fractions which are greater than 0 and less than 1:

    $$S = \{x \in F : 0 < x < 1\}$$

    where F denotes the set of all fractions. Let T denote the set of all fractions which are greater than 1:
    $$T = \{x \in F : x > 1\}$$

    Show that the sets S and T are equivalent. (*Suggestion:* Use the concept of multiplicative inverse to set up the correspondence.)
3. Show that the multiplicative inverse of a fraction (if there is one) is unique. (*Suggestion:* Use an indirect proof. Assume that a fraction n has two *distinct* multiplicative inverses x and y. Set up an equation and apply the cancellation property of multiplication of fractions. Obtain a contradiction to the assumption that $x \neq y$.)
4. The concept of multiplicative inverse is a *relation* on the set of all fractions. That

---

* A commonly used synonym for multiplicative inverse is *reciprocal.* The most standard notation for symbolizing multiplicative inverses is to employ the superscript symbol "-1." Thus the multiplicative inverse of 5 is denoted by the symbol 5^{-1}. Since the multiplicative inverse of 5 is $1/5$, this means that $5^{-1} = 1/5$. The statement, "The multiplicative inverse of $8/3$ is $3/8$," is rendered symbolically by "$(8/3)^{-1} = 3/8$." We shall not need this notation.

is, we say that two fractions are related by the relation of multiplicative inverse if and only if their product is 1. We can state this definition as follows:

$$n \text{ ® } m \text{ if and only if } nm = 1$$

(a) Explain why this relation is not reflexive.
(b) Explain why this relation is symmetric; that is, explain why if n ® m, then it necessarily follows that m ® n.
(c) Explain why the relation is not transitive.
(d) Which fractions are related to themselves by this relation?
(e) Are there any fractions not related to any fractions by this relation?

5. Solve the following equations by using the well-definedness property of multiplication of fractions and the concept of multiplicative inverse. Justify each step in your solution.

(a) $n \cdot 3/2 = 5/9$.
(b) $n \cdot (2/15 + 6/5) = 1/6$.
(c) $(2/3 + 4/5)(3/2) = (5/6)(n)$.
(d) $2n = 5/3 + 6$.
(e) $2n - 1/2 = 3/5$.

Review Questions

1. What does it mean to say that multiplication of fractions and multiplication of counting numbers agree on the counting numbers?
2. What are the properties of multiplication of fractions?
3. What does it mean to say that two fractions are multiplicative inverses of each other?
4. Which fractions possess multiplicative inverses? Which do not?
5. State an important theorem which relates multiplication of fractions and the fraction zero.

DIVISION OF FRACTIONS

Division of fractions is defined in terms of multiplication of fractions in the same way that division of counting numbers is defined in terms of multiplication of counting numbers. Defining division of fractions in this way will ensure that it will agree on the counting numbers with division of counting numbers.

Definition of Division of Fractions *If n and m are fractions, and m is different from zero, then the result of dividing n by m, denoted by $n \div m$, is that fraction q such that $n = mq$.*

Observe that division by zero is not defined. It is impossible to divide a fraction by zero for the same reason that it was impossible to divide a counting number by zero. For example, if we could divide $1/3$ by 0 then there would be some fraction n/m such that $1/3 = 0(n/m)$. But $0(n/m) = 0$, and so we would be forced to conclude that $1/3 = 0$. In order to avoid obtaining this contradiction to something we already know (namely, that $1/3$ is not equal to zero) we specifically exclude the possibility of dividing by zero.

Let us look at an example of how this definition can be used to find the quotient of two fractions.

EXAMPLE.   Divide 2/3 by 4/5.

Solution: According to the definition of division of fractions we must find (if possible) a fraction q such that

$$\frac{2}{3} = \frac{4}{5} \cdot q$$

But this is the same type of equation that we solved in our discussion of multiplicative inverse in the preceding section. As we saw there, we can solve this type of equation by multiplying both sides by the multiplicative inverse of 4/5:

$$\frac{2}{3} \cdot \frac{5}{4} = \left(\frac{4}{5} \cdot q\right)\left(\frac{5}{4}\right) \qquad \text{(Well-definedness)}$$

$$= \left(q \cdot \frac{4}{5}\right)\left(\frac{5}{4}\right) \qquad \text{(Commutivity)}$$

$$= (q)\left(\frac{4}{5} \cdot \frac{5}{4}\right) \qquad \text{(Associativity)}$$

$$= (q)(1) \qquad \text{(Multiplicative inverses)}$$

$$= q \qquad \text{(Identity)}$$

Hence $q = 2/3 \cdot 5/4 = 5/6$.

In this example we found the quotient $2/3 \div 4/5$ by multiplying 2/3 by 5/4, the multiplicative inverse of 4/5. This is a particular instance of the following general fact.

The Divide by Multiplying Theorem   *If a/b and c/d are fractions with c/d different from zero, then*

$$\frac{a}{b} \div \frac{c}{d} = \frac{a}{b} \cdot \frac{d}{c}$$

This theorem is one of the fundamental theorems insofar as computing with fractions is concerned. The theorem provides a very effective method for dividing because it changes division problems into multiplication problems, as the following examples demonstrate.

EXAMPLE 1. $\dfrac{8}{25} \div \dfrac{16}{15} = \dfrac{8}{25} \cdot \dfrac{15}{16} = \dfrac{2^3 \cdot 3 \cdot 5}{5^2 \cdot 2^4} = \dfrac{3}{2 \cdot 5} = \dfrac{3}{10}$

EXAMPLE 2. $\dfrac{2 \cdot 3^2 \cdot 7}{5^3 \cdot 11^2} \div \dfrac{2 \cdot 5^2 \cdot 7 \cdot 11}{3^4} = \dfrac{2 \cdot 3^2 \cdot 7}{5^3 \cdot 11^2} \cdot \dfrac{3^4}{2 \cdot 5^2 \cdot 7 \cdot 11}$

$$= \dfrac{2 \cdot 3^6 \cdot 7}{2 \cdot 5^5 \cdot 7 \cdot 11^3} = \dfrac{3^6}{5^5 \cdot 11^3}$$

EXAMPLE 3. $\frac{ab}{c} \div \frac{da}{bc} = \frac{ab}{c} \cdot \frac{bc}{da} = \frac{ab^2c}{cda} = \frac{b^2}{d}$

Here is a proof of the Divide by Multiplying Theorem.

The Proof: We want to prove that $a/b \div c/d = a/b \cdot d/c$. This will be true if we can prove that $a/b = (c/d)(a/b \cdot d/c)$. But this is easily proven by using the associative and commutative properties of multiplication of fractions. Here is a step-by-step verification of these facts.

(1) $\left(\frac{c}{d}\right)\left(\frac{a}{b} \cdot \frac{d}{c}\right) = \left(\frac{c}{d} \cdot \frac{a}{b}\right)\left(\frac{d}{c}\right)$	(1) Associativity of multiplication
(2) $= \left(\frac{a}{b} \cdot \frac{c}{d}\right)\left(\frac{d}{c}\right)$	(2) Commutivity of multiplication
(3) $= \left(\frac{a}{b}\right)\left(\frac{c}{d} \cdot \frac{d}{c}\right)$	(3) Associativity of multiplication
(4) $= \left(\frac{a}{b}\right)(1)$	(4) Multiplicative inverses
(5) $= \frac{a}{b}$	(5) Multiplicative identity
(6) $\frac{a}{b} = \left(\frac{c}{d}\right)\left(\frac{a}{b} \cdot \frac{d}{c}\right)$	(6) From (5) by using symmetry of equality of fractions
(7) $\frac{a}{b} \div \frac{c}{d} = \frac{a}{b} \cdot \frac{d}{c}$	(7) From (6) by using the definition of division of fractions

THE PROPERTIES OF DIVISION OF FRACTIONS

The consequences of the definition of division appear to indicate that we have been successful in defining a good division process for fractions. By examining the properties of the process we can get an even better evaluation of our definition.

1. DIVISION BY A NONZERO FRACTION IS ALWAYS POSSIBLE. This fact can be deduced from the Divide by Multiplying Theorem. For if c/d is a nonzero fraction then d/c is a fraction, and since it is always possible to multiply by d/c, the theorem tells us that it is always possible to divide by c/d.

2. DIVISION OF FRACTIONS IS WELL-DEFINED. Thus changing the names of the dividend and divisor will not affect the fraction which is their quotient. Equivalently, if n, m, a, and b are fractions such that $n = m$ and $a = b$, then the

symbols $n \div a$ and $m \div b$ are either both meaningless or both meaningful, in which case they are equal. We shall not prove this theorem.

These two properties imply that the process of division of fractions is not a binary operation but that it comes as near to being a binary operation as any "division" process can. The only reason that division of fractions is not a binary operation is that it is impossible to divide by the fraction zero.

3. DIVISION OF FRACTIONS HAS AN IDENTITY (1) AND POSSESSES THE CANCELLATION PROPERTY.   We leave the discussion of these facts to the reader.

4. DIVISION OF FRACTIONS AGREES ON THE COUNTING NUMBERS WITH DIVISION OF COUNTING NUMBERS.   In order to compare the processes of division of fractions and division of counting numbers let us use (temporarily) the following notation: Denote division of counting numbers by the symbol $\overset{C}{\div}$ and division of fractions by $\overset{F}{\div}$. Then the two division processes agree on the counting numbers in the sense that if $n \overset{C}{\div} m$ is meaningful, then $n \overset{C}{\div} m = n \overset{F}{\div} m$. Of course, it may be that $n \overset{F}{\div} m$ is meaningful when $n \overset{C}{\div} m$ is meaningless, but this is not what we are talking about. When we say that the two division processes agree on the counting numbers, we mean that when both processes can be performed upon a given pair of counting numbers the results are the same.

The Importance of Division

The process of division of fractions is important because of its relation to multiplication of fractions. Multiplication and division "undo" each other, as the following two theorem show.

Theorem 1   *If n and m are fractions and m is different from zero, then $nm \div m = n$.*

Theorem 2   *If n and m are fractions and m is different from zero, then $(n \div m)m = n$.*

Proofs of these theorems can be obtained by replacing the words *counting number* by the word *fraction* in the proofs of the corresponding theorems for counting numbers (Theorems 16 and 17, p. 69).

EXAMPLE 1.   Solve the equation $n \cdot 3/5 = 1/2$.

Solution: To solve this equation we must "undo" the effect of multiplying n by $3/5$. We can accomplish this by dividing both sides of this equation by $3/5$, and using Theorem 1 above:

$$\left(n \cdot \frac{3}{5} \right) \div \frac{3}{5} = \frac{1}{2} \div \frac{3}{5} \qquad \text{(Well-definedness of division)}$$

$$n = \frac{1}{2} \div \frac{3}{5} \qquad \text{(Theorem 1)}$$

$$n = \frac{1}{2} \cdot \frac{5}{3} \qquad \text{(Divide by Multiplying Theorem)}$$

$$n = \frac{5}{6} \qquad \text{(Definition of multiplication)}$$

This equation can also be solved without reference to division by multiplying both sides of the equation by the reciprocal of 3/5:

$$\left(n \cdot \frac{3}{5}\right) \cdot \frac{5}{3} = \frac{1}{2} \cdot \frac{5}{3} \qquad \text{(Well-definedness)}$$

$$n\left(\frac{3}{5} \cdot \frac{5}{3}\right) = \frac{1}{2} \cdot \frac{5}{3} \qquad \text{(Associativity)}$$

$$n(1) = \frac{1}{2} \cdot \frac{5}{3} \qquad \text{(Multiplicative inverses)}$$

$$n = \frac{1}{2} \cdot \frac{5}{3} \qquad \text{(Identity)}$$

$$n = \frac{5}{6} \qquad \text{(Performing multiplication)}$$

Of course multiplying both sides by 5/3 and dividing both sides by 3/5 are really the same thing in view of the Divide by Multiplying Theorem. So these methods are the same except that one of them does not use the division process. This illustrates the logical superfluousness of division of fractions. We could dispense with the process altogether if we wanted.

EXAMPLE 2. Solve the equation $n \div 3/4 = 8/3$.

Solution: There are a number of ways to solve this equation. One is to use the cancellation property of division of fractions and write

$$n \div \frac{3}{4} = 2 \div \frac{3}{4}$$

thereby obtaining the solution $n = 2$. Another way is to use the well-definedness of multiplication together with Theorem 2, p. 170:

$$n \div \frac{3}{4} = \frac{8}{3} \qquad \text{(Given equation)}$$

$$\left(n \div \frac{3}{4}\right)\left(\frac{3}{4}\right) = \left(\frac{8}{3}\right)\left(\frac{3}{4}\right) \qquad \text{(Well-definedness of multiplication)}$$

$$n = \left(\frac{8}{3}\right)\left(\frac{3}{4}\right) \qquad \text{(Theorem 2)}$$

$$n = 2 \qquad \text{(Performing multiplication)}$$

The equation can also be solved by using the definition of division of fractions:

$$n \div \frac{3}{4} = \frac{8}{3} \qquad \text{(Given equation)}$$

$$n = \left(\frac{3}{4}\right)\left(\frac{8}{3}\right) \qquad \text{(Definition of division)}$$

$$n = 2 \qquad \text{(Performing multiplication)}$$

Review Questions

1. State the definition of division of fractions.
2. How is division of fractions similar to division of counting numbers?
3. What does it mean to say that division of fractions agrees on the counting numbers with division of counting numbers?
4. How is the concept of multiplication inverse involved in a study of division of fractions?
5. State the Divide by Multiplying Theorem.
6. Write out a proof of the Divide by Multiplying Theorem.
7. What properties are possessed by division of fractions?
8. Does division of fractions possess the closure property? Explain.
9. Explain why it is always possible to divide by nonzero fractions.
10. What are the two theorems which display the way division is used in arithmetic?
11. Give an example of an equation involving fractions which can be solved by using the well-definedness property of division.
12. Give an example of an equation involving fractions which can be solved by using the cancellation property of division.

Exercises

1. Perform the indicated divisions.

   (a) $2/3 \div 4/5$.

   (b) $13/4 \div 14/8$.

   (c) $7/8 \div 4$.

   (d) $9 \div 1/2$.

   (e) $\dfrac{2^3 \cdot 3^5 \cdot 7^2 \cdot 11}{5^3 \cdot 13^2} \div \dfrac{5^2 \cdot 3^4 \cdot 2^3 \cdot 11^2 \cdot 13}{5^2 \cdot 11 \cdot 13}$.

2. Solve the equations

$$n \div 2 = 5/4 \quad \text{and} \quad 2n \div 6/5 = 1/4$$

   (a) Using the definition of division of fractions.

   (b) Using the well-definedness property of multiplication of fractions together with Theorem 2, p. 170.

   (c) Using the cancellation property of division of fractions.

   Which of these three different methods of solving these equations seems to be the most "natural"?

3. Solve the following equations any way that you want. Justify each step in your solution.

   (a) $(8/3 \cdot 4/5) \div 7/15 = n$.

   (b) $(3/2)n = 4/5$.

   (c) $15/8 = n(5/6)$.

   (d) $9/5 = (4/3)n + 4/7$.

   (e) $(8/7 - 2/3) \div 4/3 = n - 1/2$.

   (f) $(6/5 + 2)n = (14/3 + 2)$.

4. Prove Theorems 1 and 2 on p. 170.

5. Verify that the fraction 1 is an identity for division of fractions.

6. Show by example that division of fractions is neither commutative nor associative.

7. Use the Divide by Multiplying Theorem to prove that division of fractions possesses the cancellation property.

8. One brand of grocery item comes in a package weighing 8¼ ounces and costs $1.26. Another brand of the same item comes in a package weighing 7⅓ ounces and costs $0.98. Which is the better buy? (This is an example of the kind of division problem involving fractions that an average housewife is supposed to be able to solve mentally.)

THE FRACTION LINE

Constructing the Fraction Line

Draw a line and on it select arbitrarily a point which we shall call the *origin* and to the right of this point select arbitrarily another point which we shall call the *unit*. We consider now that portion of the line lying to the right of, and including, the origin. We call this a *ray* (see Fig. 36). The distance between the origin and the unit is called the *unit distance*. We may now establish a one-to-one correspondence between the fractions and a certain set of points on this ray. This correspondence is established as follows. We begin by pairing the fraction 0 with the origin. Then we pair the fraction 1 with the unit. Once we have done this the points to which the rest of the fractions correspond are automatically determined. For example, to find the point corresponding to the fraction 2/3 we divide the unit distance into three equal lengths (Fig. 37) and locate that point which lies to the right of the origin a distance equal to two of these lengths. More generally, we would locate the point corresponding to the fraction n/m by dividing the unit distance into m equal parts and then locating that point which lies to the right of the origin a distance equal to n of these m equal parts of the unit distance. In this way we locate a point of the ray corresponding to each fraction. Let the set of all such points be denoted by S. Now the correspondence we have just described between the set of fractions and the set S is a one-to-one correspondence. That is, given a fraction there corresponds to it a unique point of the set S and given a point of the set S there corresponds to it a unique fraction. By the fraction line we mean this set S of points located along the ray.

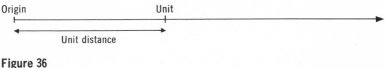

Figure 36

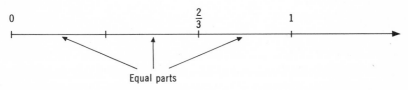

Figure 37

The reader must understand that the *numbers* which are fractions are not the same things as the *points* corresponding to the fractions. The set of numbers which are fractions is not *equal* to the set of points on the ray which correspond to the fractions; these sets are only *equivalent*. However, once we have formally acknowledged this distinction between these two sets, we find it convenient to largely ignore the distinction. Thus, simply for convenience of discussion, we shall sometimes call fractions *points* and call the points of *S fractions*. There is no danger in doing this as long as we are aware that when we, for example, talk about the fraction which lies exactly midway between the origin and the unit, we are really talking about the point which *corresponds* to the fraction 1/2. Similarly, if we talk about the point 2/3 we are really talking about the point which corresponds to the fraction 2/3.

Properties of the Fraction Line

THE DENSITY PROPERTY

Let n/m and a/b be unequal fractions and locate the points to which they correspond on the fraction line. Since these are unequal fractions one of them is less than the other. Let us suppose that $n/m < a/b$. Consider the point P which is the midpoint of the line segment between n/m and a/b (see Fig. 38). The distance from n/m to P is equal to the distance from P to a/b. Assuming that the point P corresponds to a fraction, we can say this in terms of an equation:

$$P - \frac{n}{m} = \frac{a}{b} - P$$

Let us solve this equation for P:

$$2P - \frac{n}{m} = \frac{a}{b}$$

$$2P = \frac{n}{m} + \frac{a}{b}$$

$$P = (n/m + a/b) \div 2$$

(The reader should justify each of these steps.) Thus we see that P is the *average* of the fractions n/m and a/b, and so we have proved the following theorem.

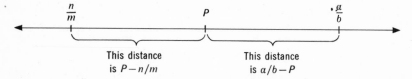

This distance   This distance
is $P - n/m$ is $a/b - P$

Figure 38

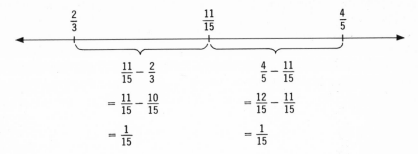

Figure 39

The Midpoint Theorem *If n/m and a/b are fractions, then the midpoint of the line segment between the points corresponding to n/m and a/b is the point corresponding to the average of n/m and a/b.*

EXAMPLE. If P is the point which is exactly midway between the points corresponding to 2/3 and 4/5, then P corresponds to the fraction

$$\left(\frac{2}{3}+\frac{4}{5}\right) \div 2 = \frac{22}{15} \div 2 = \frac{11}{15}$$

These points are illustrated in Fig. 39.

The conclusion we wish to draw from this theorem is that *between every two points of the set S there is another point of the set S*. This is a particular example of a general concept called *density*.

Definition of Density *A set of points on a line is said to have the density property if between every two distinct points of the set there is another point of the set.*

Thus the set of points corresponding to the fractions has the density property. On the other hand, the set of points corresponding to the counting numbers does not possess the density property. As a counterexample consider the counting numbers 2 and 3. There is no point corresponding to a counting number between the points corresponding to 2 and 3. Hence the set of points corresponding to the counting numbers does not possess the density property.

Exercises

1. Suppose that a/b and c/d are fractions located on the fraction line as shown below.

In the illustration the point Q is located so that its distance from a/b is exactly twice its distance from c/d. The point Q corresponds to a fraction. What fraction? (*Suggestion:* Observe first that the distance between Q and a/b is equal to twice the distance between Q and c/d. So $Q - a/b$ is twice as large as $c/d - Q$. Set up an equation and solve for Q.)

2. Find two fractions lying between 2/3 and 7/15. (*Suggestion:* Rewrite the two fractions so that they have the same denominator.)

3. Find 15 fractions lying between 2/3 and 7/15. (*Suggestion:* Rewrite the fractions so that they have the same denominator and then use the Renaming Theorem to make the denominators large enough so that the 15 desired fractions can simply be "read off.")

4. Using the Midpoint Theorem, find two fractions between n/m and a/b, where $n/m < a/b$. Illustrate the fractions you have found on the fraction line.

5. Suppose you are given fractions a/b and c/d. Describe a process by means of which you could find 100 fractions all of which are greater than the smaller of a/b and c/d and less than the larger of a/b and c/d.

6. Which of the following set of points have the density property?
    (a) The set A of points corresponding to the fractions which are greater than 1 and less than 4.
    (b) The set B of points corresponding to the fractions which when written in lowest terms have denominators equal to 5.
    (c) The set C of points corresponding to the fractions whose denominators are powers of 2.

7. Suppose S is a set of points on the fraction line.
    (a) If S is a finite set, can S possess the density property?
    (b) If S is an infinite set, does S necessarily possess the density property?

THE FRACTION LINE IS FULL OF HOLES

We intend to prove now that not every point of the ray is a point of the set S, that is, not every point of the ray corresponds to a fraction.

Construct a square of side one unit distance and let d represent the length of a diagonal of this unit square (Fig. 40). Now pick up this unit square and superimpose it on the ray so that one of its vertices coincides with the origin and the opposite vertex lies on the ray (Fig. 41). Label the point of the ray which coincides with this opposite vertex P. *We assert that the point P does not correspond to a fraction and therefore is not an element of the set S.* Before we begin the proof of this assertion we must make use of a very well-known theorem from geometry known as the Pythagorean Theorem. This theorem states that if we have a triangle one of whose interior angles (Fig. 42) is a 90 degree angle, then the lengths of the three sides of the triangle are related by the equation

$$a^2 + b^2 = c^2$$

Figure 40

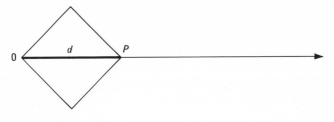

Figure 41

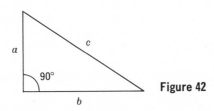

Figure 42

where *c* represents the length of the side opposite the 90 degree angle and *a* and *b* represent the lengths of the other two sides.

Now observe that the diagonal of the unit square (Fig. 40) partitions the square into two triangles. Consider either one of these triangles and observe that one of the angles of this triangle is a 90 degree angle. Hence we may apply the Pythagorean Theorem to conclude that $d^2 = 1^2 + 1^2 = 2$. Consequently, while we do not know (yet) what the number *d* itself is, we do know that the square of *d* is 2. (The reader knows that the number *d* is called the square root of 2 and is symbolized by $\sqrt{2}$. What we are going to prove is that $\sqrt{2}$ is not a fraction.)

There is also a fact from number theory that we should mention because it will be used in the proof that the point *P* does not correspond to a fraction.

Preliminary Theorem   *A counting number n is divisible by 2 if and only if n^2 is divisible by 2.*

We discussed this theorem in Exercise 3, p. 128.

We are now ready to prove that the point *P* does not belong to the set *S*. We shall accomplish this by proving that the number *d* is not a fraction.

Theorem   *The number d such that $d^2 = 2$ is not a fraction.*
The Proof: We shall prove this theorem by the *indirect method*. Hence we shall begin by assuming that *d* is a fraction. We assume that $d = n/m$, where *n* and *m* are counting numbers. Moreover, since every fraction can be written in lowest terms we may as well assume that n/m is written in lowest terms; i.e., that *n* and *m* are relatively prime.

(1) $d = n/m$, where *n* and *m* are relatively prime counting numbers	(1) This is the assumption on the basis of which we shall try to obtain a contradiction
(2) $dm = n$	(2) From (1)

(3) $d^2m^2 = n^2$
(4) $2m^2 = n^2$
(5) n^2 is divisible by 2
(6) n is divisible by 2

(7) $n = 2p$, where p is some
      counting number
(8) $n^2 = 4p^2$
(9) $2m^2 = 4p^2$
(10) $m^2 = 2p^2$
(11) m^2 is divisible by 2
(12) m is divisible by 2

(13) n and m are not relatively
      prime

(3) From (2)
(4) From (3) since $d^2 = 2$
(5) From (4)
(6) From (5) and the Prelimi-
      nary Theorem
(7) This is simply another way
      of phrasing (6)
(8) From (7)
(9) From (4) and (8)
(10) From (9)
(11) From (10)
(12) From (11) and the Pre-
      liminary Theorem
(13) From (6) and (12)

We may stop now, for statement (13) is a contradiction to something we already know. The contradiction that we have obtained is that we began with a fraction n/m that was *in lowest terms*, and we have just proven that n/m is *not in lowest terms*. Hence we either have made a mistake in the proof or the initial assumption that d is a fraction is incorrect. After a careful examination of the proof we convince ourselves that it is valid. Hence the mistake must have been in the assumption that d was a fraction. We are therefore forced to conclude that d is not a fraction. This completes the proof of the theorem.

There are many other points (infinitely many in fact) of the ray which do not correspond to fractions. One of these is the point located from the origin a distance equal to the length of the diagonal of a rectangle of sides 2 and 1. According to the Pythagorean Theorem the length of the diagonal of such a rectangle is the square root of $2^2 + 1^2 = 5$. It can be proven that $\sqrt{5}$ is not a fraction by taking our proof that $\sqrt{2}$ is not a fraction and replacing 2 everywhere in that proof by 5.

Exercises

1. Supply complete justifications for the statements in the proof of the theorem that the square root of 2 is not a fraction.
2. Prove the Preliminary Theorem. (*Suggestion:* To prove that if n is even then n^2 is even, begin by writing $n = 2x$. To prove the converse examine the prime factorization of n^2 and draw conclusions as to which primes must appear in the prime factorization of n.)
3. Prove that the square root of 5 is not a fraction. (Let d be such that $d^2 = 5$. Then $d = \sqrt{5}$. Now alter the proof that $\sqrt{2}$ is not a fraction by replacing 2 everywhere it occurs in that proof and in the Preliminary Theorem by 5. Check to see that the proof still works after these changes have been made.)

4. Prove that $\sqrt{3}$ is not a fraction.
5. Try to prove that $\sqrt{4}$ is not a fraction by using the same proof that was used to show $\sqrt{2}$ is not a fraction. The proof will break down at some stage. Where? Why does the proof break down?

Review Questions

1. What is a ray?
2. What do we mean by the fraction line? Is it really a line? Is it really a ray?
3. How is the fraction line constructed?
4. Are fractions points on the fraction line?
5. What does it mean to say that a set of points on the line has the density property?
6. How would you find three points between a given pair of points on the fraction line?
7. Explain in detail why not every point on the ray corresponds to a fraction.

THE NEED FOR MORE NUMBERS

We have seen that not every line segment can be measured by using fractions. In particular, at this stage of our development of arithmetic we cannot even measure the length of a diagonal of a square of side one unit distance. We certainly want to be able to measure this diagonal, but we cannot do it if the only numbers we have available are the fractions. There is a number which can be used to measure this diagonal and it is called an *irrational number*. We shall study irrational numbers in Chapters 8 and 9.

The System of Integers

In the last chapter we were able to enlarge the system of counting numbers so that it became possible to define a division process such that division by non-zero numbers was always possible. In this chapter we shall do the same thing relative to subtraction. We begin by defining new numbers called *negative integers*. Then we shall study the important relations and operations on the enlarged system of numbers consisting of the counting numbers together with the negative integers.

Our approach to this new number system will be motivated by our experience with the systems of counting numbers and of fractions.

THE NEW NUMBERS: THE NEGATIVE INTEGERS

As we saw in Chapter 2 the process of subtraction of counting numbers does not possess the closure property. In terms of what we want arithmetic to accomplish this is both unfortunate and unnatural. The reader can easily find problems encountered in day-to-day living that call for a new kind of number which, for example, can be used to measure such quantities as "degrees below zero."

Sample Problem   Sam arose at 10 A.M. and said to his roommate, "Boy, it sure is cold. Why, it's only 5 degrees out there." His roommate said, "You should have been up at 9. It's ten degrees warmer now than it was then." How cold was it at 9 A.M.?

If we represent the temperature at 9 A.M. by t, then we know that $5 - 10 = t$. But this equation has no solution in the system of counting numbers. Neither does it have a solution in the system of fractions. We must therefore either conclude that we cannot assign number meaning to the temperature at 9 A.M. or admit that we must invent more numbers.

We can say all of this as follows. One of the deficiencies of the system of counting numbers is that subtraction of counting numbers does not possess the closure property. What we want to do is to find some new numbers which can be used to assign meaning to all the symbols of the form $n - m$ which had no meaning in the system of counting numbers. The introduction of these new numbers will enable us to define a subtraction process which is a binary operation.

The Definition of Integer

We have seen that we want to introduce some new numbers and we have a pretty good idea of what these new numbers ought to be. Now we must find a satisfactory definition for them. Think back to the sample problem about the temperature. We all know that the temperature at 9 A.M. was five degrees below zero, symbolized by $-5°$. Just what is this temperature $-5°$? Isn't $-5°$ simply that temperature such that if it were that temperature now and got five degrees warmer, then it would be zero degrees? That is, $-5°$ is the unique temperature such that if one "adds" $5°$ to it, the result is $0°$. This idea motivates the definition of the new numbers which are called *negative integers.**

Definition of Negative Integer   *By a negative integer we shall mean a number which is the (unique) solution x of an equation of the form*

$$x + n = 0$$

where n is a counting number different from zero. The solution of this equation will be denoted by n^-.

EXAMPLES.   The equation $x + 3 = 0$ has a solution which is called a negative integer and which is denoted by the symbol 3^-. (The symbol 3^- can be read "three bar.") The symbol 5^- names the negative integer which is the solution to the equation $x + 5 = 0$. The solution to the equation $x + 17 = 0$ is the negative integer symbolized by 17^-. The negative integer 78^- is distinguished from all other numbers in that it and it alone has the property that when 78 is added to it the resulting sum is 0. This is exactly the same thing as to say that 78^- is the unique solution to the equation $x + 78 = 0$.

The set of negative integers can be tabulated as

$$\{1^-, 2^-, 3^-, 4^-, 5^-, 6^-, 7^-, \ldots\}$$

and is easily seen to be in one-to-one correspondence with the set of all nonzero counting numbers. We leave it to the reader to write out such a correspondence.

We now enlarge the set of counting numbers by using the set of all negative integers. To make our terminology more consistent we shall rename the nonzero counting numbers and call them *positive integers.* Thus the terms *nonzero counting number* and *positive integer* are synonyms. The counting number zero is neither a positive integer nor a negative integer: zero is referred to simply as

---

* The word integer is pronounced in-te-ger, *te* as in sys*te*m, and *ger* as in *ger*anium.

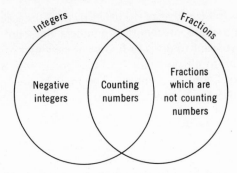

Figure 43

the integer zero. The set of numbers which are called *integers* consists of all the positive integers (i.e., nonzero counting numbers), all the negative integers, and zero.

Definition of Integer: *An integer is a number which is either a positive integer, a negative integer, or zero.*

In Fig. 43 we have illustrated by using Euler circles the relationships between the set of integers, the set of counting numbers, and the set of fractions.

There are a variety of ways to tabulate the set of all integers, the following being a sample:

$$\{0, 1, 1^-, 2, 2^-, 3, 3^-, 4, 4^-, 5, 5^-, 6, 6^-, \ldots\}$$

Given this tabulation of the set of integers the reader should be able to find a one-to-one correspondence between this set and the set of all counting numbers. This means that the set of counting numbers is *equivalent* to the set of integers. It was an exercise in the preceding chapter (Exercise 6, p. 148) to show that the set of fractions is equivalent to the set of counting numbers. Consequently we see that the sets of counting numbers, of fractions, and of integers are equivalent sets.

Review Questions

1. What is a negative integer? What is an integer?
2. Construct a one-to-one correspondence between the set of all positive integers and the set of all negative integers.
3. How could a number be tested to determine if it is equal to the negative integer 45^-? How is the integer 6^- distinguished from all other integers?
4. Illustrate by using Euler circles the relationships between the sets of counting numbers, fractions, and integers.
5. Tabulate the set of all integers.
6. A synonym for positive integer is _____.
7. The negative integers are defined in terms of what kind of numbers?

Exercises

1. Let
    C denote the set of all counting numbers,

C^+ denote the set of all nonzero counting numbers,

I denote the set of all integers

I^+ denote the set of all positive integers,

I^- denote the set of all negative integers, and

F denote the set of all fractions.

(a) Are any of these sets related by the relation of equality of sets?

(b) Show that $C \sim I$. Show that $C \sim I^+$. Explain why it is then easy to conclude that $I \sim I^+$.

(c) Are any of the sets related by the subset relation?

(d) Are any of these sets related by the proper subset relation?

(e) Are any of these sets disjoint?

(f) $I \cap C^+ = ?$ (i) $F \cup I^+ = ?$ (l) $I \cap C = ?$

(g) $F \cap I = ?$ (j) $I^- \cap I^+ = ?$ (m) $I^- \cup I^+ \cup \{0\} = ?$

(h) $F \cap I^- = ?$ (k) $I^- \cup I^+ = ?$ (n) $I^+ \cap C = ?$

The Integer Line

It is convenient to visualize the set of all integers as a set of points on a line. We pause in our discussion of the system of integers to discuss this visualization, not because it is in any way logically necessary to the development, but because it is an aid to one's intuition about integers.

We construct this visualization of the integers as follows. Draw a line and select on this line two distinct points. Call the leftmost of these two points the *origin* and the other the *unit*. Call the distance between these two points the *unit distance*. Now a very natural one-to-one correspondence between the set of integers and a certain set of points on the line suggests itself. We begin the construction of this correspondence by pairing the integer 0 with the origin and the integer 1 with the unit. To find the points corresponding to the *positive integers* we repeat the same construction as was used in constructing the counting number line. For example, to find the point corresponding to the positive integer 3 we locate the point lying to the *right* of the origin a distance equal to three unit distances. To find the points corresponding to the *negative integers* we do almost the same thing, but we locate points to the *left* of the origin. For example, the negative integer 3^- will be paired with the point lying to the *left* of the origin a distance equal to three unit distances. The negative integers are paired with points to the left of the origin and the positive integers are paired with points to the right of the origin. This correspondence between numbers and points is illustrated in Fig. 44. The reader can easily convince himself that the correspondence we have constructed is in fact a *one-to-one correspondence*

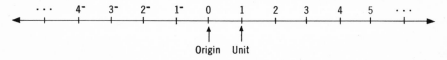

Figure 44 The integer line.

between the set of integers and a certain set of points on the line. We shall call this set of points the integer line. The reader should keep in mind that the set of integers is not equal to the set of points; these sets are only equivalent. However, we shall allow ourselves the privilege of failing to distinguish between integers and the points to which they correspond whenever it makes the discussion easier.

It is important to clearly understand the way that the integer line is used in the study of integers. Because we can visualize relations and operations involving integers, we use the integer line (1) to aid our intuition and help us see what we *ought* to do, and (2) to help us visualize what we have done *after* we have done it. But we cannot use the integer line to *do* the arithmetic; it only reflects in geometric terms what we are able to accomplish within the framework of the deductive system of integers.* Thus the integer line *per se* is not a tool of arithmetic.

Absolute Value and Algebraic Sign

Consider the integer 6^-. In terms of the location of this integer on the integer line it ought to be clear that this integer has a kind of twofold significance:

1. The integer is located a *distance* equal to 6 unit distances from the origin, and
2. The integer is located to the *left* of the origin.

Thus it appears that there are two aspects to the concept of integer, *distance* and *direction*. The distance of an integer from the origin is called the *absolute value* of the integer. The aspect of an integer having to do with the direction that integer lies from the origin is called the *algebraic sign* of the integer.

Now that we have used the integer line to get some idea of what we ought to be thinking about, we must put it aside and define these concepts within the framework of the deductive system of integers.

Definition of the Algebraic Sign of an Integer

1. *If n is a positive integer, we say that the algebraic sign of n is positive.*
2. *If n is zero, we say that n has no algebraic sign.*
3. *If n is a negative integer, we say that n has negative algebraic sign.*

EXAMPLES. The algebraic signs of 5^-, 11^-, 1^-, and 3^- are negative. The algebraic signs of 7, 3, 8, and 14 are positive. The integer 0 has no algebraic sign.

Definition of the Absolute Value of an Integer

1. *If n is a non-negative integer, then the absolute value of n is n itself;*
2. *If n^- is a negative integer (so that n is a positive integer), then the absolute value of n^- is the positive integer n.*
   If n is an integer we denote the absolute value of n by the symbol $|n|$.

It is important that the reader study the definition of absolute value very carefully and see that it says just what we said above—the absolute value of an

---

* Similar statements can be made about the fraction line and the counting number line.

Figure 45

integer is the distance of that integer from the origin on the integer line. The usefulness of this definition lies in that fact that it tells the meaning of absolute value without reference to the integer line and so may be employed in arguments (i.e., proofs) within the deductive system of integers.

EXAMPLE 1.   Since 5, 8, 0, and 1 are all non-negative integers each of these integers is equal to its absolute value. But each of the integers 5^-, 45^-, and 1^- is a negative integer, and so the absolute values of these integers are 5, 45, and 1, respectively. In symbols, $|5^-| = 5$, $|45^-| = 45$, and $|1^-| = 1$.

EXAMPLE 2.   Consider the point labeled P in Fig. 45. Since P lies to the left of the origin the algebraic sign of P is negative. Since the distance of P from the origin is equal to 6 unit distances, the absolute value of P is equal to 6. Hence P is the integer 6^-, or, more precisely, P *corresponds* to the integer 6^-.

EXAMPLE 3.   A certain integer has absolute value 7 and negative algebraic sign. What is the integer? *Answer: 7^-.*

EXAMPLE 4.   How many different integers have absolute value equal to 6? There are two—both 6^- and 6 have absolute value 6. No other integers have absolute value 6. We can visualize this in terms of the integer line by observing that 6^- and 6 are the only points situated a distance equal to six unit distances from the origin.

Review Questions

1.   What is the integer line?
2.   Describe the one-to-one correspondence between the integer line and the set of all integers.
3.   The set of points on the integer line is _____ to the set of integers.
4.   Can the integer line be used to prove facts about integers? Explain fully.
5.   In order to place an integer on the integer line there are two things you must know about that integer. What are they?
6.   State the definition of absolute value of an integer.
7.   State the definition of the algebraic sign of an integer.
8.   The absolute value of any integer is a _____.
9.   Does every integer have an absolute value? Does every integer have an algebraic sign?
10.   How are the concepts of absolute value and algebraic sign reflected in terms of the geometry of the integer line?

Exercises

1.   Define a relation on the collection of all counting numbers as follows: Say that n is related to m $(n \, \mathfrak{R} \, m)$ if and only if n and m have the same absolute value. For example, $6 \, \mathfrak{R} \, 6$ and $6 \, \mathfrak{R} \, 6^-$.

     (a) To which integers is the integer 0 related?
     (b) To which integers is the integer 1 related?
     (c) Is this relation reflexive?
     (d) Is this relation symmetric?
     (e) Is this relation transitive?

2. Define a relation on the collection of all nonzero integers as follows: Say that n is related to m ($n \mathcal{R} m$) if and only if n and m have the same algebraic sign. For example, $6^- \mathcal{R} 4^-$ but $7^- \not{\mathcal{R}} 4$.
     (a) To which integers is the integer 7 related?
     (b) To which integers is the integer 2^- related?
     (c) Discuss the properties of this relation. What kind of a relation is this?

3. Define a relation on the set of all nonzero integers as follows: Say that $n \mathcal{R} m$ if and only if n and m have the same absolute value but have different algebraic sign.
     (a) To which integers is 6 related? To which is 6^- related?
     (b) To which integers is 1^- related? To which is 1 related?
     (c) Show that this relation is not an equivalence relation.

4. Does the integer line possess the density property? Explain.

RELATIONS ON THE INTEGERS

Equality of Integers

Suppose that n and m represent integers. What ought we to mean by the statement, "The integer n is equal to the integer m"? If we think about this question in terms of the integer line a reasonable answer is that n and m ought to be equal when they correspond to the same point on the integer line. Since n and m will correspond to the same point if and only if they lie on the same side of the origin (and so have the same algebraic sign) and lie the same distance from the origin (and so have the same absolute value), we see that it is reasonable and quite natural to formulate the definition of equality of integers as follows.

Definition of Equality of Integers *Two nonzero integers are said to be equal if they have the same absolute value and the same algebraic sign. The integer zero is defined to be equal only to itself.*

This relation is an *equivalence relation* and *agrees on the counting numbers* with the relation of equality of counting numbers. In light of these expected and desirable properties and the naturalness of the definition in terms of the integer line, we may feel confident that the relation we have defined is the one we wanted.

Attention should be paid to the way that the relation of equality of integers involves the relation of equality of counting numbers. In order to determine whether two nonzero integers are equal it is necessary to be able to determine whether the counting numbers which are their absolute values are related by the relation of equality of counting numbers.

Exercises

1. Where and how is the relation of equality of counting numbers used in the definition of equality of integers?
2. Prove that equality of integers is an equivalence relation.
3. Explain why the relations of equality of integers and equality of counting numbers agree on the counting numbers.
4. Let n and m represent positive integers. Then the symbols n^- and m^- represent negative integers. Prove that $n = m$ if and only if $n^- = m^-$. (There are two theorems to be proven. Each follows easily from the definition of equality of integers.)

The Inequality Relations

The other relations on integers which we shall be interested in are the obvious four: *less than*, *greater than*, *less than or equal to*, and *greater than or equal to*. It is possible to define these relations right now, but since these definitions may be phrased more easily and naturally if we wait until after we have defined addition of integers we shall do that.

ADDITION OF INTEGERS

In light of our experience with the systems of counting numbers and fractions it is clear that one of the first operations we ought to define is an operation which we would call addition of integers. This operation should, in some way not yet explicitly stated, relate to the operation of addition of counting numbers. Our problem now is to invent a definition for such an operation.

The Definition

The invention of almost anything follows a three-step pattern. First, specifications are drawn up listing the characteristics the thing we are trying to invent ought to possess. Second, we employ our knowledge, intuition, and any other resources that bear upon the problem to actually construct the thing we want. Third, the thing we have constructed must be tested to determine whether we have done what we set out to do; that is, to determine whether the thing we have invented meets the specifications we laid down at the outset.

How does this process apply to the invention of an arithmetic operation? We begin by stipulating the properties that the operation we intend to invent (i.e., to define) ought to possess. These properties are derived from our knowledge of arithmetic. Then a definition is constructed. Finally we test this definition to make sure that it does in fact possess the properties we specified it ought to have. If the operation should prove not to possess one or more of these properties, then we have to go back and rework the definition until it does meet the specifications laid down at the outset.

THE SPECIFICATIONS: THE PROPERTIES THAT ADDITION OUGHT TO POSSESS

What are some of the properties that an operation to be called *addition of integers* ought to possess? There is one property that is forced upon us by the definition of negative integer. According to that definition it *must* be true that if n is a positive integer, then

$$n^- + n = 0$$

But surely there are some other properties that the operation ought to possess. What are some of them?

1.   Since every counting number is an integer, it is reasonable to expect that the operation of addition of integers should *agree on the counting numbers* with the operation of addition of counting numbers. For this reason we shall put it into the definition that the two operations should give the same result when applied to positive integers.

2.   The operation should possess the *closure* property and consequently the *well-definedness* property. It should be both *commutative* and *associative*. It should possess an *identity*, namely 0. It should possess the *cancellation* property. We want the operation to possess these properties because the operation of addition of counting numbers possesses them and because we want the system of integers to be a natural extension of the system of counting numbers.

3.   We have already remarked that whatever properties we choose to stipulate the operation should possess, the operation must possess the property that $n^- + n = 0$ whenever n is a positive integer. Because we also want the operation to be commutative, it is reasonable to insist that the operation be such that

$$n + n^- = n^- + n = 0$$

for every positive integer n.

These are the properties that we want the operation to possess. Keeping the desired properties constantly in mind, we now begin the second phase—the construction of the definition.

CONSTRUCTING THE DEFINITION OF ADDITION OF INTEGERS

From the foregoing consideration of the properties that the operation ought to possess we see that the definition should begin with the following:

Case 1   If n and m are positive integers, then their sum as integers should equal their sum as counting numbers.

Case 2   For every integer n it should be true the $0 + n = n + 0 = n$.

Case 3   For every positive integer n it should be true that $n + n^- = n^- + n = 0$.

Now a careful examination of this partial definition shows that we have defined the sum of integers in all cases except two. We have not yet said (Case 4) how to add two negative integers or (Case 5) how to add integers of different algebraic sign and different absolute value. We shall consider these cases separately.

First let us consider the problem of constructing the definition in Case 4, the case that both summands are negative integers. Suppose n^- and m^- represent negative integers. We seek to determine a reasonable meaning for the symbol $n^- + m^-$. At this stage of the development of the system of integers the only thing we know about these integers is what the definition of integer tells us. We know that

$$n^- + n = 0 \quad \text{and} \quad m^- + m = 0$$

But then, if addition of integers is to be well-defined, we may write

$$(n^- + n) + (m^- + m) = 0 + 0 = 0$$

This, if addition of integers is to be associative, means that

$$n^- + [n + (m^- + m)] = 0$$

which, if addition of integers is to be associative, means that

$$n^- + [(n + m^-) + m] = 0$$

which, if addition of integers is to be commutative, means that

$$n^- + [(m^- + n) + m] = 0$$

which, if addition of integers is to be associative, means that

$$n^- + [m^- + (n + m)] = 0$$

which, if addition of integers is to be associative, means that

$$(n^- + m^-) + (n + m) = 0$$

But this last equation tells us that $n^- + m^-$ represents the solution of the equation $x + (n + m) = 0$. On the other hand, we already know (how?) that the solution of this equation is represented by $(n + m)^-$. Hence we may conclude that

$$n^- + m^- = (n + m)^-$$

Because of the reasonableness of this argument we are inclined to make it a part of the definition that

Case 4   If n^- and m^- are negative integers, then $n^- + m^- = (n + m)^-$.

EXAMPLE 1.   The sum of 18^- and 4^- is $(18 + 4)^-$ or 22^-. This is reasonable because $18^- + 4^-$ is the solution of the equation $x + 22 = 0$:

$$\begin{aligned}
(18^- + 4^-) + 22 &= (18^- + 4^-) + (4 + 18) \\
&= 18^- + [4^- + (4 + 18)] \\
&= 18^- + [(4^- + 4) + 18] \\
&= 18^- + [0 + 18] \\
&= 18^- + 18 \\
&= 0
\end{aligned}$$

EXAMPLE 2. The sum of 6^- and 3^- is 9^- since $6^- + 3^- = (6 + 3)^- = 9^-$.

EXAMPLE 3. $(8^- + 4^-) + (3^- + 2^-) = (8 + 4)^- + (3 + 2)^- = 12^- + 5^- = (12 + 5)^-$
$= 17^-$.

Exercises

1. Find the following sums. Whenever you add two integers state which part of the definition you are using.

   (a) $3^- + 1^- = ?$

   (b) $(3^- + 6^-) + 2^- = ?$

   (c) $2 + (3 + 4) = ?$

   (d) $(3 + 3^-) + 6^- = ?$

   (e) $(14^- + 17^-) + 31 = ?$

   (f) $2^- + (1^- + 1^-) = ?$

   (g) $2^- + (1 + 1) = ?$

   (h) $(16^- + 32^-) + (14^- + 6^-) = ?$

2. In the manner of the general argument on p. 189, show why we defined addition of integers so that

   (a) $5^- + 4^- = 9^-$.   (b) $18^- + 34^- = 52^-$.

3. Show in the manner of Example 1, p. 189, that

   (a) $5^- + 4^-$ is the solution of the equation $x + 9 = 0$ and so $5^- + 4^- = 9^-$.

   (b) $32^- + 18^-$ is the solution of the equation $x + 50 = 0$ and so $32^- + 18^- = 50^-$.

We now know how to add integers in all cases except Case 5, in which one of the summands is positive, the other is negative, and the absolute values of the summands are not equal. (If the absolute values of the summands are equal Case 3 tells us how to add them.) We consider such addition problems now.

In inventing a reasonable meaning for the symbol $n + m^-$ where n is a positive integer, m^- is a negative integer, and $n \neq m$, we must consider two possibilities.

Subcase 5a	Subcase 5b
The absolute value of the positive summand (n) is greater than the absolute value of the negative summand (m).	The absolute value of the positive summand (n) is less than the absolute value of the negative summand (m).
Examples	*Examples*
$5 + 2^- = ?$	$5^- + 2 = ?$
$16 + 8^- = ?$	$16^- + 8 = ?$
$13 + 7^- = ?$	$13^- + 7 = ?$

We shall discuss these two subcases separately. First we shall settle the question of how to add if Case 5a holds and then we shall settle the question of how to add if Case 5b holds.

Let us begin the consideration of Case 5a by looking at a specific example, the addition problem $7 + 3^- = ?$ Consider the following argument based upon facts we already know about counting numbers and the properties we desire addition of integers to possess. We already know (Theorem 11, p. 61), that

$$7 = (7 - 3) + 3$$

Then, if addition of integers is to be well-defined, we should be able to write

$$7 + 3^- = [(7 - 3) + 3] + 3^-$$

which, if addition of integers is to be associative, means that

$$7 + 3^- = (7 - 3) + (3 + 3^-)$$

and since we already know that $3 + 3^-$ is equal to 0, we get

$$7 + 3^- = (7 - 3) + 0$$

or

$$7 + 3^- = 7 - 3$$

Thus we see that it appears reasonable to say that the sum of 7 and 3^- ought to be equal to $7 - 3$ or 4.

Now let us repeat this argument in the general case. Assume that n is a positive integer, that m^- is a negative integer, and that $n > m$. Just as in the example above we begin by writing

$$n = (n - m) + m$$

Then, if addition of integers is to be well-defined, we can write

$$n + m^- = [(n - m) + m] + m^-$$

from which we obtain, if addition of integers is to be associative,

$$n + m^- = (n - m) + (m + m^-)$$

Since we know that $m + m^- = 0$, we may then write

$$n + m^- = (n - m) + 0$$

or

$$n + m^- = n - m$$

Thus we are led to make it a part of the definition of addition of integers that $n + m^-$ should be equal to $n - m$ for summands n and m^- with $n > m$. But since we also expect this operation to be commutative, it is not unreasonable to define the sum $m^- + n$ to be equal to $n + m^-$. On the basis of these considerations we make it a part of the definition that

Case 5a If n is a positive integer, if m^- is a negative integer, and if $n > m$, then $m^- + n = n + m^- = n - m$.

EXAMPLE 1.   According to what has been said the sum of 17 and 5^- should be equal to $17 - 5$ or 12. The sum of 6 and 4^- is $6 - 4$ or 2. $7 + 1^- = 7 - 1 = 6$.

EXAMPLE 2. $(15 + 9^-) + 2^- = (15 - 9) + 2^- = 6 + 2^- = 6 - 2 = 4$.

EXAMPLE 3. $(18 + 13^-) + (12 + 6^-) = (18 - 13) + (12 - 6) = 5 + 6 = 11$.

EXAMPLE 4. $34 + (19^- + 13^-) = 34 + (19 + 13)^- = 34 + 32^- = 34 - 32 = 2$.

Exercises

1. Find the sums. Each time you add two integers tell which part of the definition you are using.

   (a) $6 + (2^- + 2^-) = ?$

   (b) $(6 + 3^-) + (1^- + 1^-) = ?$

   (c) $(45^- + 2^-) + (100 + 6^-) = ?$

   (d) $(6 + 12) + (6^- + 12^-) = ?$

   (e) $(6 + 6^-) + (6^- + 6^-) = ?$

   (f) $(17^- + 19) + 6 = ?$

   (g) $(1^- + 1) + (1 + 1^-) = ?$

   (h) $(76 + 27^-) + 40^- = ?$

   (i) $[(100 + 29^-) + 13^-] + 9^- = ?$

   (j) $3^- + [45^- + (98 + 16^-)] = ?$

2. In the manner of the discussion of the problem $7 + 3^- = ?$ given on p. 190, explain why it is a good idea to define addition in such a way that

   (a) the sum of 18 and 15^- is 3.

   (b) the sum of 11 and 10^- is 1.

   (c) the sum of 16^- and 20 is 4.

All that remains to be done is to decide on the sum in Case 5b, the case that the positive summand has absolute value less than the absolute value of the negative summand. Let us consider an example first, the problem $4 + 6^- = ?$ We seek to determine a reasonable meaning for the symbol $4 + 6^-$. But since we already know that

$$6^- = 4^- + (6 - 4)^-$$

(which follows from Case 4 of the definition) we can write, if addition of integers is to be well-defined,

$$4 + 6^- = 4 + [4^- + (6 - 4)^-]$$

which, if addition of integers is to be associative, means that

$$4 + 6^- = (4 + 4^-) + (6 - 4)^-$$

which, since we already know that $4 + 4^- = 0$, means that

$$4 + 6^- = 0 + (6 - 4)^- = (6 - 4)^-$$

Thus we see that it appears reasonable to say that the sum of 4 and 6^- ought to be $(6 - 4)^-$ or 2^-.

Now we shall apply this same line of reasoning to the general case. Thus let n be a positive integer and m^- be a negative integer such that $n < m$. Since we already know that

$$m^- = n^- + (m - n)^-$$

(Case 4 of the definition) we can, if addition of integers is to be well-defined, write

$$n + m^- = n + [n^- + (m - n)^-]$$

which, if addition of integers is to be associative, means that

$$n + m^- = (n + n^-) + (m - n)^-$$

Since $n + n^- = 0$ we then have

$$n + m^- = 0 + (m - n)^-$$

or

$$n + m^- = (m - n)^-$$

The argument leads us to make it a part of the definition of addition of integers that $n + m^-$ should be equal to $(m - n)^-$ for summands n and m^- with $n < m$.

Case 5b If n is a positive integer, m^- is a negative integer, and $n < m$, then $m^- + n = n + m^- = (m - n)^-$.

EXAMPLE 1. The sum of 15 and 34^- is equal to $(34 - 15)^-$ or 19^-. The sum of 12^- and 5 is equal to $(12 - 5)^-$ or 7^-.

EXAMPLE 2. $(15^- + 9) + 2^- = (15 - 9)^- + 2^- = 6^- + 2^- = (6 + 2)^- = 8^-$.

EXAMPLE 3. $(13^- + 8) + (19 + 5^-) = (13 - 8)^- + (19 - 5) = 5^- + 14 = 14 - 5$ $= 9$.

EXAMPLE 4. $34^- + (16 + 17^-) = 34^- + (17 - 16)^- = 34^- + 1^- = (34 + 1)^- = 35^-$.

Exercises

1. Find the sums. Each time you add two integers tell which part of the definition you are using.
    (a) $13^- + 6 = $?
    (b) $13^- + (6 + 7^-) = $?
    (c) $(13^- + 6) + 7^- = $?
    (d) $(18^- + 9^-) + 42 = $?
    (e) $18^- + (9^- + 42) = $?
    (f) $27^- + [16 + (31^- + 5)] = $?
    (g) $16^- + (32^- + 8^-) = $?
    (h) $16^- + (32 + 8^-) = $?
    (i) $(16^- + 12) + (12^- + 16) = $?
    (j) $[(37^- + 17) + 15] + 10^- = $?
2. In the manner of the discussion of the addition problem $4 + 6^- = $? on p. 192, explain why it is a good idea to define addition in such a way that
    (a) the sum of 15^- and 6 is 9^-.
    (b) the sum of 5^- and 4 is 1^-.
    (c) the sum of 10^- and 8 is 2^-.

We have now completed the definition of addition of integers. Collecting together our conclusions in Cases 1 through 5 we obtain the definition.

Definition of the Operation of Addition of Integers

1. *If n and m are positive integers, then the sum of n and m as integers is equal to their sum as counting numbers.*
2. *If n is an integer, then $0 + n = n + 0 = n$.*
3. *If n is a positive integer, then $n^- + n = n + n^- = 0$.*
4. *If n^- and m^- are both negative integers, then $n^- + m^- = (n + m)^-$.*
5. *If n is a positive integer and m^- is a negative integer, then*

$$m^- + n = n + m^- = \begin{cases} n - m, \text{ if } n > m \\ (m - n)^-, \text{ if } n < m \end{cases}$$

TESTING THE DEFINITION: THE PROPERTIES OF ADDITION OF INTEGERS

We have found a definition for the operation which we want to call addition of integers. The invention of this operation was based upon the consideration of the properties we wanted the operation to possess. But have we really defined the operation we wanted? Is it possible that we have made an error and that the operation we have defined is not, for example, commutative? Could it be that we have defined an operation which does not possess an identity? In fact, we have made no mistakes and the operation we have defined is just what we wanted. First of all, it is clear that the operation we have defined *agrees on the counting numbers* with the operation of addition of counting numbers. We specifically formulated the definition so that this would be so. Refer to parts 1 and 2 of the definition to see this. Our definition also is consistent with the definition of negative integer in that the sum of a positive integer n and the corresponding negative integer n^- is zero. This is part 3 of the definition. Lastly, the operation possesses the same six properties as does addition of counting numbers: the properties of *closure* (and consequently *well-definedness*), *commutivity*, *associativity*, *identity* (0), and *cancellation*. These properties are discussed in the exercises which follow.

Review Questions

1. What properties did we want the operation called addition of integers to possess?
2. How did we decide upon a reasonable way to define the sum of the negative integers n^- and m^-? Explain fully.
3. How did we decide upon a reasonable way to define the sum of a positive integer n and a negative integer m^- in the case that $n > m$?
4. How did we decide upon a reasonable way to define the sum of a positive integer n and a negative integer m^- in the case that $n < m$?
5. What is the definition of the operation of addition of integers?
6. What properties are possessed by this operation?

Exercises

1. Explain why addition of integers possesses the closure property. (*Suggestion:* Consider each of the five cases separately.)
2. Make up a proof which shows that addition of integers is commutative in the case that both summands are negative integers. That is, prove that $n^- + m^- = m^- + n^-$ if n^- and m^- are negative integers. Which property of addition of counting numbers is involved?
3. Find a proof of the associative property in the case that all three summands are negative integers. Why do any three positive integers associate with respect to addition of integers?
4. Explain why zero is the identity for the operation of addition of integers.
5. Suppose that n^-, m^-, and p^- are negative integers such that $n^- + p^- = m^- + p^-$. Prove that $n^- = m^-$. That is, prove that the cancellation property holds when all

three integers are negative integers. Why does this property hold when all three integers are positive integers?

6. Each of the following equations can be solved by using only the properties of addition of integers. For example, the equation

$$n + 2^- + 3 = 7^-$$

can be solved as follows:

(1)	$n + 2^- + 3 = 7^-$	(1)	Given equation
(2)	$n + 1 = 7^-$	(2)	$2^- + 3 = 1$
(3)	$n + 1 = 8^- + 1$	(3)	$7^- = 8^- + 1$
(4)	$n = 8^-$	(4)	Cancellation property of addition of integers

Solve each of the following equations in like manner giving reasons for each step.

(a) $n + 7^- = 14$.

(b) $14^- + 6 = n + 2^-$.

(c) $3^- + 2^- + 4 = n + 7^-$.

(d) $n + 28^- = 13^- + 6$.

(e) $n + 4^- = 6^- + (13 + 17^-)$.

7. Solve each of these equations by using the well-definedness property of addition of integers. Justify each step.

(a) $n + 6 = 25^-$.   (d) $n + 2^- + 3 = 18^-$.

(b) $n + 6 = 25$.   (e) $4^- + n + 5 = 13^- + 5^-$.

(c) $23^- + n = 14$.   (f) $16 + n = 16$.

8. Suppose that n and m represent integers. Consider the non-negative integers $|n|$ and $|m|$. Explain by means of counterexamples why it is not necessarily true that

$$|n + m| = |n| + |m|$$

Can you find a correct relationship between the non-negative integers $|n + m|$ and $|n| + |m|$?

Additive Inverse

The usefulness of the system of fractions is reflected in the fact that every nonzero fraction has a multiplicative inverse. It was this fact that enabled us to prove the important Divide by Multiplying Theorem. There is a parallel concept of equal importance in the system of integers called *additive inverse*.

Definition of Additive Inverse   *If n and m are integers such that $n + m = 0$, then m is called the additive inverse of n.*

EXAMPLES.   Since $5^- + 5 = 0$, 5 is the additive inverse of 5^-. Moreover since $5 + 5^- = 0$, 5^- is the additive inverse of 5. The additive inverse of 7^- is 7, since $7^- + 7 = 0$. The additive inverse of 0, 0^-, is equal to itself: $0 = 0^-$.

It should be obvious that every integer possesses a unique additive inverse.

As we shall see in our discussion of subtraction of integers the concept of additive inverse is extremely important. It is because every integer has an additive inverse that we will be able to invent a subtraction operation which possesses the closure property.

It is useful to note the parallel between the concepts of multiplicative inverse in the system of fractions and of additive inverse in the system of integers. In

$$\text{fact, two } \begin{Bmatrix} \text{fractions} \\ \text{integers} \end{Bmatrix} \text{ are } \begin{Bmatrix} \text{multiplicative} \\ \text{additive} \end{Bmatrix} \text{ inverses of each other}$$

$$\text{if their } \begin{Bmatrix} \text{product} \\ \text{sum} \end{Bmatrix} \text{ is equal to the } \begin{Bmatrix} \text{multiplicative} \\ \text{additive} \end{Bmatrix} \text{ identity.}$$

We need a symbol to denote additive inverses. For the time being we shall use the superscript symbol "$^-$" to denote additive inverses. Thus for example the statement, "The additive inverse of 5^- is the positive integer 5," would be rendered symbolically as

$$(5^-)^- = 5$$

This means that such symbols as 57^- can be interpreted in two ways. The symbol 57^- can be regarded as naming the negative integer 57^- or as naming the additive inverse of the positive integer 57. Of course, which interpretation is used is immaterial since the negative integer 57^- and the additive inverse of the positive integer 57 are the same number.

EXAMPLE 1.   The additive inverse of 6 is represented by the symbol 6^-. The additive inverse of 6^- is denoted by the symbol $(6^-)^-$, or more simply 6^{--}, and is equal to the positive integer 6: $6^{--} = 6$.

EXAMPLE 2.   If n represents an integer (positive, negative, or 0), then the additive inverse of n is denoted by n^-. The reader is cautioned not to think of a symbol like n^- as representing a negative integer just because of the superscript symbol $^-$. Indeed, n^- might represent a positive integer. In fact, n^- will represent a positive integer whenever the symbol n represents a negative integer. Examine the following table.

If $n =$	then $n^- =$
4	4^-
3^-	3
0	0
1	1^-
15^-	15

Review Questions

1.   Are there any integers which are their own additive inverses?
2.   Does every integer have an additive inverse?
3.   Does any integer have more than one additive inverse?
4.   What can be said about the additive inverse of a negative integer?
5.   Which integers have multiplicative inverses?
6.   Discuss the parallel between the concepts of multiplicative inverse and additive inverse.

7. The fractions are to the integers as one is to _____.
8. Under what circumstances will the symbol m^- represent a negative integer? Under what circumstances will it represent a positive integer?

Exercises

1. $6^{---} = ?, 6^{-----} = ?, n^{-----------} = ?, n^{---------} = ?$
2. What is the algebraic sign of $n^{-------}$ if n represents a negative integer? If n represents a positive integer?
3. Solve each of the following equations for n. Justify each step.
   (a) $n^- = 5$.
   (b) $(6 + 5^-)^- = n$.
   (c) $n^- = 5^- + (4^- + 11)^-$.
   (d) $n = [(9^- + 11)^- + (3^- + 6)^-]^-$.
4. Prove that the additive inverse of an integer is unique. (*Suggestion:* Use an indirect proof. Assume that an integer has two additive inverses. Employ the cancellation property of addition of integers. Cf. Exercise 3, p. 166.)
5. The concept of additive inverse is a relation on the set of all integers. Write $n \, \Re \, m$ to mean that m is the additive inverse of n. For example, $6 \, \Re \, 6^-$, $16^- \, \Re \, 16$, and $5 \, \Re \, 5^-$. Prove that this relation is symmetric. Find examples which show that this relation is neither reflexive nor transitive.

Some Theorems About Addition of Integers

Many of the theorems which we proved in Chapter 2 and which dealt with the operation of addition of counting numbers have analogs for the system of integers. For example, the analog of Theorem 3, p. 52, is

Theorem *Let n, m, and p represent integers. If $p + n = p + m$, then $n = m$.*

The proof of this theorem for integers is similar to the proof of Theorem 3. All one has to do to get a proof of this theorem is to change "counting number" to "integer" in the proof for Theorem 3. In searching for true statements about addition of integers, then, a very good place to begin looking is with the theorems already known concerning addition of counting numbers. We shall not, however, spend much time going back to discover which of these theorems have analogs in the new system. The reader has been working with these ideas sufficiently long now that he should be able to judge which will have analogs in the system of integers.

The most interesting consequences of the definition of addition of integers are those which do not have analogs in the system of counting numbers, those theorems which do not stem from theorems about addition of counting numbers. The following theorem is an example of this kind of theorem.

Additive Inverse Theorem *If n and m are integers, then $(n + m)^- = n^- + m^-$.*

The proof of this theorem is included in the exercises. Note that this theorem says something we do not already know only when n and m are not both positive integers, for if n and m are both positive then the theorem follows directly from part 4 of the definition of addition. This theorem is one of the most frequently used theorems in the system of integers and has great application in problems involving subtraction. We shall use it in the next section.

Exercises

1. (a) State the analogs for the system of integers of Theorem 1, p. 51, and Theorem 9, p. 55.
    (b) By making the appropriate changes in the proofs of Theorems 1 and 9, construct proofs for the analogs you found in part (a).
2. Supply justifications for the statements in the following proof of the Additive Inverse Theorem. We have abbreviated the proof considerably. Where more than one justification is in fact necessary you need only give the one most important justification.
    The Proof:
    (1) $(n + m) + (n^- + m^-) = (m + n) + (n^- + m^-)$
    (2) $\qquad\qquad\qquad\quad = m + (n + n^-) + m^-$
    (3) $\qquad\qquad\qquad\quad = m + 0 + m^-$
    (4) $\qquad\qquad\qquad\quad = m + m^-$
    (5) $\qquad\qquad\qquad\quad = 0$
    (6) $n^- + m^- = (n + m)^-$
3. Additive inverse is a concept in the system of integers. The parallel concept in the system of fractions is multiplicative inverse. Find the analog of the Additive Inverse Theorem in the system of fractions. That is, find a statement which might be called the Multiplicative Inverse Theorem in the system of fractions and which parallels the Additive Inverse Theorem.

The Four Inequality Relations

We are now ready to define the four inequality relations in the system of integers. Let us consider the *less than* relation first.

There are two ways to motivate our definition of *less than* for integers. First of all, since the system of integers is an extension of the system of counting numbers, perhaps we should define *less than* for integers in the same way we defined *less than* for counting numbers.

Definition of the Relation of Less Than for Integers   *If n and m represent integers, then we say that n is less than m, and write $n < m$, if there is a positive integer p such that $n + p = m$.*

On the other hand, we could motivate this definition by using the integer line. It is intuitively natural to think of one integer as being less than another if the point to which it corresponds lies to the left of the point corresponding to the other integer. Translating the above definition into geometric terms, this is exactly what we get. To say that $n + p = m$ means exactly that the point corresponding to n lies p unit distances to the left of the point corresponding to m.

EXAMPLES. $6^- < 3^-$ since $6^- + 3 = 3^-$. $4^- \not< 4^-$ since there is no *positive* integer p such that $4^- + p = 4^-$. $5^- < 3$ since $5^- + 8 = 3$.

Observe that this relation *agrees on the counting numbers* with the relation of *less than* for counting numbers. Thus if n and m are non-negative integers (counting numbers), then $n < m$ (*as integers*) if $n < m$ (*as counting numbers*)

The other three inequality relations are defined in the obvious ways; we shall define *less than or equal to* and leave the others to the reader.

Definition of the Relation of Less Than or Equal to   *If n and m are integers, then we say that n is less than or equal to m, and write $n \leq m$, if there is a non-negative integer p such that $n + p = m$.*

EXAMPLES. $17^- \leq 8^-$ since $17^- + 9 = 8^-$ and 9 is a non-negative integer. $5^- \leq 5^-$ since $5^- + 0 = 5^-$ and 0 is a non-negative integer. $5 \leq 18$ since $5 + 13 = 18$ and 13 is a non-negative integer.

These relations for integers possess exactly the same properties as do the corresponding relations for counting numbers. The discussion of these properties is included in the exercises.

Exercises

1. Of the given pair of integers, which integer is the smaller? Use the definition of *less than* to justify your answers.
    (a) 6^- and 5^-.   (d) 1^- and 67^-.
    (b) 6^- and 6.   (e) 6 and 5.
    (c) 2^- and 0.

2. Arrange the integers 7, 6^-, 4^-, and 1^- in order of increasing size. Use the definition of *less than* to justify your answer.

3. Suppose that n and m represent negative integers. Complete the following statement by using the concept of absolute value: *If n and m are negative integers, then $n < m$ if and only if _____.*

4. Suppose that n and m represent integers having different algebraic sign. Complete the following statement using the concept of algebraic sign: *If n and m represent integers with different algebraic sign, then $n < m$ if and only if _____.*

5. Define the relations of *greater than* and *greater than or equal to* for integers.

6. *Less than* for integers possesses only the transitivity property. Find counterexamples to the reflexivity and symmetry of this relation. Then give justifications for the following argument which proves that the relation is transitive.
    (1) $n < m$ and $m < p$
    (2) There exist positive integers x and y such that $n + x = m$ and $m + y = p$
    (3) $n + (x + y) = (n + x) + y$
    (4) $= m + y$
    (5) $= p$
    (6) $x + y$ is a positive integer
    (7) $n < p$

7. Which of the properties of reflexivity, symmetry, and transitivity are possessed by the relations of *less than or equal to*, *greater than*, and *greater than or equal to* for integers?
8. Prove that $n \leq m$ if and only if either $n < m$ or $n = m$.
9. Paralleling the proof in Exercise 6 show that *greater than or equal to* is a transitive relation.
10. Explain why in the definition of *less than* for integers the integer p was required to be positive rather than simply nonzero.

SUBTRACTION OF INTEGERS

The Definition

After defining a binary operation called addition of integers, it is natural to define a process called subtraction of integers. We shall use the same definition schema that we used in the systems of counting numbers and of fractions; that is, we shall define subtraction in terms of addition.

Definition of Subtraction of Integers   *If n and m are integers, then the result of subtracting m from n, symbolized by n − m, is that integer d such that n = m + d.*

Comparing this definition with the corresponding definition for counting numbers, we see that the two are very similar, the only difference being that in the present definition we have not said anything about the possibility that $n - m$ might be meaningless. As we shall see, subtraction of integers has the closure property and so we do not need to mention the possibility that the integer d might not exist.

EXAMPLE 1.   To subtract 3^- from 5 we find that integer d such that $5 = 3^- + d$. From our knowledge of addition of integers it is not difficult to see that d must be 8. Then since $5 = 3^- + 8$ we may conclude that $5 - 3^- = 8$.

EXAMPLE 2.   To find $15^- - 4$ we seek that integer d such that $15^- = 4 + d$. Again, from our knowledge of addition of integers it is not difficult to see that d must equal 19^-. Hence $15^- - 4 = 19^-$.

Exercises

1. As in the examples above, use the definition of subtraction to find the following differences:
   (a) $6^- - 9 = ?$ (c) $6^- - 4^- = ?$
   (b) $6^- - 5^- = ?$ (d) $4^- - 6^- = ?$
2. Using the definition of subtraction prove this theorem:
   Theorem   *If $n - m = d$, then $n - d = m$.*

The Subtract by Adding Theorem

The definition tells us what subtraction of integers is, but it does not give us a particularly effective computational procedure for actually performing subtraction. It is the existence of additive inverses in this number system which provides the computational tool we are looking for.

The Subtract by Adding Theorem   *If n and m are integers, then* $n - m = n + m^-$.
The Proof: This proof is abbreviated and the justifications given represent only the most important or significant of all the justifications necessary for each step.

(1)	$(n + m^-) + m = n + (m^- + m)$	(1) Associativity of addition of integers
(2)	$\qquad\qquad = n + 0$	(2) Additive inverses
(3)	$\qquad\qquad = n$	(3) Additive identity
(4)	$n = (n + m^-) + m$	(4) From (3) by using symmetry of equality
(5)	$n = m + (n + m^-)$	(5) From (4) by using commutivity of addition of integers
(6)	$n - m = n + m^-$	(6) From (5) by using the definition of subtraction of integers

⁑

This theorem tells us that we can perform subtraction by performing addition: Subtracting an integer *m* is exactly the same as adding the additive inverse of *m*. This is where the concept of *additive inverse* becomes important in the study of integers. Using the theorem we can immediately reduce all questions involving subtraction to questions involving addition. Let us look at some examples of its application to subtraction problems.

EXAMPLE 1.   Earlier we used the definition of subtraction to see that $5 - 3^- = 8$. Using the theorem we write

$$5 - 3^- = 5 + (3^-)^- = 5 + 3 = 8$$

EXAMPLE 2. $5 - 3 = 5 + (3)^- = 5 + 3^- = 2$.

EXAMPLE 3. $5^- - 3 = 5^- + (3)^- = 5^- + 3^- = 8^-$.

EXAMPLE 4. $5^- - 3^- = 5^- + (3^-)^- = 5^- + 3 = 2^-$.

In view of the Subtract by Adding Theorem and the definition of subtraction it is clear that subtraction is logically a superfluous operation in the sense that subtraction is never really performed at all. All subtraction problems are replaced by the appropriate addition problems and it is these addition problems that we actually solve. However, in our real world it would be unnatural to ignore subtraction. Many problems naturally point toward a formulation involving subtraction and this is why we study subtraction—not because we are compelled by logic to do so, but because we want to.

Review Questions

1. How is subtraction of integers defined?
2. How does the definition of subtraction of integers compare with the definition of subtraction of counting numbers?
3. Subtraction of integers is defined in terms of _____.
4. What is the Subtract by Adding Theorem?
5. The Subtract by Adding Theorem provides a connection between the concepts of _____ and _____.
6. How is the Subtract by Adding Theorem proven?

Exercises

1. Solve the following subtraction problems by using the Subtract by Adding Theorem and solve them also by applying the definition of subtraction of integers.

    (a) $5^- - 6 = ?$ (d) $56^- - 89^- = ?$

    (b) $7^- - 5^- = ?$ (e) $5 - 6^- = ?$

    (c) $19 - 18^- = ?$ (f) $0 - 5^- = ?$

2. Solve these subtraction problems by using the Subtract by Adding Theorem.

    (a) $6 - (5 + 7^-)^- = ?$ (e) $16^- - (5^- - 10) = ?$

    (b) $(9 - 8^-) + 5 = ?$ (f) $16^- + (5^- - 10) = ?$

    (c) $(6^- + 5^-) - 3^- = ?$ (g) $16^- - (5^- + 10) = ?$

    (d) $3^- - (4^- + 3^-) = ?$ (h) $(5^- - 10) - 16^- = ?$

3. Rewrite each of the following symbols in such a way that the only operation involved is addition of integers. This can be accomplished by appropriate applications of the Subtract by Adding Theorem and the Additive Inverse Theorem.

    (a) $n - (m - p)$.   (f) $a - [b - (c - d)]$.

    (b) $n - (m + p)$.   (g) $a - [b - (c + d)]$.

    (c) $(a - b) + (c - d)$.   (h) $e - [(a - b) - (c - d)]$.

    (d) $(a - b) - (c - d)$.   (i) $e - [(a - b) - (c + d)]$.

    (e) $(b - c) + a + (x - y)$.   (j) $[(a - b) - c] - (d - e)$.

4. Where in the proof of the Subtract by Adding Theorem was the well-definedness property of addition of integers used?
5. Compare the Divide by Multiplying Theorem and the Subtract by Adding Theorem. In what way are these two theorems similar?

The Properties of Subtraction of Integers

1. SUBTRACTION OF INTEGERS POSSESSES THE CLOSURE PROPERTY. This is by far the most important property of subtraction of integers and is the most significant aspect of the system of integers. Indeed it was to obtain a subtraction process with this property that the integers were invented in the first place. Here is a proof of this fundamental fact.

Theorem *If n and m represent integers, then the symbol n − m represents a unique integer.*

The Proof:

(1) n and m represent integers   (1) Hypothesis

(2) m^- represents a unique integer

(2) m is an integer and every integer has a unique additive inverse

(3) $n + m^-$ represents a unique integer

(3)   Addition of integers possesses the closure property

(4) $n - m$ represents a unique integer

(4)   From (3) and the Subtract by Adding Theorem which states that $n - m$ and $n + m^-$ have the same meaning

❋

We see that in contrast to the other subtraction processes we have defined subtraction of integers is a *binary operation*.

As usual we find it convenient to reformulate the uniqueness part of the closure property in a special way and to give this reformulation a special name.

The Well-Definedness Property of Subtraction of Integers   *If n, m, a, and b represent integers such that n = m and a = b, then n − a = m − b.*

Formulated in this way the property says that the names used to symbolize the minuhend and subtrahend have no effect upon the number which is their difference. It may also be interpreted as saying that equals subtracted from equals are equal.

2.   SUBTRACTION OF INTEGERS POSSESSES AN IDENTITY (0) AND POSSESSES THE CANCELLATION PROPERTY.   We leave the verification of these facts as exercises.

3.   SUBTRACTION OF INTEGERS AGREES ON THE COUNTING NUMBERS WITH SUBTRACTION OF COUNTING NUMBERS.   This fact follows from the way these two subtraction operations are defined in terms of addition and the fact that addition of integers agrees on the counting numbers with addition of integers.

4.   SUBTRACTION OF INTEGERS IS NEITHER COMMUTATIVE NOR ASSOCIATIVE. We leave it to the reader to find examples which prove this.

Many of the theorems we proved for subtraction of counting numbers have analogs for integers. In particular, the following theorems (which are analogs of Theorems 10 and 11, p. 61) obtain. These theorems display explicitly the connection between addition and subtraction of integers.

Theorem 1   *If n and m are integers, then* $(n + m) - m = n$.

Theorem 2   *If n and m are integers, then* $(n - m) + m = n$.

Exercises

1.   Give counterexamples
   (a)   involving only positive integers

(b)   involving only negative integers

(c)   involving both positive and negative integers

which show that subtraction of integers is not commutative and is not associative.

2.   Supply justifications for the following theorems which show that subtraction of integers possesses an identity and possesses the cancellation property.

(a)   **Theorem**   *Zero is an identity for subtraction of integers.*

(1) $n - 0 = n + 0^-$

(2) $n + 0^- = n + 0$

(3) $n + 0 = n$

(4) $n - 0 = n$

(b)   **Theorem**   *Subtraction of integers possesses the cancellation property.*

(1) $n - p = m - p$

(2) $n - p = n + p^-$

$m - p = m + p^-$

(3) $n + p^- = m + p^-$

(4) $n = m$

3.   Use the Subtract by Adding Theorem to prove the following theorems.

(a)   **Theorem**   *If n is an integer, then $0 - n = n^-$.*

(b)   **Theorem**   *If n and m are integers, then $(n - m)^- = n^- + m$.*

(c)   **Theorem**   *If n and m are integers, then $n - m^- = n + m$.*

4.   State the analogs in the system of integers of the following theorems from the system of counting numbers.

(a)   Theorem 12, p. 63.

(b)   Theorem 13, p. 63.

(c)   Theorem 14, p. 63.

(d)   Theorem 15, p. 63.

5.   Using the Subtract by Adding Theorem and (if necessary) the Additive Inverse Theorem, prove

(a)   The analog you found in Exercise 4(a).

(b)   The analog you found in Exercise 4(b).

(c)   The analog you found in Exercise 4(c).

(d)   The analog you found in Exercise 4(d).

6.   Are the statements below theorems? If either is not, can you find a way to change the statement so that it will be a theorem?

(a)   *If n, m, and p are integers and if $n < m$, then $n - p < m - p$.*

(b)   *If n, m, and p are integers and if $n < m$, then $p - n < p - m$.*

7.   If n, m, a, and b are integers and if $n - a = m - b$, then what is $n + b$ equal to? Give your answer in the form of a theorem. Supply a proof for your theorem.

MULTIPLICATION OF INTEGERS

The Definition

How ought we to define a binary operation on the set of all integers which will extend in a natural way the binary operation of multiplication of counting numbers? To find such an operation we shall go through the same steps as we went through to invent the operation of addition of integers.

THE SPECIFICATIONS: THE PROPERTIES THAT MULTIPLICATION OUGHT TO POSSESS

In the light of what we know about multiplication of counting numbers the following list of properties is certainly reasonable and desirable:

1. The operation should *agree on the counting numbers* with the binary operation of multiplication of counting numbers.
2. The operation should possess the properties of *closure, commutivity, associativity, identity* (1), and *cancellation.*
3. The operation of multiplication of integers should share a *distributive property* with the binary operation of addition of integers. Thus it should be true that $n(m + p) = nm + np$ for all integers n, m, and p.
4. An important property of multiplication of counting numbers was that $n0 = 0n = 0$ for every counting number n. It is not unreasonable to expect that multiplication of integers should possess the same property. Hence we shall assume that $n0 = 0n = 0$ for every integer n.

Keeping these desired properties in mind we shall now proceed to the search for an appropriate definition.

CONSTRUCTING THE DEFINITION OF MULTIPLICATION OF INTEGERS

From the list of properties the new operation should possess we see how to begin the definition of multiplication of integers. Because the new multiplication operation should agree with multiplication of counting numbers, the first part of the definition should be

Case 1 If n and m are positive integers, then their product as integers should equal their product as counting numbers.

Since we want $n0 = 0n = 0$ for all integers n we shall insert this directly into the definition:

Case 2 $n0 = 0n = 0$ for every integer n.

These two cases define all possible products except two. It remains to decide upon the meaning of the product if (Case 3) one factor is positive and the other factor is negative, and if (Case 4) both factors are negative. We shall consider these two cases separately. We begin with Case 3.

Suppose that n is a positive integer and m^- is a negative integer. We seek to assign meaning to the symbol nm^-. Using known facts about the system of integers and the properties that we desire the operation of multiplication of integers to possess, we can do this by studying the sum

$$nm^- + nm$$

What we can do is to show that it is reasonable to expect that this sum should be 0. This would mean that nm^- is the *additive inverse* of nm. Observe: If multiplication and addition of integers are to share the distributive property then it is reasonable to write

$$nm^- + nm = n(m^- + m)$$

But since we already know that $m^- + m = 0$ this means that

$$nm^- + nm = n0$$

According to Case 2 of the definition of multiplication of integers $n0$ is equal to 0. Hence we see that

$$nm^- + nm = 0$$

This last equation tells us that the symbol nm^- represents the additive inverse of the positive integer nm. Since the symbol $(nm)^-$ also represents this additive inverse we may conclude that

$$nm^- = (nm)^-$$

This argument motivates us to make it a part of the definition that nm^- should be equal to the negative integer $(nm)^-$. Since we also want this operation to be commutative, we shall insert the following into the definition:

Case 3   If n is a positive integer and m^- is a negative integer, then $(m^-)n = n(m^-) = (nm)^-$.

EXAMPLE 1.   The product of 6 and 3^- is the additive inverse of the product of 6 and 3: $6(3^-) = (6 \cdot 3)^- = 18^-$.

EXAMPLE 2. $(1^-)(1) = (1)(1^-) = (1 \cdot 1)^- = 1^-$.

EXAMPLE 3.   The product of 3 and 7^- ought to be 21^- since the sum of $(3)(7^-)$ and 21 is zero:

$$\begin{aligned}
(3)(7^-) + 21 &= (3)(7^-) + (3)(7) \\
&= (3)(7^- + 7) \\
&= (3)(0) \\
&= 0
\end{aligned}$$

That is, $(3)(7^-)$ is the additive inverse of 21 and so we put $(3)(7^-) = 21^-$.

Exercises

1. As in Example 3 immediately above, show why it is reasonable to say that the product of
    (a)   5 and 7^- should be equal to the additive inverse of 35.

(b)   4 and 8^- should be equal to the additive inverse of 32.

(c) 7^- and 2 should equal 14^-.

2.   Find the solution of these equations. Whenever two integers are multiplied tell which part of the definition you are using.

(a) $6^-(7) = n$.

(b) $6^-(3) + 7^- = n$.

(c) $6^-(4) - 17^- = n$.

(d) $6^-(7 + 5^-) = n$.

(e) $(14^- - 7^-)(2) = n$.

(f) $(14^- - 7^-)(6^- + 8)(2^- - 4^-) = n$.

(g) $(6^- + 10)(4^- + 1^-) = n$.

(h) $(2^-)(6) + (6^-)(2) = n$.

(i) $(8^-)(10^-) - [(8)(4^- + 2)] = n$.

(j) $(18^- + 6)(20^- + 6 + 7^-) = n$.

3.   In Example 3 above, the first step in the argument was to replace 21 by (3)(7). How did we know that the product of the *integers* 3 and 7 was equal to the *integer* 21?

4.   If n is a positive integer and m is a negative integer, complete the statement:

$$nm = (n \cdot \ ?)^-$$

5.   Another way to motivate Case 3 of the definition of multiplication of integers is to recognize that because we want multiplication and addition of integers to share the distributive property it is possible to think of this product as repeated addition. For example,

$$
\begin{aligned}
(7^-)(3) &= (7^-)(1 + 2) \\
&= (7^-)(1) + (7^-)(2) \\
&= 7^- + (7^-)(2) \\
&= 7^- + [(7^-)(1 + 1)] \\
&= 7^- + [(7^-)(1) + (7^-)(1)] \\
&= 7^- + [7^- + 7^-] \\
&= 7^- + 7^- + 7^- \\
&= 21^-
\end{aligned}
$$

Using the list of properties that we want multiplication to possess together with what we already know about the system of integers, explain why we think each of the steps in this argument is reasonable. Then use this same kind of argument to find the product of 4 and 5^-.

It only remains to decide upon the meaning of the product in Case 4, the case when both factors are negative integers. So suppose that n^- and m^- are negative integers. We seek to assign meaning to the symbol n^-m^-. Using known facts about the system of integers and the properties that we want multiplication of integers to possess, we can do this by studying the sum

$$n^-m^- + (nm)^-$$

We can argue that it is entirely reasonable to expect that this sum should be 0. This would mean that n^-m^- is the additive inverse of $(nm)^-$. But the additive inverse of $(nm)^-$ is nm. Hence we could conclude that $n^-m^- = nm$. Here is the argument: Consider the integers n^- and m. According to Case 3 of the definition of multiplication the product of these integers is $(nm)^-$. Consequently since addition of integers is well-defined we can write

$$n^-m^- + (nm)^- = n^-m^- + n^-m$$

Then, if multiplication and addition of integers are to share the distributive property, we should be able to write

$$n^-m^- + (nm)^- = n^-(m^- + m)$$

which means that

$$n^-m^- + (nm)^- = n^-(0)$$

or that

$$n^-m^- + (nm)^- = 0$$

This equation tells us that n^-m^- is the additive inverse of $(nm)^-$; that is, it tells us

$$n^-m^- = [(nm)^-]^- = nm$$

Because this argument is reasonable we are led to make it a part of the definition that the product of two negative integers should be equal to the product of their absolute values:

$$(n^-)(m^-) = nm$$

Hence we finish off the definition of multiplication of integers with

Case 4   If both n^- and m^- are negative integers, then $n^-m^- = nm$.

EXAMPLE 1.   The product of 6^- and 4^- is the product of the absolute values $|6^-|$ and $|4^-|$:

$$6^-(4^-) = |6^-| \cdot |4^-| = 6 \cdot 4 = 24$$

EXAMPLE 2.   The product of 18^- and 1^- is $18 \cdot 1$ or 18.

EXAMPLE 3. $(4^-)[(2^-)(3)] = (4^-)(2 \cdot 3)^- = (4^-)(6)^- = 4^-(6^-) = |4^-| \cdot |6^-| = 4 \cdot 6 = 24$.

EXAMPLE 4.   Repeating the general argument used above we can show that the product $(2^-)(3^-)$ ought to be equal to 6 as follows:

$$\begin{aligned}
(2^-)(3^-) + 6^- &= (2^-)(3^-) + (2^-)(3) \\
&= (2^-)(3^- + 3) \\
&= (2^-)(0) \\
&= 0
\end{aligned}$$

That is, $(2^-)(3^-)$ is the additive inverse of 6^-,

$$(2^-)(3^-) = (6^-)^-$$

and this means that $(2^-)(3^-) = 6$.

Exercises

1.   In the manner of Example 4 immediately above show why it is reasonable to make the definition of multiplication of integers such that
    (a) $(5^-)(7^-)$ is equal to 35.
    (b) $(1^-)(1^-)$ is equal to 1.
    (c) $(6^-)(2^-)$ is equal to 12.

2. Find the solutions of the following equations.
   (a) $[(6^-)(3^-)](2) = n.$
   (b) $6^-(2^- + 4) + 6(7^-) = n.$
   (c) $3^- - 4(2^- + 3) = n.$
   (d) $(6^- - 3) - 3^-(2^- - 3) = n.$
   (e) $(14^- + 6^-) - 3^-(1^- + 6) = n.$
   (f) $(3^-)^2(4^-)^3 = n.$
   (g) $(16^-)^0(2^-) = n.$
3. If n and m represent negative integers, complete the statement:

$$nm = |n| \cdot \ ?$$

4. In Exercise 5, p. 207, we saw that we could interpret the product of a positive factor and a negative factor as being repeated addition. Is this interpretation possible if both factors are negative integers?

Examining Cases 1 and 4 of the definition of multiplication we see that if the factors n and m have the same algebraic sign, then their product is equal to the product of their absolute values:

$$nm = |n| \cdot |m|$$

On the other hand, from Case 3 we see that if n and m have different algebraic signs, then their product is the additive inverse of the product of their absolute values:

$$nm = (|n| \cdot |m|)^-$$

Consequently we can most conveniently formulate the definition as follows:

Definition of the Operation of Multiplication of Integers
1. *If n and m are integers which have the same algebraic sign, then $nm =$ $|n| \cdot |m|$.*
2. *If n and m are integers with different algebraic sign, then $nm = (|n| \cdot |m|)^-$*
3. *If one of the integers n and m is zero, then $nm = 0$.*

Thus multiplication of nonzero integers is a sort of two-step process. First, the absolute value of the product is found by multiplying the absolute values of the factors: $|nm| = |n| \cdot |m|$. Second, the algebraic sign of the product is determined. If both factors have the same algebraic sign, then the product is positive; otherwise the product is negative. Seen in this light the problem of multiplying nonzero integers is reduced essentially to the problem of multiplying counting numbers, i.e., of multiplying the counting numbers which are the absolute values of the factors.

TESTING THE DEFINITION: THE PROPERTIES
OF MULTIPLICATION OF INTEGERS

Now we must verify that the operation we have defined is in fact the operation we sought when we began the search for a "multiplication of integers" operation. It is evident from the definition that this new operation *agrees on the counting numbers* with multiplication of counting numbers. (Which part of the definition states this?) Also, the definition explicitly tells us that $n0 = 0n = 0$ for every integer n. One can show that this new multiplication operation possesses the *closure* property and hence the *well-definedness* property. That is, multiplication of integers is a *binary operation*. Also, multiplication of integers is *commutative* and *associative*, possesses an *identity* (1), and possesses the *cancellation* property.* Finally, multiplication of integers shares a *distributive* property with addition. Thus the operation we have defined possesses all of the properties we stipulated it should possess.

Exercises

1. Explain why multiplication of integers has the closure property. (*Suggestion:* Consider each of the different cases in the definition and show that in each case the result of the operation is a unique integer.)
2. Explain why multiplication of integers is commutative. (*Suggestion:* Consider the three cases of the definition separately.) Do you need to use any of the properties of multiplication of counting numbers? If so, which ones?
3. Show that any three negative integers associate with respect to multiplication of integers. (*Suggestion:* Let the negative integers be n^-, m^-, and p^-. Then compute $n^-(m^-p^-)$ and $(n^-m^-)p^-$ and explain why these are equal.)
4. It is immediate that any three positive integers associate with respect to multiplication of integers. Why is it immediate?
5. Show that the integer 1 is an identity for multiplication.
6. Multiplication and addition share the distributive property. So do multiplication and subtraction. These statements may be combined and written together:

$$n(m \pm p) = nm \pm np$$

   Verify that both distributive properties are true when
   (a) $n = 6^-$, $m = 5$ and $p = 2^-$.
   (b) $n = 6$, $m = 5^-$, and $p = 3^-$.
   (c) $n = 4^-$, $m = 5^-$, and $p = 3^-$.
7. **Theorem** *If n and m are integers, then $nm = 0$ if and only if at least one of n and m is zero.*

   (a) This theorem consists of two other theorems one of which is true by virtue of the definition of multiplication of integers. Explain.
   (b) Explain why the other theorem is true also.
8. Explain why 0 cannot be cancelled with respect to multiplication.
9. If n and m are positive integers, then

$$(n^-)^m = \begin{cases} n^m, & \text{if } m \text{ is even} \\ (n^m)^-, & \text{if } n \text{ is odd} \end{cases}$$

   Explain.

---

* Keep in mind that when we say that multiplication has the cancellation property, we mean that $np = mp$ implies $n = m$ *if p is not zero.*

10. Make up some equations which illustrate how the cancellation property of multiplication of integers can be used to solve equations.
11. Prove that if n is an integer, then $(n)(1^-)$ is the additive inverse of n. (*Suggestion:* Add $(n)(1^-)$ to $n = (n)(1)$.)
12. Use the result of Exercise 11 to prove that if n and m are integers, then $nm = n^-m^-$. (*Suggestion:* Write $n^- = (n)(1^-)$ and similarly for m^-.)
13. Use the result of Exercise 11 to prove that if n and m are integers, then $n(m^-) = (nm)^-$.
14. Prove that if n is an integer, then $(n^-)^- = n$.

Review Questions

1. Before constructing the definition of multiplication of integers we stipulated some properties that we wanted the operation to possess. What were these properties?
2. What is the argument we used to motivate our definition of multiplication in the case that one factor is negative and the other is positive?
3. What is the argument we used to motivate our definition of multiplication in the case that both factors are negative?
4. State a definition for multiplication of integers.
5. What properties are possessed by the operation of multiplication of integers?

DIVISION OF INTEGERS

How should we define an operation which will extend in a natural way the operation of division of counting numbers? From our experience with division of counting numbers and division of fractions it is natural to try to define the operation as follows:

Definition of the Operation of Division of Integers *If n and m are integers, and if m is not zero, then the result of dividing n by m, denoted by the symbol $n \div m$, is that integer q such that*

$$n = mq$$

provided such an integer q exists. If no such integer q exists, then n cannot be divided by m.

EXAMPLE 1. Since $6^- = (3)(2^-)$, the definition of division tells us that $6^- \div 3 = 2^-$.

EXAMPLE 2. 75^- divided by 5, $75^- \div 5$, is equal to 15^- since 15^- is the solution of the equation $75^- = (5)(?)$.

EXAMPLE 3. $6^- \div 5$ is meaningless since there is no integer q such that $6^- = (5)(q)$.

Suppose that n and m are integers such that $n \div m$ is meaningful; that is, suppose that there exists an integer q such that

$$n = mq$$

This equation tells us that

$$|n| = |mq|$$

But since $|mq| = |m| \cdot |q|$, this means that

$$|n| = |m| \cdot |q|$$

Now because $|n|$, $|m|$, and $|q|$ are all counting numbers, it follows from the definition of division of counting numbers that

$$|q| = |n| \div |m|$$

Hence we see that the absolute value of the quotient q is equal to the quotient of the absolute values of n and m.

EXAMPLES.   The absolute value of $156^- \div 12$ is equal to $|156^-| \div |12|$ or $156 \div 12$ or 13.

The absolute value of the quotient $n \div m$ can be easily computed by using the absolute value of n and the absolute value of m. How is the algebraic sign of the quotient determined from the algebraic signs of n and m? The equation

$$n = mq$$

together with our understanding of multiplication of integers shows us that

1.   if n and m have the same algebraic sign, then q must be a positive integer, while if
2. n and m have different algebraic sign, then q must be negative.

EXAMPLES.

$n =$	$m =$	Algebraic Sign of the Quotient $n \div m$	Absolute Value of the Quotient $n \div m$	Quotient $n \div m$
6^-	3^-	$+$	$6 \div 3$, or 2	2
6^-	3	$-$	$6 \div 3$, or 2	2^-
15	3^-	$-$	$15 \div 3$, or 5	5^-
100	20^-	$-$	$100 \div 20$, or 5	5^-
14^-	7	$-$	$14 \div 7$, or 2	2^-
14^-	7^-	$+$	$14 \div 7$, or 2	2

The process of division of integers has the following properties.

1.   Division of integers *agrees on the counting numbers* with division of counting numbers.
2.   Division of integers is *well-defined,* has an *identity* (1), and possesses the *cancellation* property. The *well-definedness property* for this process is stated as follows: If n, m, a, and b represent integers such that $n = m$ and $a = b$, then the symbols $n \div a$ and $m \div b$ are either both meaningless or both meaningful, in which case they are equal.

The following exercises are concerned with these properties and some of the consequences of the definition.

Exercises

1. Solve the following equations.
   (a) $(3^-)(4) \div 2 = n$.
   (b) $12^- \div (3^-)(4^-) = n$.
   (c) $(6^- + 2^-) \div 4 = n$.
   (d) $[(6^- + 12^-) \div 4^-] + 10 = n$.
   (e) $3^-(6^- \div 2) = n$.
   (f) $n + 6^- = (3^- \div 1^-)(4 \div 4)$.
   (g) $(2^-)(n) + 3^- = (4^- + 3) \div 1^-$.
   (h) $(6^-)(2)(n) + 4^- = (6^- + 20) + 2$.
   (i) $(n + 2^-) \div 3^- = 9^-$.
   (j) $32 \div (n + 6^-) = 2^-$. (*Suggestion*: Multiply by $n \div 6^-$.)
   (k) $(32 + n) \div 6^- = 21$.
   (l) $[5^- + 3^-(4 + 5^-)] \div 2n = 1^-$.
2. Prove that 1 is an identity for division of integers.
3. Find counterexamples which involve both positive and negative integers and which show that division of integers is not commutative and is not associative.
4. Explain why $|n \div m| = |n| \div |m|$, provided $n \div m$ is meaningful.
5. Let n and m represent integers such that $|n|$ is divisible by $|m|$.
   (a) Explain why $n^- \div m^- = n \div m$.
   (b) Explain why $n^- \div m = (n \div m)^-$.
6. State the well-definedness and cancellation properties of division of integers.
7. Explain why division by zero is impossible in the system of integers.

Review Questions

1. How is division of integers defined?
2. How is the algebraic sign of the quotient determined?
3. How is the absolute value of the quotient determined?
4. What properties are possessed by division of integers?

NOTATION

In order to distinguish more forcefully between the related concepts of subtraction and additive inverse, we have been placing the symbol "−" in the superscript position to denote additive inverses. From now on we shall use the more usual notation for additive inverse by placing a dash in the prefix position. In the same way we shall denote negative integers by the symbols $-1, -2, -3, -4, -5, \ldots$, instead of by the symbols $1^-, 2^-, 3^-, 4^-, \ldots$. Consequently the symbol "−" is used in three different ways:

1. It may denote the binary operation of subtraction of integers.

2. It may denote additive inverses.
3. It may be used as a part of the symbol for a negative integer.

EXAMPLE. In the symbol $5 - 6$ the dash could only mean subtraction. In the symbol $5 + {}^-6$ the dash could only mean additive inverse or negative integer. That is, $5 + {}^-6$ could mean either $5 + (6)^-$ or $5 + 6^-$. The symbol $-5 - {}^-6$ means $5^- - 6^-$.

Exercises

1. Rewrite each of the following expressions using the prefix bar notation.
    (a) $5^- - 6$.   (c) $(3^- - 4^-)^-$.
    (b) $5^- {}^- - 6^-$.   (d) $(2 - 3^-)^- - (4^- + 5)^-$.
2. Rewrite each of the following symbols using the superscript bar notation.
    (a) $-3 - 2$.   (f) $-3 - {}^- - 4$.
    (b) $3 - 2$.   (g) $- {}^-3 - 4$.
    (c) $3 + {}^-2$.   (h) $-(3 - 11) - 5$.
    (d) $-3 + {}^- - 2$.   (i) $-(-3 - 4) - {}^-5$.
    (e) $-3 + {}^-2$.   (j) $-(-3 + {}^-4) - (-4 - {}^-6)$.
3. Is $-p^2$ equal to $(-p)(-p)$ or to $-(p)(p)$ or does it make no difference?
4. Is $3 - 5^2$ equal to $3 - 25$ or to $(3 - 5)(3 - 5)$?

CHAPTER 7

The Rational Number System

In Chapter 5 we learned how to extend the system of counting numbers to improve upon the division process. Division of counting numbers could only rarely be performed but in the extended number system (the system of fractions) division could be performed as long as the divisor was not zero. However, in extending the system of counting numbers to the system of fractions we did not improve upon the subtraction process—witness the fact that subtraction of counting numbers and subtraction of fractions possess exactly the same properties. Then in Chapter 6 we extended the system of counting numbers again. The purpose of this second extension was to improve upon the subtraction process, for subtraction of counting numbers did not possess the closure property but the subtraction process in the extended system (the system of integers) did. The extension from the counting numbers to the integers did not, however, improve upon the division process—witness the fact that division of counting numbers and division of integers possess exactly the same properties. These two extensions of the system of counting numbers therefore went in different directions, the first in the direction of improving division but not subtraction and the second in the direction of improving subtraction but not division. In this chapter we shall discuss a third extension of the system of counting numbers which goes in both of these directions at once. This extension will improve both division and subtraction in the sense that in the new system subtraction will be a binary operation and division by nonzero numbers will always be possible. The new system of numbers will be called the *rational number system*.

The idea behind this new extension of the system of counting numbers is not complicated; indeed we already have in hand all the techniques needed to accomplish the extension. We shall begin with the system of integers and extend this system in exactly the same way that we previously extended the system of counting numbers to obtain the system of fractions. Because this extension will be handled just as the extension to the fractions was handled, in the resulting extended system division by nonzero numbers will always be possible. Moreover, since we begin with a number system in which subtraction is a binary operation, subtraction in the extended system will also be a binary operation.

THE NUMBERS CALLED RATIONAL NUMBERS

Recall how we defined the fractions in terms of the counting numbers. We began with the counting numbers and then considered all equations of the form

$$a = bx$$

where a and b were counting numbers and b was not zero. The fractions were then defined to be the solutions of these equations. In this way the fractions developed from the counting numbers. Now we shall do exactly the same thing using the integers in place of the counting numbers. We shall consider equations of the same form and the solutions of these equations will be called *rational numbers*.

Definition of Rational Number   *A rational number is a number which is the (unique) solution of an equation of the form*

$$a = bx$$

where a and b represent integers and b is different from zero. The solution of the equation a = bx is symbolized by a/b.

The most notable aspect of this definition is its similarity to the definition of fraction. Indeed, as the definition shows, the rational numbers evolve from the integers in the same way that the fractions evolve from the counting numbers.

EXAMPLES.   The solution of the equation $-2 = -3x$ is the rational number represented by the symbol $-2/-3$. The rational number denoted by $7/-4$ is that number which is the solution of the equation $7 = -4x$.

Every fraction and every integer is a rational number.   Consider a fraction n/m. According to the definition of fraction this number is the solution of the equation $n = mx$. But since n and m are counting numbers they are also integers. This means that n/m is a rational number. Consider the integer n. We have seen that n is the solution of the equation $n = 1x$. But the solution of this equation is by definition a rational number. Hence n is a rational number.

The set-theoretic relationships between the various systems of numbers are illustrated by Euler circles in Fig. 46.

Exercises

1. Let
    C denote the set of all counting numbers,
    F denote the set of all fractions,

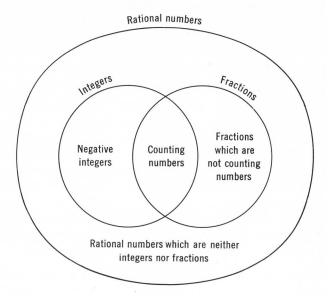

Rational numbers

Integers   Fractions

| Negative integers | Counting numbers | Fractions which are not counting numbers |

Rational numbers which are neither integers nor fractions

Figure 46

I denote the set of all integers, and

R denote the set of all rational numbers.

(a)   Prove that $C \subset R$, $F \subset R$, and $I \subset R$.

(b)   Prove that $(C \cup I \cup F) \subset R$.

2.   The counting numbers are to the fractions as the _____ are to the rational numbers. The fractions are to the rational numbers as the _____ are to the _____.

3.   Prove that the set of all rational numbers is equivalent to the set of all counting numbers.

RELATIONS ON THE SET OF RATIONAL NUMBERS

The principal relations on the set of rational numbers are *equality, less than, greater than, less than or equal to,* and *greater than or equal to.* These relations have very nearly the same meaning for the rational numbers as they did for the fractions.

Equality

Since the rational numbers were developed from the integers in the same way that the fractions were developed from the counting numbers, it is not unreasonable to try to define equality of rational numbers in the same way that we defined equality of fractions.

Definition of the Relation of Equality of Rational Numbers *If a/b and c/d are rational numbers, then we say that a/b is equal to c/d, and write a/b = c/d, if da = bc.*

EXAMPLE 1. $-2/3 = -4/6$ since $(6)(-2) = (3)(-4)$.

EXAMPLE 2. $0/17 = 0/-78$ since $(-78)(0) = (17)(0)$.

The relation of equality of rational numbers is an *equivalence relation*. We shall omit the verification of this because it is almost exactly the same as the verification of the fact that equality of fractions is an equivalence relation (see Exercise 1, p. 145). The only difference is that the proof now will involve integers and rational numbers instead of counting numbers and fractions.

We observed in Chapter 5 that the aspect of the system of fractions which makes things complicated is that each fraction has many different names of the form *a/b*. Examples 1 and 2 above show that the same is true of the rational numbers. There is a Renaming Theorem for rational numbers which tells us how to obtain "new" rational number names from "old" names.

Renaming Theorem *If a/b is a rational number, and if n is a nonzero integer, then a/b = an/bn.*

EXAMPLES.

$$\frac{2}{3} = \frac{2(-1)}{3(-1)} = \frac{-2}{-3}$$

$$\frac{-4}{5} = \frac{-4(-1)}{5(-1)} = \frac{4}{-5}$$

$$\frac{10}{-15} = \frac{2(5)}{-3(5)} = \frac{2}{-3} = \frac{2(-1)}{-3(-1)} = \frac{-2}{3}$$

$$\frac{-6}{5} = \frac{-12}{10} = \frac{-18}{15} = \frac{-24}{20} = \frac{-30}{25} = \cdots$$

$$\frac{-6}{5} = \frac{6}{-5} = \frac{12}{-10} = \frac{18}{-15} = \frac{24}{-20} = \frac{30}{-25} = \cdots$$

As the first two examples above show it is possible to change the name of a rational number in such a way that the algebraic signs of the numerator and denominator are changed. This is accomplished simply by multiplying numerator and denominator by -1. The principal use of this is to rewrite rational numbers so that their denominators are positive. We shall adopt the convention that unless there is a good reason for doing otherwise, all rational numbers are to be written so that their denominators are positive. This convention is helpful in that it makes computations involving rational numbers more closely resemble computations involving fractions.

In the third of the preceding examples we see how a rational number may be *written in lowest terms* by using the Renaming Theorem. The technique is the same as with fractions. When we say that a rational number is written in lowest terms, we mean that the absolute values of the numerator and denominator are relatively prime.

EXAMPLE.

$$\frac{70}{-105} = \frac{(70)(-1)}{(-105)(-1)} = \frac{-70}{105}$$

$$= \frac{(-2)(35)}{(3)(35)} = \frac{-2}{3}$$

In this example we used the Renaming Theorem to write the rational number with positive denominator, and we used it to divide numerator and denominator by 35.

The Renaming Theorem can also be used to write given rational numbers so that they have the same denominator. Thus the concept of *least common denominator* (LCD) is meaningful for rational numbers just as it was for fractions. Generally speaking, to write two rational numbers with the same least common denominator we first rename the rational numbers so that their denominators are positive and then proceed exactly as with fractions. The principal reason for always writing rational numbers with positive denominators is so that their denominators can be handled just as we handled the denominators of fractions.

EXAMPLE.   Write the rational numbers $-3/4$ and $2/-5$ so that they have the same least positive denominator.

Solution: We begin by renaming the rational numbers so that their denominators are positive: $-3/4$ already has a positive denominator and $2/-5 = (2)(-1)/(-5)(-1) = -2/5$. Then we proceed exactly as with fractions. The least common multiple of 4 and 5 is 20, so

$$\frac{-3}{4} = \frac{(-3)(5)}{(4)(5)} = \frac{-15}{20}$$

and

$$\frac{-2}{5} = \frac{(-2)(4)}{(5)(4)} = \frac{-8}{20}$$

Exercises

1. Rename each rational number so that its denominator is positive and the number is written in lowest terms. Justify each step.
    (a) $-27/-3$.   (c) $35/-105$.
    (b) $27/-3$.   (d) $18/(-9)(-5)$.
2. Rename each of the following pairs of integers so that they have the same *least* positive integer denominator. Justify each step.
    (a) $2/3$ and $1/-4$.
    (b) $8/-9$, $2/-27$, and $-1/18$.
    (c) $2/-105$, $-6/35$, $3/14$, and $-7/-28$.

3. Rename each of these rational numbers so that each has the given integer for denominator.
    (a) $2/5$; -25.
    (c) $7/-3$; 9.
    (e) n/m; $-m$.
    (b) $7/-3$; -9.
    (d) $-8/2$; -1.
    (f) $-n/(-m)$; m^2.
4. Complete the theorem:

    Theorem $a/b = n/b$ if and only if _____.

    (a) Prove your theorem.
    (b) Use your theorem to solve these equations:
          (i) $n/-3 = 1/4$.   (ii) $(n - 2)/6 = 4/-5$.
5. Prove the Renaming Theorem for rational numbers.
6. Prove that equality of rational numbers is an equivalence relation. (*Suggestion:* Cf. Exercise 1, p. 145.)
7. Equality of rational numbers agrees on the fractions with equality of fractions and agrees on the integers with equality of integers. Explain.

The Inequality Relations

The reader should review the definition of *less than* for fractions. Keeping in mind that the rational numbers are built upon the integers in the same way that the fractions were built upon the counting numbers, the following definition seems as if it *might be a reasonable way* to define the relation of *less than* for rational numbers.

Trial Definition   If a/b and c/b are rational numbers, then we shall say that a/b is less than c/b if $a < c$.

This definition appears reasonable; but before we accept it as final we ought to check it against some of the properties that we feel the relation ought to possess. According to this definition it is true that $-5/ - 1 < -4/ - 1$ since $-5 < -4$. But $-5/ - 1 = 5/1 = 5$ and $-4/ - 1 = 4/1 = 4$. Thus according to this definition of *less than* the rational number 5 is less than the rational number 4. This means that we have defined a relation to be called *less than* which does not *agree on the counting numbers* with *less than* for counting numbers. This is certainly not desirable. We must find a way to change our definition so that this will not happen. A little study will reveal that the trouble arose because we permitted the denominators of the rational numbers being compared to be negative integers. If we require that the denominators be positive, then everything is all right.

Definition of the Relation of Less Than for Rational Numbers   *If a/b and c/b are rational numbers written with the same positive denominators, then we say that a/b is less than equal to c/b, and write $a/b < c/b$, if $a < c$.*

We leave it to the reader to define the other three inequality relations and to discuss the properties of all four inequality relations.

Exercises

1. Determine the properties of *less than* for rational numbers. Verify your answers either by proofs or by giving counterexamples.
2. State the definitions and discuss the properties of the other three inequality relations.
3. Arrange the following rational numbers in order of increasing size from left to right.
   (a) $-2/3$, -1, 1, 0, $2/5$, $2/-1$, $1/2$.
   (b) $-2/3$, $2/3$, $1/-3$, $4/-3$, $4/3$, $-3/3$, $-3/-3$.
4. In the definition of *less than* for rational numbers it was necessary to stipulate that the denominator b should be positive. Give two examples which show that if this restriction were omitted from the definition, then the resulting definition would yield undesirable results. Explain fully.
5. Based upon our knowledge of the system of fractions the following conjecture might appear plausible: *If a/b and c/d are rational numbers, then $a/b < c/d$ if and only if $da < bc$.* (Cf. Exercise 5, p. 152.) However this conjecture is false. Find four counterexamples to this conjecture.
6. State the Law of Trichotomy for rational numbers.

Review Questions

1. Why did we define equality of rational numbers as we did?
2. It is always possible to rewrite a rational number whose denominator is negative so that it will have a positive denominator. Explain why we can always do this.
3. What does it mean to say that a rational number is written in lowest terms?
4. What does it mean to say that equality of rational numbers agrees on the fractions with equality of fractions?

PROCESSES ON THE SET OF RATIONAL NUMBERS

The discussion of addition, subtraction, multiplication, and division of rational numbers parallels the discussion of these processes for fractions.

Addition

Definition of the Operation of Addition of Rational Numbers *If a/b and c/b are rational numbers, then $a/b + c/b = (a + c)/b$.*

Clearly addition is a two-step process:

1. Rename the rational numbers so that they have the same denominator. While it is not *necessary* that this common denominator be positive, it is generally more convenient if it is chosen positive.
2. Add the numerators of the rational numbers. Thus the only addition that is performed involves integers—the integers which are the numerators.

This operation *agrees on the fractions* with addition of fractions and it *agrees on the integers* with addition of integers. The operation we have defined possesses the properties of *closure* (and hence *well-definedness*), *commutativity*, *associativity*, *identity* (0), and *cancellation*.

EXAMPLE. $\dfrac{4}{5} + \dfrac{3}{-4} + \dfrac{7}{-10} = ?$

Solution: Since our preference is to work with rational numbers which have positive denominators, we begin by renaming the summands so that their denominators are positive. The problem then becomes

$$\frac{4}{5} + \frac{-3}{4} + \frac{-7}{10} = ?$$

We may now proceed exactly as with fractions:

$$\frac{4}{5} + \frac{-3}{4} + \frac{-7}{10} = \frac{16}{20} + \frac{-15}{20} + \frac{-14}{20}$$

$$= \frac{16 + -15 + -14}{20}$$

$$= \frac{-13}{20}$$

The answer $-13/20$ is written in lowest terms since $|-13|$ and $|20|$ are relatively prime.

Exercises

1. Perform the following additions.
    (a) $-2/3 + 1/-9 + 3/-18$.
    (b) $4/-9 + -2/24 + -5/-18$.
    (c) $n/-m + 2/p + -1/mp + 1/-p^2$, where n, m, and p represent integers.
2. Recall that there is a way to add fractions without first renaming the summands so that they have the same denominator. (Refer to Exercise 6, p. 157.) We can also add rational numbers without having to perform this preliminary step. We use the theorem:
    Theorem *If a/b and c/d are rational numbers, then $a/b + c/d = (da + bc)/bd$.*
    Use this theorem to perform these additions without first renaming the summands:
    (a) $-2/3 + 1/-9$.
    (b) $-5/-9 + 3/-4$.
    (c) $n/-m + 2/m$, where n and m represent integers.
3. Solve these equations using only addition and its properties. Explain each step.
    (a) $n + -1/3 = 5/-4$.   (b) $n + 1/3 = 8/3 + -7/2$.

THE ADDITIVE INVERSE OF A RATIONAL NUMBER

Since the system of fractions did not involve the idea of "negativeness" there was no concept of additive inverse in that system. But in the system of rational numbers we are able to define additive inverses. If a/b is a rational number, then by the *additive inverse* of a/b we mean the solution of the equation

$$\frac{a}{b} + x = 0$$

It is not difficult to see that every rational number has an additive inverse. For if a/b is any rational number, $-a/b$ is also a rational number and

$$\frac{a}{b} + \frac{-a}{b} = \frac{a + -a}{b} = \frac{0}{b} = 0$$

so that $-a/b$ is the additive inverse of a/b.

Just as the prefix symbol "$-$" was used to denote additive inverse in the system of integers, the same symbol is used to denote additive inverse in the system of rational numbers. Thus the additive inverse of a/b is denoted by $-(a/b)$. This means that there are in fact three different ways to denote the additive inverse of a rational number. Since $-(a/b) = -a/b$ and since $-a/b = (-a)(-1)/(b)(-1) = a/-b$, each of the three symbols

$$-\left(\frac{a}{b}\right), \quad \frac{-a}{b}, \quad \text{and} \quad \frac{a}{-b}$$

represents the additive inverse of a/b.

EXAMPLES. We have written the additive inverses of the given rational numbers in the three different ways just mentioned.

The Rational Number $\dfrac{a}{b}$	Its Additive Inverse Written in the Form		
	$-\left(\dfrac{a}{b}\right)$	$\dfrac{-a}{b}$	$\dfrac{a}{-b}$
$\dfrac{-6}{5}$	$-\left(\dfrac{-6}{5}\right)$	$\dfrac{6}{5}$	$\dfrac{-6}{-5}$
$\dfrac{7}{-5}$	$-\left(\dfrac{7}{-5}\right)$	$\dfrac{-7}{-5}$	$\dfrac{7}{5}$
$\dfrac{-5}{-3}$	$-\left(\dfrac{-5}{-3}\right)$	$\dfrac{5}{-3}$	$\dfrac{-5}{3}$
$\dfrac{2}{3}$	$-\left(\dfrac{2}{3}\right)$	$\dfrac{-2}{3}$	$\dfrac{2}{-3}$

Finally, let us record now for use in our discussion of subtraction a theorem of frequent application in computations. This theorem is the analog for rational numbers of the Additive Inverse Theorem for integers.

Additive Inverse Theorem *If x and y are rational numbers, then $-(x + y) = -x + -y$.*

EXAMPLE 1. The additive inverse of the sum $-3 + 5$ is denoted by $-(-3 + 5)$ and according to this theorem is equal to $-(-3) + -(5)$ or -2.

EXAMPLE 2. The additive inverse of $2/3 + 4/5$ can be found by first adding $2/3$ and $4/5$, obtaining $22/15$, and then taking the additive inverse of this sum, obtaining the answer $-(22/15)$ or $-22/15$. On the other hand according to the Additive Inverse Theorem we can also find this additive inverse by adding the additive inverses of $2/3$ and $4/5$:

$$-\left(\frac{2}{3} + \frac{4}{5}\right) = -\left(\frac{2}{3}\right) + -\left(\frac{4}{5}\right) \qquad \text{(Additive Inverse Theorem)}$$

$$= \frac{-2}{3} + \frac{-4}{5} \qquad \text{(Rewriting)}$$

$$= \frac{-10}{15} + \frac{-12}{15} \qquad \text{(LCD)}$$

$$= \frac{-22}{15} \qquad \text{(Performing addition)}$$

Exercises

1. As in the examples on p. 223 write the additive inverses of the following rational numbers in three ways.
   (a) $-2/3$.   (d) $-2/-3$.
   (b) $2/-3$.   (e) $0/6$.
   (c) $2/3$.   (f) -6.
2. Using the Additive Inverse Theorem write the additive inverse of each of the following rational numbers.
   (a) $2/3 + -7/2$.   (c) $-2/-3 + 7/-2$.
   (b) $-2/3 + 7/2$.   (d) $2/-3 + -7/2$.
3. The concept of additive inverse can be regarded as a relation on the set of all rational numbers. Representing this relation by the symbol $\Re$, we define the relation $\Re$ as follows: If n and m are rational numbers, then $n \Re m$ means that m is the additive inverse of n. Which of the properties of a relation are possessed by this relation? (Cf. Exercise 5, p. 197.)
4. Prove the Additive Inverse Theorem for rational numbers by showing that $(x + y) + (-x + -y) = 0$ for all rational numbers x and y. Why does this prove the theorem?

POSITIVE AND NEGATIVE RATIONAL NUMBERS

Suppose that a/b is a nonzero rational number. Then the nonzero integers a and b have the same algebraic sign or they have different algebraic sign. Let us consider these two possibilities separately.

THE INTEGERS a AND b HAVE THE SAME ALGEBRAIC SIGN.   In this case if necessary we can use the Renaming Theorem to rename the rational number so that
its numerator and denominator are both positive. For example, $-2/-3$ can be
written as $2/3$. Since every rational number which can be represented by a
numeral whose numerator and denominator are both positive integers is a
fraction, we conclude that if the numerator and denominator of a/b have the
same algebraic sign, then the rational number a/b is a fraction. Such rational
numbers are called *positive rational numbers.*

THE INTEGERS a AND b HAVE DIFFERENT ALGEBRAIC SIGN.   In this case we
can write the rational number a/b in the form $-(a/b)$ where a/b is a fraction.
For example,

$$\frac{-2}{3} = -\left(\frac{2}{3}\right) \quad \text{and} \quad \frac{4}{-5} = -\left(\frac{4}{5}\right)$$

Hence each rational number whose numerator and denominator have different
algebraic sign is the additive inverse of a fraction. Such rational numbers are
called *negative rational numbers.*

From these observations we conclude that every nonzero rational number is
either a fraction or the additive inverse of a fraction. But since zero is a fraction,
the final conclusion is that *every rational number is either a fraction or the additive inverse of a fraction.* Thus the rational numbers are related to the fractions
in the same way that the integers are related to the counting numbers. That is,

$$\text{every}\left\{\begin{array}{l}\text{integer}\\\text{rational number}\end{array}\right\}\text{ is either a }\left\{\begin{array}{l}\text{counting number}\\\text{fraction}\end{array}\right\}\text{ or the additive inverse of a}$$

$$\left\{\begin{array}{l}\text{counting number}\\\text{fraction}\end{array}\right\}.\text{ This means that we could have developed the rational}$$

numbers from the fractions by using the same techniques as were used to develop
the integers from the counting numbers. We would begin by defining the negative
rational numbers to be solutions of the equations of the form

$$x + \frac{a}{b} = 0$$

where a/b is a nonzero fraction. Then we would define a rational number to be
a number which is either a negative rational number or a fraction.

Thus there are two ways to obtain the rational numbers, from the integers
by using the same procedures as we used to develop the fractions from the
counting numbers, or from the fractions by using the same procedures we used

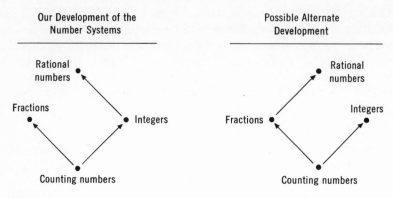

Figure 47

to develop the integers from the counting numbers (see Fig. 47). Both ways give rise to exactly the same number system.

Review Questions

1. How is addition of rational numbers defined?
2. What are the properties of addition of rational numbers?
3. What do we mean by the additive inverse of a rational number? Which rational numbers have additive inverses? Which rational numbers are equal to their additive inverse? What is the symbol used to denote the additive inverse of a rational number x?
4. State the Additive Inverse Theorem.
5. What is a positive rational number? What is a negative rational number?
6. Every rational number is either a _____ or the _____ of a _____.
7. There are two different ways to develop the system of rational numbers. Explain.

Exercises

1. Show that every positive rational number is greater than zero and that every negative rational number is less than zero.
2. (a) Prove that if n and m are rational numbers such that $n < m$, then there is a positive rational number p such that $n + p = m$.
   (b) Prove that if n and m are rational numbers and if there is a positive rational number p such that $n + p = m$, then $n < m$.
   (c) Combine the statements of parts (a) and (b) into one statement of the "if and only if" form.

Subtraction

Definition of the Operation of Subtraction of Rational Numbers *If a/b and c/d are rational numbers, then $a/b - c/d$ is that rational number x such that $a/b = c/d + x$.*

EXAMPLE. $3/4 - 7/3 = ?$

Solution: According to the definition we must find the rational number x such that

$$\frac{3}{4} = \frac{7}{3} + x$$

If we rename the rational numbers so that they have the same positive denominator,

$$\frac{9}{12} = \frac{28}{12} + x$$

then it is not difficult to see that x must equal $-19/12$ since

$$\frac{28}{12} + \frac{-19}{12} = \frac{28 + -19}{12} = \frac{9}{12}$$

Therefore $3/4 - 7/3 = -19/12$.

An appreciation of this definition is necessary in order to know *what* subtraction is, but the definition itself does not provide a particularly good way to actually perform subtraction. Because the system of rational numbers is in a sense a combination of the systems of fractions and integers, there are two ways to conveniently perform subtraction. The first of these ways stems from the system of fractions and is the analog of the Subtraction Theorem for fractions.

Subtraction Theorem *If a/b and c/b are rational numbers, then $a/b - c/b = (a - c)/b$.*

The second way to perform subtraction stems from the system of integers and is the analog of the Subtract by Adding Theorem for integers.

Subtract by Adding Theorem *If x and y are rational numbers, then $x - y = x + -y$.*

Here are some examples of how these theorems can be used to perform subtraction.

EXAMPLE 1. $2/3 - -7/3 = ?$

Solution 1: Using the Subtraction Theorem we write

$$\frac{2}{3} - \frac{-7}{3} = \frac{2 - -7}{3} \qquad \text{(Subtraction Theorem)}$$

$$= \frac{2 + --7}{3} \qquad \text{(Subtract by Adding Theorem for integers)}$$

$$= \frac{2 + 7}{3} \qquad (--7 = 7)$$

$$= \frac{9}{3} \qquad \text{(Addition of integers)}$$

$$= 3 \qquad \text{(Lowest terms)}$$

Solution 2: Using the Subtract by Adding Theorem we write

$$\frac{2}{3} - \frac{-7}{3} = \frac{2}{3} + -\left(\frac{-7}{3}\right) \qquad \text{(Subtract by Adding Theorem)}$$

$$= \frac{2}{3} + \frac{7}{3} \qquad \text{(?)}$$

$$= \text{etc.}$$

EXAMPLE 2. $1/2 - (3/4 + 7/3) = ?$

Solution 1: Using the Subtraction Theorem we write

$$\frac{1}{2} - \left(\frac{3}{4} + \frac{7}{3}\right) = \frac{6}{12} - \left(\frac{9}{12} + \frac{28}{12}\right) \qquad \text{(LCD)}$$

$$= \frac{6}{12} - \frac{37}{12} \qquad \text{(Performing addition)}$$

$$= \frac{6 - 37}{12} \qquad \text{(Subtraction Theorem)}$$

$$= \frac{-31}{12} \qquad \text{(Subtraction of integers)}$$

Solution 2: Solving this problem using the Subtract By Adding Theorem requires the use of the Additive Inverse Theorem:

$$\frac{1}{2} - \left(\frac{3}{4} + \frac{7}{3}\right) = \frac{1}{2} + -\left(\frac{3}{4} + \frac{7}{3}\right) \qquad \text{(Subtract by Adding Theorem)}$$

$$= \frac{1}{2} + \left[-\left(\frac{3}{4}\right) + -\left(\frac{7}{3}\right)\right] \qquad \text{(Additive Inverse Theorem)}$$

$$= \frac{1}{2} + \left[\frac{-3}{4} + \frac{-7}{3}\right] \qquad \text{(Rewriting the additive inverses)}$$

$$= \text{etc.}$$

In Solution 2 before anything else was done the problem was turned into an addition problem. It remains to write the rational numbers over their LCD and to perform the addition. We leave this part of the solution to the reader.

Subtraction of rational numbers possesses the *closure property* and thus is a binary operation. This can be proved by using either the Subtraction Theorem or the Subtract by Adding Theorem. For example, if rational numbers x and y are given, then the Subtract by Adding Theorem states that $x - y$ has the same meaning as $x + -y$. But since addition of rational numbers has the closure property, $x + -y$ represents a unique rational number. Hence $x - y$ represents a unique rational number.

Subtraction of rational numbers possesses an *identity* (0) and has the *cancellation property*. These and some other properties of the operation are discussed in the exercises which follow.

Review Questions

1. How is subtraction of rational numbers defined?
2. What are the properties of subtraction of rational numbers?
3. State the Subtraction Theorem. This theorem stems from the system of _____.
4. State the Subtract by Adding Theorem. This theorem stems from the system of _____.
5. Explain why subtraction of rational numbers possesses the closure property.

Exercises

1. Perform the following subtractions by using the definition of subtraction.
   (a) $-2/3 - 4/5$.   (b) $-7/5 - 3/-8$.
2. The theorems which display the importance of subtraction are

   Theorem 1 *If a/b and c/d are rational numbers, then $(a/b + c/d) - c/d = a/b$.*

   Theorem 2 *If a/b and c/d are rational numbers, then $(a/b - c/d) + c/d = a/b$.*

   Prove Theorem 1 by using the Subtraction Theorem and prove Theorem 2 by using the Subtract by Adding Theorem.
3. Solve the following equations. Explain each step.
   (a) $n - 2/3 = (4/5 - 2/4)$.
   (b) $n + (6/7 + -2/3) = 2/3 - -5/6$.
   (c) $(1/2)n + 1/3 = -4/5$.
   (d) $1/3 - (1/2)n = 5$.
   (e) $2/3 + n = -4/5 + 2n$.
   (f) $n = (2/3 - 4/5) - 1/2$.
   (g) $n + 2/5 = -3/2 + 2/3$.
   (h) $n - 1/4 = 4/-5 - 2/3$.
   (i) $n = [(-6 - 2/5) - 1/3] - 1/2$.
4. Prove the Subtraction Theorem. (*Suggestion:* Pattern a proof after the proof of the Subtraction Theorem for fractions.)
5. Prove the Subtract by Adding Theorem. (*Suggestion:* Pattern a proof after the proof of the Subtract by Adding Theorem for integers.)
6. The theorem which enables one to perform subtraction of rational numbers without first writing the rational numbers with the same denominator is:

   Theorem *If a/b and c/d are rational numbers, then $a/b - c/d = (da - bc)/bd$.*

   (a) Prove this theorem.
   (b) Use the theorem to perform the following subtractions
       (i) $-2/3 - 4/-5$.   (ii) $a/b - -a/b$.
7. We know that since addition is associative it is possible to remove the parentheses in an expression such as $n + (m + p)$ and write simply $n + m + p$. However, if an expression involves both addition and subtraction (or subtraction alone) then to remove the parentheses it is necessary to first replace all subtractions by the appropriate additions. Do this with the following expressions. Write each of these expressions as a sum of rational numbers with positive denominators with all parentheses removed.
   (a) $2 - (2/3 + 4/5)$.
   (b) $(2/4 - 1/3) - (2/5 + 1/7)$.

(c) $(1/2 + 5/-4) - [3 - (3/5 - -6/3)]$.

8. Prove that subtraction of rational numbers is neither commutative nor associative. Prove that 0 is an identity for the operation.

9. Using the Subtract by Adding Theorem and the fact that addition of rational numbers possesses the cancellation property, prove that subtraction of rational numbers possesses the cancellation property.

10. Prove that if x and y are rational numbers, then $x - -y = x + y$.

Multiplication

Definition of the Operation of Multiplication of Rational Numbers   *If a/b and c/d are rational numbers, then $a/b \cdot c/d = ac/bd$.*

It is not difficult to see that this multiplication operation *agrees on the fractions* with multiplication of fractions. It also *agrees on the integers* with multiplication of integers and *agrees on the counting numbers* with multiplication of counting numbers. Multiplication of rational numbers possesses the *closure property* and so is a binary operation. The operation is *commutative, associative,* has an *identity* (1), and possesses the *cancellation property*. Lastly, multiplication of rational numbers shares a *distributive property* with each of the operations of addition and subtraction of rational numbers: $n(m \pm p) = nm \pm np$. In short, this multiplication operation is similar to all the other multiplication operations we have studied.

THE MULTIPLICATIVE INVERSE OF A RATIONAL NUMBER

The multiplicative inverse of a rational number is defined in exactly the same way that the multiplicative inverse of a fraction was defined. Given a rational number a/b we define the *multiplicative inverse* of a/b to be the solution of the equation $a/b \cdot x = 1$. We can immediately draw three conclusions:

1. Zero does not have a multiplicative inverse.
2. The multiplicative inverse of a nonzero rational number a/b is unique.
3. The multiplicative inverse of a nonzero rational number a/b is b/a.

Exercises

1. Let a/b, c/d, and e/f be rational numbers. Verify by direct computation that $(a/b)(c/d + e/f) = (a/b)(c/d) + (a/b)(e/f)$.

2. Prove that if a/b, c/d, and e/f are rational numbers, then $(a/b)(c/d - e/f) = (a/b)(c/d) - (a/b)(e/f)$.

3. Prove that the multiplicative inverse of a nonzero rational number is unique.

4. Solve the following equations and justify each step.
   (a) $(2/3)n - 4/5 = 1/2$.   (b) $2/3 - (1/7)n = 5/21$.

5. Prove that multiplication of rational numbers is both commutative and associative.

6. Prove that 1 is an identity for multiplication of rational numbers. Then prove that 1 is the *only* identity for this operation. (*Suggestion:* Use an indirect proof and begin by assuming that there are two *distinct* identities.)
7. Use the cancellation property of multiplication of integers to prove that multiplication of rational numbers possesses the cancellation property. Then use the well-definedness of multiplication of rational numbers to prove the same result.
8. Let a/b and c/d be rational numbers such that $a/b \neq 0$ and $a/b \cdot c/d = 0$. Draw a conclusion and prove your result.

Division

Definition of Division of Rational Numbers *If a/b and c/d are rational numbers and if c/d is not equal to zero, then $a/b \div c/d$ is that rational number q such that $a/b = c/d \cdot q$.*

Because of the similarity between the definitions of division of fractions and division of rational numbers the Divide by Multiplying Theorem for fractions has an analog for rational numbers.

Divide by Multiplying Theorem *If a/b and c/d are rational numbers and c/d is different from zero, then $a/b \div c/d = a/b \cdot d/c$.*

This theorem is proven in exactly the same way that the corresponding theorem for fractions was proved. The theorem shows that division by the nonzero rational number c/d is possible whenever the multiplicative inverse of c/d exists. But every nonzero rational number has a multiplicative inverse and consequently *division by nonzero rational numbers is always possible*. Hence while division of rational numbers does not possess the closure property, it comes as near to possessing this property as a division process can.

Division of real numbers is *well-defined*, has an *identity* (1), and possesses the *cancellation property*. Also, division shares a distributive property with both addition and subtraction: $(x \pm y) \div z = (x \div z) \pm (y \div z)$. Lastly, this division process *agrees* with each of the other three division processes we have studied.

Exercises

1. Explain why in the definition of division of rational numbers the divisor must be different from zero.
2. Prove the Divide by Multiplying Theorem.
3. Use the Divide by Multiplying Theorem and the cancellation property of multiplication to prove that division possesses the cancellation property.
4. **Theorem** *Division of rational numbers is well-defined. That is, if a/b, c/d, $e/f \neq 0$, and $g/h \neq 0$ are rational numbers such that $a/b = c/d$ and $e/f = g/h$, then $a/b \div e/f = c/d \div g/h$.*

   Prove this theorem.

5. Verify by direct computation that if a/b, c/d, and e/f are rational numbers, then
   (a) $(a/b + c/d) \div e/f = (a/b \div e/f) + (c/d \div e/f)$.
   (b) $(a/b - c/d) \div e/f = (a/b \div e/f) - (c/d \div e/f)$.
6. Perform these divisions using only the definition of division of rational numbers.
   (a) $1/3 \div -2/5$.   (b) $-6/7 \div 4/-3$.
7. The importance of division of rational numbers lies in its connection with multiplication as displayed by the following pair of theorems.

   Theorem 1   *If a/b and c/d are rational numbers and $c/d \neq 0$, then $(a/b \cdot c/d) \div c/d = a/b$.*

   Theorem 2   *If a/b and c/d are rational numbers and $c/d \neq 0$, then $(a/b \div c/d) \cdot c/d = a/b$.*

   (a) Prove Theorem 1.   (b) Prove Theorem 2.
8. Solve the following equations. Explain each step.
   (a) $n \div 1/2 = -4$.   (c) $(-1/3 \cdot 6/5)n = -6$.
   (b) $n = (-2/3 \cdot 6/7) \div 2/-7$.   (d) $n(-2/3) = 4/5 - 3/2$.
9. Write the following expressions in the form n/m where n and m represent integers. All the letters in these expressions represent integers.
   (a) $(a/b + c/d)(e/f)$.   (c) $(a/b - c/d)(a/b + c/d)$.
   (b) $(1/a + 2/b)(c/1 + 1/2)$.   (d) $(a/b + c/d) \div (3/b)(-4/d)$.
10. **Theorem**   *If a/b and c/d are rational numbers and if $c/d \neq 0$, then $a/b \div c/d = (a \div c)/(b \div d)$.*

   This theorem states that division can be performed in the same way that multiplication is performed. That is, the statement

   $$\frac{a}{b} * \frac{c}{d} = \frac{a * c}{b * d}$$

   is true when the symbol $*$ represents either the operation of multiplication or the process of division.
   (a) Prove the theorem. (*Suggestion:* $a/b = a \div b$.)
   (b) Use this theorem to perform the following divisions:
        (i) $-5/7 \div 8/-14$.
        (ii) $8/-9 \div 9/-8$.
11. Solve these equations. Justify each step.
   (a) $2(x + 4) = -12$.   (g) $s/3 - s/5 = 1/2$.
   (b) $11n - (3n - 4) = -20$.   (h) $n - (n - 1)/3 = 1/2$.
   (c) $5(2t - 1) - 7(3t - 2) = 9$.   (i) $(u - 2)/3 - (u + 1)/4 = -1$.
   (d) $-(n + 6) = 2$.   (j) $2x + 3 = x - 5/2$.
   (e) $-5(6 - n) = -15$.   (k) $1/(r - 1) = -2/3$.
   (f) $(1/5)(x - 3) = -3/10$.   (l) $1/(r - 1) + -3/4 = 9/-2$.

Review Questions

1. State the definition of multiplication of rational numbers.
2. What are the properties of multiplication of rational numbers?
3. State the definition of multiplicative inverse.

4. Which rational numbers possess multiplicative inverses? Which rational numbers are equal to their multiplicative inverses?
5. State the definition of division of rational numbers.
6. What are the properties of division of rational numbers?
7. State the Divide by Multiplying Theorem.
8. Explain why division of rational numbers does not have the closure property but division by nonzero rational numbers is always possible.

THE RATIONAL NUMBER LINE

The rational number line is constructed in much the same way as the other number lines we have studied. First points called the *origin* and the *unit* are selected. Then points are chosen to correspond to the positive rational numbers (fractions) in exactly the same way points were chosen to correspond to the fractions in the construction of the fraction line. To find points corresponding to the negative rational numbers (additive inverses of fractions), points are chosen in the obvious way to the left of the origin. Thus the rational number line resembles the fraction line to the right of the origin, and the left half of the rational number line is the reflection of the right half across the origin.

Since, very roughly speaking, the rational number line consists of two fraction lines laid end to end and pointing in opposite directions, it is predictable that these two number lines will possess similar properties. In particular,

1. The rational number line has the *density property*.
2. The rational number line has "holes." There are points on the line which do not correspond to any rational number.

We leave the discussion of these properties to the reader.

Exercises

1. Describe in detail how the rational number line is constructed by giving the one-to-one correspondence between rational numbers and points.
2. Prove that the rational number line has the density property by proving that if a/b and c/d are distinct rational numbers, then their average is a rational number less than the larger of the given rational numbers and greater than the smaller.
3. Explain why the rational number line has "holes." Give at least two examples of points on the line which do not correspond to rational numbers. (*Suggestion:* Use what you know about the fraction line and the fact that the rational number line and the fraction line resemble each other to the right of the origin.)
4. It has become popular in the elementary grades to use the word "opposite" as a synonym for additive inverse. Explain by using the rational number line why this word is a natural one to use as a synonym for additive inverse.

INEQUALITIES

Conditional Inequalities

An *inequality* is an expression involving one of the four inequality relations. Examples of inequalities are

$$6 \leq 7$$
$$4 - 3 > 0$$
$$-5(6) \geq -100$$
$$n + 2 > 4$$
$$2n - 3 \leq \frac{5}{6}$$
$$\frac{n - 2}{3} < \frac{-6}{7}$$

The first three of these inequalities are called *absolute inequalities* because they involve specific numbers and are true statements. The last three are called *conditional inequalities* because they involve unspecified numerals. The three conditional inequalities do not express statements; that is, they are neither true nor false. However, each of these conditional inequalities will produce a statement when the unspecified numeral n is specified to represent a particular number. For example, if in the conditional inequality

$$n + 2 > 4$$

we specify that n should represent 0 then the resulting statement,

$$0 + 2 > 4$$

is false. However if n is specified to represent the rational number 5/2, then the resulting statement,

$$\frac{5}{2} + 2 > 4$$

is true. If n represents 6 then the resulting statement $6 + 2 > 4$ is true. The numbers 5/2 and 6 are called *solutions* of the given conditional inequality. By a *solution* of a conditional inequality we mean a specification of the unspecified numeral which produces a true statement. Clearly a conditional inequality may have many different solutions and so it is meaningful to talk about the set of solutions of a conditional inequality. This set of solutions is called the *solution set* of the inequality. For simplicity we shall refer to conditional inequalities simply as inequalities from now on.

In this section we shall be concerned with finding the solution sets of inequalities. We shall first examine some inequalities whose solution sets may be determined simply by inspection. Then we shall state some theorems which can be used to help in finding solution sets. As we shall see, finding solution sets of inequalities can be very much like finding solutions of equations, but there are some differences which make the study of inequalities more complicated than the study of equations.

Finding Solution Sets by Inspection

First we must observe that just as was the case with equations it is meaningless to ask for solutions to inequalities without also specifying the number system from which these solutions are to be drawn. For example the inequality $n < 7$ has a different solution set relative to the system of counting numbers than it does relative to the system of integers. In the system of counting numbers the solution set of $n < 7$ is $\{0, 1, 2, 3, 4, 5, 6\}$ while in the system of integers the solution set is $\{6, 5, 4, 3, 2, 1, 0, -1, -2, -3, -4, -5, \ldots\}$.

Here are some examples of inequalities and their solution sets. It is expected that these inequalities are sufficiently transparent that their solution sets can be determined simply by inspection.

EXAMPLE 1. The inequality $n + 2 < 6$ has the solution set $\{0, 1, 2, 3\}$ in the system of counting numbers. In the system of integers the solution set is $\{0, 1, 2, 3, -1, -2, -3, -4, \ldots\}$. In the rational number system (henceforth denoted by the letter R) the solution set of this inequality is most easily described as $\{x \in R : x < 4\}$.

EXAMPLE 2. The inequality $2 - n > 0$ has the solution set $\{0, 1\}$ in the system of counting numbers, $\{0, 1, -1, -2, -3, -4, \ldots\}$ in the system of integers, and $\{x \in R : x < 2\}$ in the system of rational numbers.

It is sometimes helpful to illustrate the solution sets of inequalities by using the number line. The next examples demonstrate one way to illustrate solution sets.

EXAMPLE 3. In the system of counting numbers the inequality $n - 1 < 7$ has the solution set $\{1, 2, 3, 4, 5, 6, 7\}$. We shall illustrate such finite sets as shown in Fig. 48.

EXAMPLE 4. In the system of integers the inequality $n - 1 < 7$ has the solution set $\{1, 2, 3, 4, 5, 6, 7, 0, -1, -2, -3, -4, \ldots\}$ which is illustrated in Fig. 49.

Figure 48

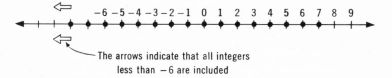

The arrows indicate that all integers less than -6 are included

Figure 49

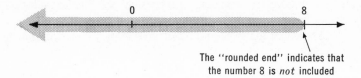

The "rounded end" indicates that
the number 8 is *not* included

Figure 50

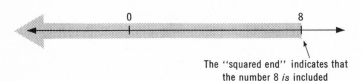

The "squared end" indicates that
the number 8 *is* included

Figure 51

EXAMPLE 5.   In the system of rational numbers the inequality $n - 1 < 7$ has the solution set $\{x \in R : x < 8\}$, This set is illustrated in Fig. 50. Figure 50 is intended to convey the information that the rational number 8 is *not* including in the solution set being illustrated. Figure 51 shows how we would illustrate the set of all rational numbers which are less than *or equal to* 8.

EXAMPLE 6.   The solution set of the inequality $3 \div n < 5$ is
$\{1, 3\}$ in the system of counting numbers,
$\{1, 3, -1, -3\}$ in the system of integers,
$\{x \in F : x > 3/5\}$ in the system of fractions,
$\{x \in R : x < 0 \text{ or } x > 3/5\}$ in the system of rational numbers.
These solution sets are illustrated in Fig. 52.

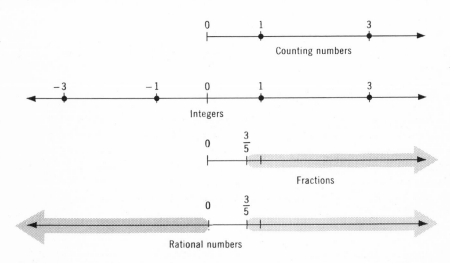

Figure 52

Exercises

1. Find the solution sets of the following inequalities in each of the four number systems. You should be able to find these solution sets by inspection. Illustrate the the solutions sets in the manner indicated in the text.

   (a) $n - 1 > 6$.

   (b) $n + 1 < 6$.

   (c) $2n - 1 \geq 0$.

   (d) $2n + 1 \leq 0$.

   (e) $2 - n > 0$.

   (f) $2 - n < 0$.

   (g) $2 - n \geq 3$.

   (h) $2 - n < 3$.

   (i) $1 \div n < 2$.

   (j) $5 \div n > 3$.

2. Sometimes two inequalities are combined into one inequality. For example, the inequality

$$3 \leq n < 7$$

   is the combination of the two inequalities

$$3 \leq n \quad \text{and} \quad n < 7$$

   The solution set of such an inequality is the intersection of the solutions sets of the two inequalities from which it is formed. Thus the solution set, relative to the system of integers, of the inequality $3 \leq n < 7$ is the set $\{3, 4, 5, 6, 7, \ldots\} \cap \{6, 5, 4, 3, 2, 1, 0, -1, -2, \ldots\} = \{3, 4, 5, 6\}$. Each of the following inequalities is to be solved in the system of integers. Begin by identifying the two inequalities of which each given inequality is a combination. Illustrate the solution set of each inequality.

   (a) $3 \leq n < 7$.

   (b) $3 \leq n + 1 \leq 6$.

   (c) $-3 \leq 2n + 1 \leq 12$.

   (d) $4 < n < 2$.

   (e) $-3 \leq n < 5$.

   (f) $-3 \leq n > 5$.

   (g) $-3 \geq n < 5$.

   (h) $-3 \geq n > 5$.

   (i) $-4 > n > 5$.

3. Find the solution sets of the following inequalities in the system of rational numbers. Illustrate each solution set.

   (a) $1/2 < n < 5/3$.

   (b) $-2/3 \leq n < 1$.

   (c) $-2/3 \geq n > 1$.

   (d) $-2/3 \geq 2n > -1$.

   (e) $0 < n + 1 \leq 4$.

   (f) $-1 \leq n - 2 \leq 5$.

Theorems About Inequalities

There are three basic theorems concerning the four inequality relations which relate them to the processes of addition, subtraction, multiplication, and division. We are going to state and prove these three theorems for the relation of *less than*, but each of the theorems has an analog for each of the other three inequality relations as well. We shall ask the reader to supply these analogs and, in some cases, to supply proofs for them. But before stating the theorems let us state a preliminary theorem which can be used to shorten and simplify the proofs of the three theorems.

Preliminary Theorem *Let x and y be rational numbers. Then $x < y$ if and only if there is a positive rational number k such that $x + k = y$.*

We have given the statements which comprise a proof of this theorem in the exercises and shall not prove the theorem here.

The Preliminary Theorem has analogs for the other three inequality relations and the reader should pause now to write out these analogs. In two of them the rational number k should be taken to be non-negative instead of positive.

The first of the three theorems we are going to prove deals with the addition of a rational number to both sides of an inequality. We know that because of the well-definedness of addition of rational numbers, the same rational number may be added to both sides of an equation and this theorem says that we can do the same thing to an inequality.

Theorem 1 *If x, y, and z are rational numbers such that $x < y$, then $x + z < y + z$.*

The Proof:

(1) $x < y$	(1) Hypothesis
(2) There is a positive rational number k such that $x + k = y$	(2) From (1) by using the Preliminary Theorem
(3) $(x + k) + z = y + z$	(3) From (2) by using?
(4) $(x + z) + k = y + z$	(4) ?
(5) $x + z < y + z$	(5) From (4) by using the Preliminary Theorem

⌘

It follows from the Theorem 1 that the same rational number z can be *subtracted* from both sides of the inequality $x < y$ to produce the inequality $x - z < y - z$. This is because the subtraction of z from both sides is the same as the addition of the additive inverse of z, $-z$, to both sides. That is, if $x < z$, then Theorem 1 tells us that $x + -z < y + -z$, from which it follows by the Subtract by Adding Theorem that $x - z < y - z$.

The next theorem has to do with the multiplication of both sides of an inequality by the same *positive* rational number.

Theorem 2 *If x, y, and z are rational numbers, if z is a positive rational number, and if $x < y$, then $xz < yz$.*

The Proof:

(1) $x < y$	(1) ?
(2) There is a positive rational number k such that $x + k = y$	(2) ?
(3) $(x + k)z = yz$	(3) From (2) by using ?
(4) $xz + kz = yz$	(4) From (3) by using ?
(5) kz is a positive rational number	(5) ?
(6) $xz < yz$	(6) ?

⌘

It follows from the second theorem that both sides of an inequality can be divided by the same positive rational number. For if $x < y$ is the given inequality and z is the positive rational number, then the division of both sides of $x < y$ by z is the same as the multiplication of both sides of $x < y$ by the positive rational number which is the multiplicative inverse of z.

The reason that it was necessary to specify that the rational number z in Theorem 2 be positive is that the theorem is false if z is a negative number. For example, if we multiply both sides of the true statement $6 < 8$ by -1 we get the false statement $-6 < -8$. But observe that if we multiply both sides of the inequality $6 < 8$ by the negative rational number -1 and at the same time replace the *less than* relation by the *greater than* relation, we get a true statement:

$$-6 > -8$$

As another example consider the inequality $-2 < 3$. If we simply multiply both sides of this inequality by the negative rational number $-1/2$, we get a false statement, namely, the statement

$$1 < \frac{-3}{2}$$

However, if at the same time that we multiply both sides by the negative rational number $-1/2$ we also replace $<$ by $>$ we get a true statement:

$$1 > \frac{-3}{2}$$

When we replace the *less than* relation by the *greater than* relation in this way we say that we have *reversed the sense of the inequality*. These two examples then appear to tell us that we can multiply both sides of an inequality by the same negative rational number if at the same time we also reverse the sense of the inequality. This is the content of the last theorem.

Theorem 3   *If x, y, and z are rational numbers, if z is a negative rational number, and if $x < y$, then $xz > yz$.*
The Proof:

(1) $x < y$	(1) Hypothesis
(2) There is a positive rational number k such that $x + k = y$	(2) ?
(3) $(x + k)z = yz$	(3) From (2) by using ?
(4) $xz + kz = yz$	(4) ?
(5) $xz = yz + -kz$	(5) From (4) by adding $-kz$ to both sides
(6) $-kz$ is a positive rational number	(6) ?

(7) $xz > yz$ (7) From (5) and (6) by using the analog of the Preliminary Theorem for *greater than*.

⁑

Since the division of both sides of the inequality $x < y$ by the same negative rational number z is the same as the multiplication of both sides of $x < y$ by the multiplicative inverse of z (which is also negative) Theorem 3 implies that both sides of an inequality may be divided by the same negative rational number if the sense of the inequality is reversed.

The content of the three theorems may be summarized as follows:

1. The same rational number may be added to or subtracted from both sides of an inequality without reversing the sense of the inequality.
2. Both sides of an inequality may be multiplied or divided by the same positive rational number without reversing the sense of the inequality.
3. Both sides of an inequality may be multiplied or divided by the same negative rational number by reversing the sense of the inequality.

The three theorems which have been proven in terms of the *less than* inequality relation may be stated in terms of any one of the other three inequality relations. The reader should now write out these analogs in full.

Exercises

1. Use the theorems of this section to rewrite the inequality
    (a) $2/3 > 4/16$ so that the right side is an integer.
    (b) $-2/7 \leq 3/4$ so that the left side is positive.
    (c) $4 - 1/3 > 5/2$ so that the left side is 4.
    (d) $3/5 \leq -4/-5 + 2/7$ so that the right side is an integer.
    (e) $-5/3 \geq -5/4$ so that the left side is an even positive integer.
    (f) $-3 > -5$ so that the right side is 15.
2. State the analogs of the Preliminary Theorem for the inequality relations of *greater than*, *less than or equal to*, and *greater than or equal to*.
3. State the analogs of the three theorems for the inequality relations of *greater than*, *less than or equal to*, and *greater than or equal to*.
4. The Preliminary Theorem is a combination of two other theorems which we shall call Theorems A and B. Supply justifications for these proofs of Theorems A and B.

    Theorem A *If x and y are rational numbers such that $x < y$, then there is a positive rational number k such that $x + k = y$.*
    The Proof:
    (1) Write $x = a/b$ and $y = c/b$, where b is a positive integer
    (2) $a/b < c/b$
    (3) $a < c$
    (4) There is a positive integer t such that $a + t = c$
    (5) $(a + t)/b = c/b$
    (6) $a/b + t/b = c/b$

(7) t/b is a positive rational number

Theorem A then follows from statements (6) and (7) by taking the number k to be t/b.

Theorem B   *If x and y are rational numbers and if there is a positive rational number k such that $x + k = y$, then $x < y$.*

The Proof:

(1)   Write $x = a/b$, $y = c/b$, and $k = d/b$, where b and d are positive integers.

(2) $a/b + d/b = c/b$

(3) $a + d = c$

(4) $a < c$

(5) $a/b < c/b$

Theorem B then follows from statement (5) since $x = a/b$ and $y = c/b$.

5.   In Exercise 2 you found the analog of the Preliminary Theorem for the relation of *greater than*. Prove this analog.

6.   In Exercise 3 you found the analogs of the three theorems for the relation of *greater than*. Prove these analogs.

7.   Earlier we observed that the following test for determining whether one rational number is less than another is incorrect: $a/b < c/d$ if and only if $da < bc$ (see Exercise 5, p. 221). This statement can be made correct if we add another hypothesis.

Theorem *If a/b and c/d are rational numbers written so that their denominators have the same algebraic sign, then $a/b < c/d$ if and only if $da < bc$.*

If the denominators of the rational numbers a/b and c/d have different algebraic sign, then we get another theorem.

Theorem *If a/b and c/d are rational numbers written so that their denominators have different algebraic sign, then $a/b < c/d$ if and only if $da > bc$.*

(a)   Prove each of these theorems.

(b)   State the analogs of these theorems for the other inequality relations.

8.   Explain why the following statements are true.

(a)   If $x + y > z + y$, then $x > z$.

(b)   If $xz \geq yz$ and if z is positive, then $x \geq y$.

(c)   If $xz \leq yz$ and if z is negative, then $x \geq y$.

(d)   If $xz + w > yz + w$, then $x > y$ if z is positive and $x < y$ if z is negative.

(e)   If $x^2 > x$ and x is positive, then $x > 1$.

(f)   If $x^2 > x$ and x is negative, then $x < 0$.

(g)   If $x^2 > x$, then either $x > 1$ or $x < 0$.

(h)   If $x < 0$, then $x^2 > x$.

(i)   If $x > 1$, then $x^2 > x$.

(j)   If $x > 1$ or $x < 0$, then $x^2 > x$.

(k) $x^2 > x$ if and only if $x < 0$ or $x > 1$.

(l) $x^2 \not> x$ if and only if $0 \leq x \leq 1$.

(m) $x^2 \leq x$ if and only if $0 \leq x \leq 1$.

Using the Theorems to Find Solution Sets

We shall now restrict our attention to inequalities to be solved in the system of rational numbers. In this system inequalities may be solved by using the three theorems just proved in much the same way that equations are solved. Very roughly speaking, the idea is to use the theorem to somehow "isolate" the unspecified numeral on one side of the inequality. Here are some examples of how this is done and why doing it produces the desired solution set.

EXAMPLE 1.   Find the solution set of the inequality $2n - 5 \geq -2$.

Solution: Just as with equations we seek to "isolate" the unspecified numeral on one side of the inequality. We can accomplish this by applying the theorems as follows:

$2n - 5 \geq -2$ (Given inequality)

$2n \geq -2 + 5$ (Applying Theorem 1 to add 5 to both sides)

$2n \geq 3$ (Simplifying)

$n \geq \dfrac{3}{2}$ (Applying Theorem 2 to multiply both sides by 1/2, which is the same as dividing both sides by 2.)

Now what we have accomplished is this: By application of the theorems we have obtained from the given inequality a new inequality (namely, the inequality $n \geq 3/2$) whose solution set may be determined by inspection alone. In and of itself this is no great accomplishment, but it can be proved that *the solution set of the original inequality is the same as the solution set of the simpler inequality.* Hence by finding the solution set of the simpler inequality, we have in fact found the solution set of the original inequality. That is, we have used the given inequality to find a new inequality whose solution set may be determined by inspection and *which has the same solution set as the given inequality.* Using the theorems we replaced the given inequality by another simpler inequality having the same solution set and then solved the simpler inequality by inspection. Therefore the solution set is $\{x \in R : x \geq 3/2\}$.

EXAMPLE 2.   Find the solution set of $n/2 + 4/3 < -1$.

Solution: We apply the theorems to isolate the unspecified numeral on one side of the inequality:

$\dfrac{n}{2} + \dfrac{4}{3} < -1$ (Given inequality)

$\dfrac{n}{2} < -1 + \dfrac{-4}{3}$ (Applying Theorem 1 by adding $-4/3$ to both sides. We could have obtained the same result by subtracting 4/3 from both sides.)

$\dfrac{n}{2} < \dfrac{-7}{3}$ (Simplifying)

$n < \left(\dfrac{-7}{3}\right)(2)$ (Applying Theorem 2 to multiply both sides by 2.)

$n < \dfrac{-14}{3}$ (Simplifying)

The result of applying these theorems has been to obtain from the given inequality a simpler inequality, the inequality $n < -14/3$, whose solution set may be determined by inspection and which has the same solution set as the given inequality. We conclude therefore that the solution set of the given inequality is $\{x \in R : x < -14/3\}$.

EXAMPLE 3. Find the solution set of $2 - n < 3$.

Solution:

$2 - n < 3$ (Given inequality)

$n - 2 > -3$ (Multiplying both sides by -1. Note that we have had to reverse the sense of the inequality.)

$n > -3 + 2$ (Adding 2 to both sides)

$n > -1$ (Simplifying)

The new inequality we have obtained by applying the theorems has the same solution set as the given inequality and this solution set is seen by inspection to be $\{x \in R : x > -1\}$.

EXAMPLE 4. Find the solution set of the inequality

$$\frac{4 - 7n}{-2} \leq -\frac{6}{5}$$

Solution:

$\dfrac{4 - 7n}{-2} \leq -\dfrac{6}{5}$ (Given inequality)

$4 - 7n \geq \left(-\dfrac{6}{5}\right)(-2)$ (Multiplying both sides by -2 and reversing the sense of the inequality)

$4 - 7n \geq \dfrac{12}{5}$ (Simplifying)

$7n - 4 \leq \dfrac{-12}{5}$ (Multiplying both sides by -1)

$7n \leq \dfrac{-12}{5} + 4$ (Adding 4 to both sides)

$7n \leq \dfrac{8}{5}$ (Simplifying)

$n \leq \left(\dfrac{8}{5}\right)\left(\dfrac{1}{7}\right)$ $\left(\text{Multiplying both sides by } \dfrac{1}{7}\right)$

$n \leq \dfrac{8}{35}$ (Simplifying)

The sequence of applications of the theorems has given us an inequality whose solution set may be determined simply by inspection. The solution set of the last inequality is $\{x \in R : x \leq 8/35\}$. Since this solution set is the same as the solution set of the given inequality we have found the solution set of the given inequality.

Exercises

1. Find the solution sets of the following inequalities in the system of rational numbers. Use the theorems. Justify each step.

(a) $n - 3 \leq -4$.

(b) $(n - 3)/4 \leq 7/2$.

(c) $(n - 3)/-4 \leq 7/2$.

(d) $(2n - 5)(-1) \geq -5$.

(e) $(2n - 5)/16 \leq 7/4$.

(f) $-4/5 \leq 2n + 1/2 < 6$. (*Suggestion:* Consider the two inequalities $-4/5 \leq 2n + 1/2$ and $2n + 1/2 < 6$ and form the intersection of their solution sets. Cf. Exercise 2, p. 237.)

(g) $2/3 \leq (n + 3)/-2 \leq 1$.

(h) $(4 - n)/2 < -5$.

(i) $3 \leq 4 - n \leq 7$.

(j) $(3 - 2n)/-2 \geq 2/3$.

(k) $-2(n - 3) < 8$.

CHAPTER 8

Decimal Numerals

Heretofore our attention has been directed toward numbers and we have been concerned with numerals only in that names must be given to numbers before they can be discussed. We shall now change the direction of our study and concern ourselves with a particular system of numeration by means of which rational numbers can be symbolized. In this chapter we shall study the *decimal system of numeration.*

INTRODUCTION TO DECIMAL NUMERALS

The numerals that we have used to represent counting numbers in this book are called *decimal numerals* or *Hindu-Arabic numerals.* The decimal system of numeration is generally believed to have originated in India and to have been transmitted to the West in the thirteenth century. The principal system used in the West immediately prior to the introduction of the Hindu-Arabic system was the Roman numeral system. That system was remarkably inefficient and while it survived into the Middle Ages, as soon as the decimal system became generally known it completely disappeared from everyday use.

How then is the decimal system superior to the Roman numeral system? There are two aspects of the decimal system called the concepts of *place holder* and *place value* which display this superiority. To introduce these concepts we shall consider first the way that decimal numerals are used to name counting numbers. Later we shall extend the system so that all rational numbers can be named with decimal numerals.

The Concept of Place Value

Within the decimal system for naming counting numbers there are certain distinguished counting numbers called *digits.* These are the numbers zero through nine and are represented by the special symbols 0, 1, 2, 3, 4, 5, 6, 7, 8, and 9, which are called *digit symbols*. All the other counting numbers are named by blocks of two or more of these digit symbols. For example, the block

$$4567$$

represents a counting number. In this numeral the digit symbol 7 is said to occupy the *units place*. The digit symbol 6 occupies the *tens place*, 5 occupies the *hundreds place*, and 4 occupies the *thousands place*. Obviously these places are named (from right to left) by using powers of ten. The digit symbol 7 is in the 10^0 place; 6 is in the 10^1 place, 5 is in the 10^2 place, and 4 is in the 10^3 place. The other places to the left of the thousands place are named by using successively larger powers to ten.

Now in the block 4567 the digit symbols 4, 5, and 6 do not represent the counting numbers four, five, and six. The meaning of a digit symbol in a block of digit symbols is called its *place value* and by definition this place value is equal to the product of the digit represented by the digit symbol and the value of the place which that digit symbol occupies. Thus in the block 4567 the digit symbol 4 represents the counting number which is the product of 4 and 10^3, or 4000. The digit symbol 5 represents the product of 5 and 10^2, or 500, the digit symbol 6 represents the product of 6 and 10^1, or 60, and the symbol 7 represents the product of 7 and 10^0, or 7. Thus the place value of a digit symbol in a block of digit symbols depends upon (1) the digit represented by that digit symbol and (2) the place occupied by that digit symbol.

We have given meaning to each of the digit symbols in a block of digit symbols. Now we can give meaning to the block. By definition, *a block of digit symbols represents the number which is the sum of the place values of the digit symbols comprising the block*. The block 4567 represents the counting number which is the sum of the place values 4000, 500, 60, and 7. A block of digit symbols therefore is nothing more than a convenient abbreviation of the sum of its place values. Thus the numeral 4567 is simply an abbreviation for the expression $4000 + 500 + 60 + 7$. To fully grasp the significance of the decimal system of numeration it is essential that this fact be well understood. When one looks at the numeral "51" he should think "50 + 1." It is this sum which is important, the abbreviation is simply a convenience.

The Concept of Place Holder

The sum

$$4(1000) + 5(10) + 6(1)$$

is the kind of sum which can be abbreviated by a decimal numeral. The decimal numeral which abbreviates this sum has the digit symbol 4 in the thousands place, the symbol 5 in the tens place, and the symbol 6 in the units place. That is, the abbreviation for this sum is the numeral

4		5	6
Thousands Place	Hundreds Place	Tens Place	Units Place

there being no digit symbol in the hundreds place. We must somehow record the fact that there is no digit symbol in the hundreds place. There are many different ways to convey this information. Any one of the following symbols could be used:

$$4\text{-}56$$
$$4 * 56$$
$$4 \cdot 56$$
$$4(\ )56$$
$$4\ 56$$

In fact in some of the early Hindu-Arabic manuscripts the symbol · was used. Thus 4 · was written for forty and 4 · 1 for four hundred one. We call such a symbol a *place holder* because its only function as far as the numeral is concerned is to convey the information that no digit symbol occupies that place— it "holds the place open." Of course, today we use the digit symbol 0 as the place holder. It is possible to do this because the digit symbol 0 has place value of zero wherever it occurs in a block of digit symbols. Consequently the insertion of this digit symbol into a place to hold that place does not change the meaning of the block.

Extending the Concept of Place Value

By appropriately extending the concept of place value, we shall be able to represent fractions by decimal numerals. We accomplish this extension by creating places to the right of the units place and assigning place values to digit symbols occurring in these new places. The first place to the right of the units place is called the *tenths place*, the second place is called the *hundredths place*, the third place is called the *thousandths place*, and so on. Thus the places to the right of the units place are given value by using the multiplicative inverses of the powers of ten.

	Thou-sands	Hun-dreds	Tens	Units	Tenths	Hun-dredths	Thou-sandths	
. . .	10^3	10^2	10^1	10^0	$\dfrac{1}{10^1}$	$\dfrac{1}{10^2}$	$\dfrac{1}{10^3}$	. . .

Since places are named according to their position relative to the units place we must somehow clearly identify the units place. This is done by placing a dot called the *decimal point* immediately to the right of the units digit. The decimal point is used to instruct the reader as to which digit symbol occupies the units place. This information is vital because the place values of all the digit symbols depend upon the correct identification of the units place digit symbol. Of course, if all the places to the right of the units place are unoccupied, then we need not use the decimal point. The units place in this case is understood to be the right-most place.

The *place value* assigned to a digit symbol occurring in a place to the right of the units place is the product of the digit represented by that digit symbol and the value of the place which the symbol occupies. For example, in the block 45.6789

the place value of the digit symbol 6 is 6(1/10) or 3/5
the place value of the digit symbol 7 is 7(1/100) or 7/100
the place value of the digit symbol 8 is 8(1/1000) or 1/125
the place value of the digit symbol 9 is 9(1/10000) or 9/10000

We have seen how to extend the concept of place value to the right of the units place. It remains now to assign meaning to decimal numerals which have digit symbols occurring to the right of the units place. We shall do this in the next two sections. As we shall see it is not difficult to assign meaning to decimal numerals in which only *finitely* many digit symbols appear to the right of the units place, but to assign meaning to numerals in which *infinitely* many digit symbols appear to the right of the decimal place units place is another problem altogether and must be handled differently.

Review Questions

1. What are digits? What are digit symbols?
2. What is meant by the place value of a digit symbol in a block of digit symbols? How is this place value determined?
3. What is the meaning of a decimal numeral which has no digit symbols to the right of the units place?
4. What is the function of the decimal point?
5. What is a place holder? Why are place holders needed in the decimal system?
6. Why can the symbol 0 be used as a place holder? Why can't the symbol 6 be used as a place holder?

Exercises

1. Identify the place values of the digit symbols in the numerals below.
   - (a) 189.
   - (b) 101.
   - (c) 1,687,324.
   - (d) 80.014.
   - (e) .0000000001.
   - (f) 9000.0010.
   - (g) 0.
   - (h) 93,000,135.

2. Find the decimal numerals which abbreviate the following sums. In some cases it will be necessary to rearrange the terms or to insert extra terms. In these cases first rewrite the sums so that all terms appear and the terms are in the correct order before making the abbreviation.
   (a) $8(1000) + 6(100) + 3(10) + 0(1)$.
   (b) $8(1000000) + 6(100000) + 5(10000) + 7(1000)$.
   (c) $8(1) + 5(100) + 7(1000)$.
   (d) $4(1000) + 6(1)$.
3. Is there any mathematical reason why the decimal point could not be placed between the tens digit and the units digit, provided of course that everyone would agree to do this?
4. The British name the places differently that do the Americans. Consult a dictionary for the meaning of the word *billion*. (A good dictionary will give both British and American meanings.) Which is the billions place in Great Britain? Which is the billions place in the United States? Who has more money, a billionaire in Liverpool or a billionaire in San Francisco?

TERMINATING DECIMAL NUMERALS

In this section we shall discuss a rather special kind of decimal numeral called a *terminating* decimal numeral. A decimal numeral is said to terminate if it has only finitely many digit symbols occurring to the right of the decimal point. Not all decimal numerals are of this kind. The reader may recall from his own elementary school days that the fraction 1/3 when written as a decimal numeral is written as $0.33333\cdots.$* (The ellipsis symbol indicates that the digit symbol 3 occurs in every place to the right of the decimal point.) Numerals such as this one are called *nonterminating* decimal numerals, and we shall discuss this kind of numeral in the next section.

We have already seen how to assign meaning to terminating decimal numerals which have no digit symbols to the right of the units place. We assign meaning to all other terminating decimal numerals in the same way. That is, by definition *a terminating decimal numeral represents the number which is the sum of the place values of its digit symbols*. For example, the terminating decimal numeral 2.34 represents the sum of the place values of the digit symbols comprising the numeral. Therefore $2.34 = 2(1) + 3(1/10) + 4(1/100)$. The terminating decimal numeral 0.145 represents the number which is the sum of the place values $1(1/10)$, $4(1/100)$, and $5(1/1000)$.

With this definition of the meaning of a terminating decimal numeral the following theorem becomes almost obvious.

Theorem   *Every terminating decimal numeral names a fraction.*
The Proof: According to our definition a terminating decimal numeral represents that number which is the sum of the place values of the digit symbols

---

* We shall adopt the convention that if no digit symbols occur to the left of the decimal point we shall place a 0 in the unit's place. This is done to fix the location of the decimal point more firmly.

occurring in the numeral. But each of these place values is a fraction and the sum of fractions is a fraction, hence the numeral represents a fraction.

⁘

We may conclude therefore that while every terminating decimal numeral names a fraction, not every fraction (e.g., 1/3) is named by a terminating decimal numeral. The next theorem identifies the fractions which can be named by terminating decimal numerals.

Theorem   *A fraction a/b (written in lowest terms) can be represented by a terminating decimal numeral if and only if the denominator has the form*

$$2^n 5^m$$

where n and m are counting numbers.

We shall not prove this theorem, but let us consider some examples of it.

EXAMPLE 1.   According to the theorem the fraction

$$\frac{17}{2^3 5^4}$$

should be representable by a terminating decimal numeral. Let us verify this by direct calculation. We begin by adjusting the denominator so that the prime factors 2 and 5 appear with the same exponent:

$$\frac{17}{2^3 5^4} = \frac{17 \cdot 2}{2^4 5^4} = \frac{34}{2^4 5^4}$$

Having done this we can now apply Theorem 2, p. 120, and get

$$\frac{17}{2^3 5^4} = \frac{34}{2^4 5^4} = \frac{34}{10^4}$$

So far what we have accomplished is to write the given fraction so that its denominator is a power of ten. Now we can find the terminating decimal numeral name for this fraction by decomposing this fraction into a sum of fractions which can then be abbreviated by a terminating decimal numeral. Observe:

$$\frac{34}{10^4} = \frac{30 + 4}{10000} = \frac{30}{10000} + \frac{4}{10000}$$

$$= \frac{3}{1000} + \frac{4}{10000}$$

$$= \frac{0}{10} + \frac{0}{100} + \frac{3}{1000} + \frac{4}{10000}$$

$$= 0.0034$$

A close examination of Example 1 will convince the reader that the method used there to write $17/2^3 5^4$ as a terminating decimal numeral is perfectly general.

That is, the same method may be applied to any fraction whose denominator has the prescribed form to obtain a terminating decimal numeral.

EXAMPLE 2.   The theorem also states that if a fraction is represented by a terminating decimal numeral, then it can be written with a denominator of the form $2^n 5^m$. Let us verify that this is true for the particular terminating decimal numeral 4.156. We begin by replacing the terminating decimal numeral by the sum which it abbreviates:

$$4.156 = 4 + \frac{1}{10} + \frac{5}{100} + \frac{6}{1000}$$

Then we perform addition of fractions:

$$4.156 = \frac{4000}{1000} + \frac{100}{1000} + \frac{50}{1000} + \frac{6}{1000}$$

$$= \frac{4000 + 100 + 50 + 6}{1000}$$

$$= \frac{4156}{1000}$$

$$= \frac{4156}{10^3}$$

At this point we have written the fraction represented by the given terminating decimal numeral so that it has a denominator which is a power of ten. If we continue by writing this fraction in lowest terms we get the special denominator we wanted:

$$4.156 = \frac{4156}{10^3} = \frac{4156}{2^3 5^3} = \frac{2078}{2^2 5^3} = \frac{1039}{2^1 5^3}$$

The denominator of this fraction is $2^1 5^3$ and so has the form that the theorem said it would have.

The method used in this example is perfectly general and will work for any terminating decimal numeral in place of 4.156.

Review Questions

1. What is a terminating decimal numeral?
2. What is a nonterminating decimal numeral?
3. What does the symbol $\cdots$ in $0.33333 \cdots$ mean?
4. Explain why every terminating decimal numeral represents a fraction.
5. How can one identify a fraction which can be represented by a terminal decimal numeral?
6. We have illustrated a general method for writing a fraction whose denominator has the form $2^n 5^m$ as a terminating decimal numeral. Describe this method.
7. We have illustrated a general method for writing a terminating decimal numeral as a fraction whose denominator has the form $2^n 5^m$. Describe this method.

Exercises

1. Use the theorem of this section to identify the fractions which can be represented by terminating decimal numerals.

    (a) 16/144.   (e) 5/33.   (i) 1/2.
    (b) 16/125.   (f) 3/75.   (j) 1/5.
    (c) 71/200.   (g) 3/50.   (k) 1/25.
    (d) 14/625.   (h) 42/9.   (l) 1/4.

2. Each of the following fractions is to be rewritten as a terminating decimal numeral in the manner of Example 1. Justify each step.

    (a) 7/125.   (b) 59/200.   (c) 45/250.   (d) 14/625.

3. Each of the following terminating decimal numerals is to be rewritten as an ordinary fraction written in lowest terms in the manner of Example 2. Justify each step.

    (a) 17.78.   (b) 0.156.   (c) 1897.45.   (d) 0.0013.

NONTERMINATING DECIMAL NUMERALS

A *nonterminating decimal numeral* is a decimal numeral which has a digit symbol in *every* place to the right of the decimal point. We have seen one example of such a numeral, namely, 0.3333 · · · · . Other examples are

> 0.11111 · · ·
> 0.121231234123451234561234567712345678 · · ·
> 0.101001000100001000001000000010000000 · · ·
> 16.1212121212 · · ·

Now it is easy enough to say that a nonterminating decimal numeral is one which has lots of digit symbols, but it is not quite so easy to verify that we have said something meaningful. That is, it is not so easy to verify that these symbols are actually numerals—that they are in fact the names of numbers. We could for instance define a *zilch numeral* to be a numeral with digit symbols in every place to the *left* of the decimal point. But what we could not do would be to assign meaning to such a symbol, for this kind of symbol does not represent a number and so is not really a numeral at all. Calling a symbol a numeral does not automatically mean that the symbol represents a number. We have to verify that the symbol we are calling a numeral does in fact represent some number. This is just what we must do for the nonterminating decimal numerals.

We have seen how to attach meaning to a terminating decimal numeral; we simply add up the place values of the numeral. What meaning can we attach to a nonterminating decimal numeral? For example, consider the nonterminating numeral

$$0.3333 \cdot \cdot \cdot *$$

---

* We are using this particular nonterminating numeral as our example because the reader is familiar with it already. Our concern here is not with whether the reader *believes* that this numeral represents the fraction 1/3, it is with the mathematical foundation for this belief.

We might try to attach meaning to this nonterminating numeral in the same way that we attached meaning to the terminating numerals: we would write down the symbol

$$\frac{3}{10} + \frac{3}{100} + \frac{3}{1000} + \frac{3}{10000} + \frac{3}{100000} + \cdots$$

But this does not help us at all, for at our present level of understanding the symbol we have just written down is quite meaningless. The difficulty we have gotten into by writing down this "infinite sum" is that addition of fractions is a binary operation and this symbol involves infinitely many summands. How can we add these infinitely many summands together if we can add only two fractions at a time? Do we even know that the sum of infinitely many fractions makes any sense at all? What do we mean by the "sum" of infinitely many fractions? We have opened up a veritable Pandora's box of questions. The difficulty is that we cannot make sense out of "infinite sums" if the only tool we possess is the binary operation of addition. We must find some new tool to use in trying to attach meaning to these nonterminating numerals. Equivalently, the understandings which enabled us to attach meaning to terminating decimal numerals are insufficient to enable us to attach meaning to nonterminating decimal numerals. We need a new tool and that tool is the concept of "convergence to zero." Before we try to assign meaning to nonterminating decimal numerals, then, we must discuss this concept.

Convergence to Zero

Consider the nonterminating decimal numeral $0.3333\cdots$. From this numeral we can obtain an infinite list of *terminating* decimal numerals:

$$0.3$$
$$0.33$$
$$0.333$$
$$0.3333$$
$$0.33333$$
$$0.333333$$
$$\cdot$$
$$\cdot$$
$$\cdot$$

These terminating decimal numerals are called the *partial sums* of the nonterminating decimal numeral $0.3333\cdots$. These terminating numerals are called *sums* because they are just that—each of them is the sum of its place values. They are called *partial* sums because each of them consists of a part of the nonterminating decimal numeral symbol $0.3333\cdots$. It is clear that given any nonterminating decimal numeral we can obtain from it such a list of partial sums.

EXAMPLE. The partial sums of the nonterminating decimal numeral
0.121231234123451234561 2 · · · are

$$0.1$$
$$0.12$$
$$0.121$$
$$0.1212$$
$$0.12123$$
.
.
.

Referring again to the nonterminating decimal numeral 0.3333 · · · , let us compute the differences between the fraction 1/3 and the partial sums of this numeral:

$$\frac{1}{3} - 0.3 = \frac{1}{3} - \frac{3}{10} = \frac{10}{30} - \frac{9}{30} = \frac{1}{30}$$

$$\frac{1}{3} - 0.33 = \frac{1}{3} - \frac{33}{100} = \frac{100}{300} - \frac{99}{300} = \frac{1}{300}$$

$$\frac{1}{3} - 0.333 = \frac{1}{3} - \frac{333}{100} = \frac{1000}{3000} - \frac{999}{3000} = \frac{1}{3000}$$

$$\frac{1}{3} - 0.3333 = \frac{1}{30000}$$

$$\frac{1}{3} - 0.33333 = \frac{1}{300000}$$

$$\frac{1}{3} - 0.333333 = \frac{1}{3000000}$$

.
.
.

Next consider the *sequence* of these differences:

$$\frac{1}{30}, \ \frac{1}{300}, \ \frac{1}{3000}, \ \frac{1}{30000}, \ \frac{1}{300000}, \ \frac{1}{3000000}, \ \cdots$$

This sequence of fractions is illustrated in Fig. 53. (In Fig. 53 the scale has been distorted so that we might picture more of the fractions in this sequence.)

Looking at Fig. 53, let us describe the "behavior" of this sequence of fractions. It is obvious that the fractions in this sequence are getting closer and closer to zero. But is this not all we can say. Consider the sequence of fractions

$$\frac{11}{10}, \ \frac{101}{100}, \ \frac{1001}{1000}, \ \frac{10001}{10000}, \ \frac{100001}{100000}, \ \cdots$$

which is illustrated in Fig. 54. The fractions in the sequence in Fig. 54 are not behaving in exactly the same way as the fractions in Fig. 53. The fractions in Fig. 53 are not only getting closer and closer to zero, they are getting *arbitrarily close* to zero in the sense that if we are given an arbitrarily small distance we can find a fraction in the sequence which is less than that distance from zero. We cannot say the same of the fractions in Fig. 54. For example, it is not possible to find a fraction in Fig. 54 which is within distance 1/2 of zero.

We say that the fractions in Fig. 53 are *converging to zero*. Without trying to formulate a precise mathematical definition of what this means, let us agree that to say that a sequence of fractions *converges to zero* if given any arbitrarily small distance it is possible to find a fraction in the sequence such that it and all the fractions following it in the sequence are less than that distance from zero. For example, with regard to the sequence

$$\frac{1}{30}, \frac{1}{300}, \frac{1}{3000}, \frac{1}{30000}, \frac{1}{300000}, \ldots$$

given the distance 1/100 it is possible to find a fraction such that that fraction and all the fractions which follow it in the sequence lie within a distance of 1/100 of zero. In fact, the fraction 1/300 and all of the fractions following 1/300 in the sequence lie within a distance of 1/100 from zero.

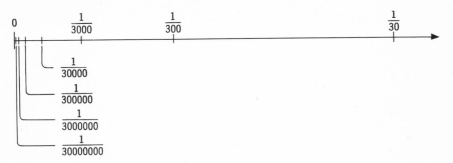

Figure 53 (Distorted scale.)

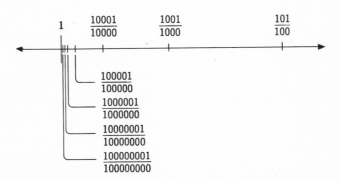

Figure 54 (Distorted scale.)

EXAMPLE 1.   The sequence of fractions 1/2, 1/3, 1/4, 1/5, 1/6, . . . converges to zero (see Fig. 55).

EXAMPLE 2.   The sequence of fractions 1/10, 1/100, 1/1000, . . . converges to zero and is illustrated in Fig. 56.

EXAMPLE 3.   The sequence 4/3, 34/33, 334/333, 3334/3333, . . . does not converge to zero (see Fig. 57). In fact the fractions in this sequence are all greater than 1, and so clearly the sequence cannot converge to zero. The fact that the fractions in the sequence are getting smaller and smaller is irrelevant, they are not getting arbitrarily smaller.

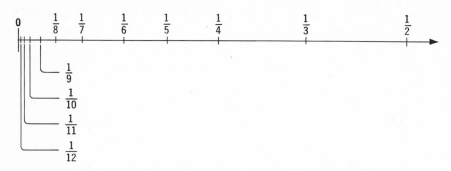

Figure 55   (Distorted scale.)

Figure 56   (Distorted scale.)

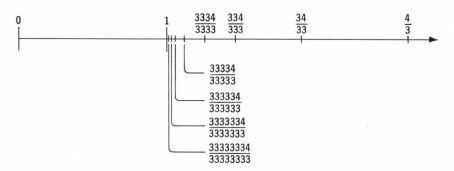

Figure 57   (Distorted scale.)

Review Questions

1. What is a nonterminating decimal numeral?
2. Give an example of a nonterminating decimal numeral and explain why meaning cannot be assigned to the numeral by using the same ideas that were used to assign meaning to the terminating decimal numerals.
3. What are partial sums?
4. What does it mean to say that a sequence of fractions converges to zero?
5. What does it mean to say that the fractions of a sequence of fractions get arbitrarily close to the origin?
6. If the fractions in a sequence get smaller and smaller, must it be true that the fractions converge to zero?

Exercises

1. Each of the following sequences of fractions converges to zero. Find the first fraction in each sequence which is less than (i) 1/100, (ii) 1/1000, (iii) 1/1000000, and (iv) 1/100000000.
    (a)   1, 1/2, 1/3, 1/4, 1/5, 1/6, ...
    (b)   1, 1/2, 1/4, 1/8, 1/16, 1/32, ...
    (c)   1/20, 1/200, 1/2000, 1/20000, ...
    (d)   3/5, 3/55, 3/555, 3/5555, 3/55555, ...
2. Find a sequence of fractions which does not get closer and closer to zero but does get closer and closer to 3. Find a sequence of fractions which gets closer and closer to both 0 and 3.
3. Find a sequence of fractions which gets closer and closer to 5 but does not get arbitrarily close to 5.

Assigning Meaning to Nonterminating Decimal Numerals

The concept of convergence to zero is the concept we need to be able to assign meaning to nonterminating decimal numerals. By definition, *we say that a nonterminating decimal numeral represents a fraction a/b if the sequence of differences between the fraction a/b and the partial sums of the nonterminating decimal numeral converges to zero.* For example, we have seen that the differences between $1/3$ and the partial sums of the nonterminating decimal numeral $0.33333 \cdots$ converge to zero. Therefore *by definition* the numeral $0.33333 \cdots$ represents $1/3$. Here are some more examples.

EXAMPLE 1.   According to the definition the nonterminating decimal numeral $0.12121212121212 \cdots$ represents the fraction $4/33$. We can see this by computing the differences between $4/33$ and the partial sums of the decimal numeral:

$$\frac{4}{33} - 0.1 = \frac{4}{33} - \frac{1}{10} = \frac{40}{330} - \frac{33}{330} = \frac{7}{330}$$

$$\frac{4}{33} - 0.12 = \frac{4}{33} - \frac{12}{100} = \frac{400}{3300} - \frac{396}{3300} = \frac{4}{3300}$$

$$\frac{4}{33} - 0.121 = \frac{4}{33} - \frac{121}{1000} = \frac{4000}{33000} - \frac{3993}{33000} = \frac{7}{33000}$$

$$\frac{4}{33} - 0.1212 = \frac{4}{330000}$$

$$\frac{4}{33} - 0.12121 = \frac{7}{3300000}$$

$$\frac{4}{33} - 0.121212 = \frac{4}{33000000}$$

.
.
.

The sequence of differences is

$$\frac{7}{330}, \quad \frac{4}{3300}, \quad \frac{7}{33000}, \quad \frac{4}{330000}, \quad \frac{7}{3300000}, \quad \frac{4}{33000000}, \quad \cdots$$

This sequence converges to zero and therefore according to the definition stated above, the numeral $0.12121212 \cdots$ represents the fraction 4/33.

The reader is no doubt curious as to where the fraction 4/33 came from in Example 1. In a later section we will show how to find this fraction given the nonterminating decimal numeral.

EXAMPLE 2.   According to the definition the numeral $0.55555 \cdots$ does *not* represent the fraction 7/9 since the sequence of differences between 7/9 and the partial sums of $0.55555 \cdots$ do not converge to zero:

$$\frac{7}{9} - 0.5 = \frac{7}{9} - \frac{5}{10} = \frac{70}{90} - \frac{45}{90} = \frac{25}{90}$$

$$\frac{7}{9} - 0.55 = \frac{7}{9} - \frac{55}{100} = \frac{700}{900} - \frac{495}{900} = \frac{205}{900}$$

$$\frac{7}{9} - 0.555 = \frac{7}{9} - \frac{555}{1000} = \frac{7000}{9000} - \frac{4995}{9000} = \frac{2005}{9000}$$

$$\frac{7}{9} - 0.5555 = \frac{20005}{90000}$$

$$\frac{7}{9} - 0.55555 = \frac{200005}{900000}$$

.
.
.

These differences are illustrated in Fig. 58. As the figure shows these differences cannot converge to zero because none of them are less than 2/9:

$$\frac{25}{90} > \frac{20}{90} = \frac{2}{9}$$

$$\frac{205}{900} > \frac{200}{900} = \frac{2}{9}$$

$$\frac{2005}{9000} > \frac{2000}{9000} = \frac{2}{9}$$

$$\frac{20005}{90000} > \frac{20000}{90000} = \frac{2}{9}$$

$$\frac{200005}{900000} > \frac{200000}{900000} = \frac{2}{9}$$

.
.
.

EXAMPLE 3.   The nonterminating decimal numeral in Example 2 represents the fraction 5/9. The reader should compute the differences between 5/9 and the partial sums of 0.55555 · · · and observe that these differences converge to zero. (The differences are 5/90, 5/900, 5/9000, ...)

Our last example is very important because it shows that the decimal representation of a fraction is not necessarily unique. That is, some fractions have more than one decimal numeral!

EXAMPLE 4.   Consider the nonterminating decimal numeral 0.99999 · · · . We pull the

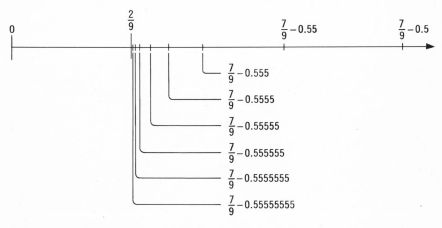

Figure 58   (Distorted scale.)

fraction 1 out of the air (the reader will soon learn how to perform this trick) and compute the differences between 1 and the partial sums of this numeral:

$$1 - 0.9 = 1 - \frac{9}{10} = \frac{1}{10}$$

$$1 - 0.99 = 1 - \frac{99}{100} = \frac{1}{100}$$

$$1 - 0.999 = \frac{1}{1000}$$

$$1 - 0.9999 = \frac{1}{10000}$$

$$1 - 0.99999 = \frac{1}{100000}$$

.

.

.

These differences are converging to zero (see Example 2, p. 256). Therefore according to the definition which assigns meaning to nonterminating decimal numerals, the nonterminating decimal numeral 0.99999 · · · represents the fraction 1. Thus the *distinct* decimal numerals 1 and 0.99999 · · · both represent the same fraction and so consequently 1 = 0.99999 · · · · . We shall continue the discussion of non-uniqueness of decimal representations on p. 268.

Very often students have some trouble in reconciling the result of the last example with their intuition about numbers. The basis of this trouble is that they are (consciously or not) trying to assign meaning to the nonterminating decimal numeral 0.99999 · · · by using what they know about terminating decimal numerals. If one knew and understood only terminating decimal numerals then he would be very likely to think that, in some sense which he could not make very precise, the "number" 0.99999 · · · ought to be "a little less than 1." But this is not so, for according to our definition this numeral represents a number which is not "a little less than 1" but represents the number 1 itself.

On the other hand, many students understand that if our definition assigning meaning to nonterminating decimal numerals is accepted, then there is no choice but to agree that 0.99999 · · · names the number 1. But they are nevertheless unhappy with the result. They understand the logic but dislike the consequences of that logic. There is nothing at all wrong with this attitude. In fact at every opportunity we have made the point that definitions are made the way they are because we approve of the consequences of those definitions. If a definition gives rise to unpleasant results, then we go back and try to change the definition so that the unpleasant consequences will not result. However, the fact of the matter is that in the present situation no unpleasant consequences have resulted. Everything we have said about nonterminating decimal numerals is entirely consistent with the rest of mathematics.

Review Questions

1. It is asserted that the value of a certain nonterminating decimal numeral is the fraction a/b. How would you go about verifying this assertion? On what would you base your verification?

Exercises

1. Show that the given nonterminating decimal numeral represents the given fraction by showing that the differences between the fraction and the partial sums of the numeral converge to zero. Draw number lines to illustrate these differences.
   (a) 0.433333 · · · and 13/30.   (c) 0.4141414141 · · · and 5/11.
   (b) 0.1111 · · · and 1/9.   (d) 1.6666666 · · · and 5/3.
2. Show that 0.83333 · · · ≠ 7/6 by showing that the differences between 7/6 and the partial sums of 0.83333 · · · do not converge to zero. Explain why these differences do not converge to zero. Illustrate on the number line.
3. Consider the nonterminating decimal numeral 0.499999 · · · . Find the fraction represented by this numeral. (*Suggestion:* We do not as yet have a general procedure for finding this fraction so you will have to use your imagination. You might try looking at the partial sums.) Prove that your fraction is represented by this numeral by appealing to the definition of the meaning of a nonterminating decimal numeral.
4. Explain why 0.6363636363 · · · = 7/11.
5. It is possible to regard every terminating decimal numeral as a nonterminating decimal numeral by inserting the digit symbol 0 in all empty places to the right of the units place. For example, the terminating numeral 0.5 and the nonterminating numeral 0.50000000 · · · both represent the same fraction, 1/2. Most of the time we would rather deal with terminating numerals than nonterminating numerals and so we would not want to do this. Sometimes, however, it is a convenience to be able to regard all decimal numerals as nonterminating numerals.
   (a) Prove that 0.5 and 0.500000 · · · each represents the fraction 1/2. (*Suggestion:* To show that 0.500000 · · · represents 1/2 use the notion of convergence to zero.)
   (b) Prove that 5.67 and 5.6700000 · · · represent the same fraction.

Classifying Nonterminating Decimal Numerals

In the next section we will need to refer to an important classification of nonterminating decimal numerals and so we shall discuss that method of classification now.

Among the nonterminating decimal numerals we have seen so far are the following, each of which has a special characteristic:

0.33333 · · ·	0.11111 · · ·
16.1212121212 · · ·	0.4141414141 · · ·
0.55555 · · ·	1.66666 · · ·
0.99999 · · ·	0.833333 · · ·
0.433333 · · ·	0.6363636363 · · ·

The common characteristic shared by each of these numerals is that each involves a digit symbol or a block of digit symbols repeated over and over. That is, to the right of some particular place each numeral consists of a block of digit symbols repeated indefinitely. Such numerals are called *repeating decimal numerals*. The block of digit symbols that is repeated is called (surprisingly enough) the *repeating block* of the numeral. The following table displays the repeating block of each of these numerals and the place in which that block begins to repeat.

Repeating Numeral	*Repeating Block*	*Place Where the Block Begins to Repeat*
0.33333 · · ·	3	Tenths
16.1212121212 · · ·	12	Tenths
0.55555 · · ·	5	Tenths
0.999999 · · ·	9	Tenths
0.433333 · · ·	3	Hundredths
0.11111 · · ·	1	Tenths
0.4141414141 · · ·	41	Tenths
1.66666 · · ·	6	Tenths
0.833333 · · ·	3	Hundredths
0.6363636363 · · ·	63	Tenths
Other examples are:		
15.150617171717171 · · ·	17	Hundred thousandths
32.567891789178917891 · · ·	7891	Thousandths
44.44444 · · ·	4	Hundreds
14.0130130132013201320132 · · ·	0132	Ten millionths
10.001001001001001 · · ·	001	Tenths

The following list of *nonrepeating and nonterminating* numerals is presented without verification; that is, we shall not prove that these numerals are nonrepeating. They are given simply to illustrate that nonrepeating and nonterminating numerals exist.

0.12123123412345123456123456712345678 · · ·
0.1010010001000010000010000001000000001 · · ·
0.1234567891011121314151617181920212223242 5 · · ·
0.1223334444555556666667777777888888889999999991010 · · ·

Exercises

1. Identify the repeating block and the place in which the block begins to repeat in each of these numerals.
   (a) 15.6781341341341341341 34 · · ·
   (b) 15.670670670670167016701670167016701 6701 · · ·
   (c) 55.5555555 · · ·
   (d) 17.100000000010000000001 · · ·

2. (a) List three repeating numerals which have the repeating block 123 and which begin to repeat in the hundredths place.
    (b) List three repeating numerals which have the repeating block 56 and begin to repeat in different places.
    (c) List three repeating numerals which have a repeating block consisting of exactly four digit symbols and begin to repeat in the ten thousandths place.
3. The set of all decimal numerals has been partitioned into three pairwise disjoint sets. One of these sets is the set of terminating numerals. What are the other two?
4. A repeating numeral is a _____ numeral.

THE DECIMAL NUMERAL NAMES FOR FRACTIONS

Finding the Decimal Representation

Earlier in this chapter we saw that every fraction which could be written with a denominator of the special form $2^n 5^m$ had a decimal representation. In fact, every fraction can be represented by a decimal numeral.

Theorem   *Every fraction has a decimal representation.*

This theorem is an *existence* theorem. It asserts a decimal numeral name exists for every fraction. But we do not yet know how to find that representation if the fraction does not have one of the special denominators of the form $2^n 5^m$. What is needed is a general procedure for finding these decimal numerals. As a matter of fact such a procedure is very simple; merely long divide the numerator of the fraction by its denominator. *The resulting quotient is a decimal numeral and represents the fraction n/m.* When we perform this long division one of two things will happen, either the long division process will terminate (in the event that a zero remainder is obtained at some stage) or the process will never terminate (in the event that the remainder at every stage is nonzero). The first example below illustrates the procedure in the case that a zero remainder is obtained at some stage of the long division process.

EXAMPLE 1.   To find the decimal representation of 16/125 long divide 16 by 125:

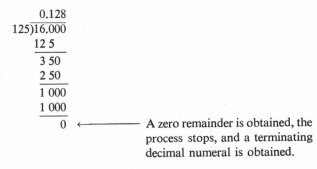

A zero remainder is obtained, the process stops, and a terminating decimal numeral is obtained.

The quotient numeral we have obtained is 0.128 and according to the general procedure this is the decimal representation of the fraction 16/125. This can be verified by replacing the numeral 0.128 by the sum which it abbreviates and simplifying:

$$0.128 = \frac{1}{10} + \frac{2}{100} + \frac{8}{1000}$$

$$= \frac{100}{1000} + \frac{20}{1000} + \frac{8}{1000}$$

$$= \frac{100 + 20 + 8}{1000}$$

$$= \frac{128}{1000} = \frac{64}{500} = \frac{32}{250} = \frac{16}{125}$$

In Example 1 we knew even before we began the long division that we would obtain a terminating decimal numeral because the denominator 125 has the special form $2^n 5^m$: $125 = 2^0 5^3$. In the next example we can predict that the numeral we will obtain will be nonterminating because the denominator is not of this special form.

EXAMPLE 2.   To find the decimal representation of 5/9 we long divide 5 by 9:

```
        0.55555 · · ·
   9)5.00000 · · ·
     4 5
     ___
      50
      45
     ___
      50
      45
     ___
      50
      45
     ___
      50
      45
     ___
      50
      45
     ___
       5
```

None of the remainders will be zero, the process will not terminate and the resulting decimal numeral will be nonterminating.

We know that the procedure has given us the correct decimal representation for 5/9 because we said earlier that 0.55555 · · · names the fraction 5/9. See Example 3, p. 259.

EXAMPLE 3.   We know that the decimal representation of the fraction 7/11 will be nonterminating since the denominator 11 cannot be written in the form $2^n 5^m$. To find this representation we long divide 7 by 11:

$$
\begin{array}{r}
0.636363\cdots \\
11)\overline{7.0000000}\cdots \\
\underline{6\,6} \\
40 \\
\underline{33} \\
70 \\
\underline{66} \\
40 \\
\underline{33} \\
70 \\
\underline{66} \\
40 \\
\underline{33} \\
70 \\
\underline{66} \\
40 \\
\end{array}
$$

We conclude that $7/11 = 0.636363636363\cdots$. (It is clear from an examination of the long division process that the digit symbols 6 and 3 will continue to appear as indicated.) This result can be verified by showing that the differences between $7/11$ and the partial sums of $0.6363636363\cdots$ converge to zero. (This was Exercise 4, p. 261.)

Review Questions

1. Describe the general method for finding the decimal representation of a fraction.
2. When applying the long division process to find the decimal representation of a fraction one of two things will happen. Discuss this.

Exercises

1. Using the long division process find the decimal representation of each of these fractions.
   (a) 1/9.   (c) 5/6.   (e) 71/675.
   (b) 21/11.   (d) 7/9.   (f) 1/11.
2. Each of the following fractions has been written with a denominator of the special form $2^n 5^m$. Therefore the decimal representation of these fractions may be found in two ways: (1) Using the long division process and (2) first writing the fraction with a denominator which is a power of ten and then writing this fraction as a sum of place values, which is then abbreviated to give the required decimal numeral.

Find the representation of these fractions in each of these two ways.
(a) 5/16.   (b) 7/8.   (c) 7/32.   (d) 73/40.
3. Find the decimal representation of the fraction 3/7 by using the long division
process and then verify that the process has given the correct numeral by studying
the differences between 3/7 and the partial sums of your numeral.

Describing the Decimal Representation of a Fraction

Every problem and example we have seen so far points directly to the following theorem.

Theorem   *The decimal representation of a fraction is either terminating or repeating.*

The fractions which can be written with a denominator of the form $2^n 5^m$ have
terminating representations and all other fractions have repeating representations. Now what is even more interesting is that the *converse* of this theorem is
also true.

Theorem   *If a decimal numeral is either terminating or repeating, then it is the
name of a fraction.*

The part of this theorem that says that a terminating numeral names a fraction
is not new, but the other part is. This raises the very natural question, "Given a
repeating decimal numeral how can I find the fraction that numeral represents?"
The theorem states that every repeating numeral names a fraction but it provides
no clue to how one might go about finding the fraction. For example, according
to the theorem the numeral $15.5617892892892892 \cdots$ names a fraction. It is
certainly desirable to be able to find a symbol of the form n/m which names the
same fraction. The examples which follow illustrate a procedure by which a
numeral of the form n/m may be obtained from a repeating numeral.

EXAMPLE 1.   Consider the repeating numeral $0.44444 \cdots$. To find the fraction represented by this numeral begin by writing

$$x = 0.44444 \cdots$$

Next multiply both sides of this equation by 10 and obtain

$$10x = 4.44444 \cdots$$

Finally, subtract x from $10x$:

$$
\begin{aligned}
10x &= 4.44444 \cdots \\
x &= 0.44444 \cdots \\
\hline
10x - x &= 4.00000 \cdots = 4
\end{aligned}
$$

But $10x - x = 10x - 1x = (10 - 1)x = 9x$. Hence

$$9x = 4 \quad \text{or} \quad x = 4/9$$

The last equation together with the first imply that

$$\frac{4}{9} = 0.44444 \cdots$$

This fact can be verified by computing the differences between 4/9 and the partial sums of the nonterminating numeral 0.44444 · · · . These differences converge to zero and therefore the conclusion that 4/9 and 0.44444 · · · name the same fraction is verified.

Now if we study this example very carefully we will see why we were able to get the result that we wanted. The given numeral (0.44444 · · ·) was repeating. Because of this we were able to multiply the given numeral by a power of ten (10^1) and obtain a second repeating numeral (4.44444 · · ·) which "agreed" with the given one in all the places to the right of the units place. Then, upon subtracting the smaller of these from the larger, we were able to obtain an equation which involved only terminating decimal numerals, the equation $9x = 4$. This equation could easily be solved for x and there was our answer: 4/9. So by obtaining a pair of repeating numerals which "agreed" to the right of the units place we were able to subtract one from the other and "wipe out" the troublesome nonterminating part of the numerals. Let's look at another example.

EXAMPLE 2.   Consider the decimal numeral 0.2323232323 · · · . We seek to find two decimal numerals, both repeating, which have exactly the same digit symbols in every place to the right of the units place. We can do this by writing

$$x = 0.2323232323 \cdots$$

and then taking as our second decimal numeral the numeral

$$100x = 23.2323232323 \cdots$$

These two are the numerals we sought because now upon subtracting,

$$
\begin{array}{r}
100x = 23.2323232323 \cdots \\
x = 0.2323232323 \cdots \\
\hline
99x = 23.0000000 \cdots = 23
\end{array}
$$

we obtain the equation $99x = 23$ and can conclude that $x = 23/99$. That is, $23/99 = 0.23232323 \cdots$.

In the first two examples the repeating block began to repeat in the tenths place. If the repeating block begins to repeat in a place to the right of the tenths place, then we must work a little harder to obtain the pair of "agreeing" numerals that we need. Here is an example.

EXAMPLE 3.   Find the fraction which is named by the repeating numeral 0.12344444444 · · · .
Solution: We begin as before by writing

$$x = 0.12344444 \cdots$$

Now remember that we are looking for two numerals which "agree" in *all* places to the right of the decimal point. We can find them by multiplying x by both 1000 and 10000:

$$1000x = 123.44444 \cdots$$
$$10000x = 1234.44444 \cdots$$

Then upon subtracting we get

$$10000x = 1234.44444 \cdots$$
$$1000x = 123.44444 \cdots$$
$$\overline{9000x = 1111.00000 \cdots = 1111}$$

So $x = 1111/9000$ and consequently $0.12344444 \cdots$ and $1111/9000$ name the same fraction.

Review Questions

1. How can the decimal numeral of a fraction be described?
2. Given a decimal numeral, how can one tell whether or not it represents a fraction?
3. Describe the method used to find the fraction represented by a given repeating decimal numeral.
4. Suppose one is given a repeating decimal numeral which begins to repeat in the tenths place and whose repeating block is composed of n (n a counting number) digit symbols. A pair of "agreeing" decimal numerals can be found by taking the given numeral as one of these and taking as the other the given numeral multiplied by what power of ten?
5. Suppose in a given repeating numeral the repeating block starts to repeat in the nth place to the right of the decimal point and is composed of m digit symbols. Describe how you would obtain a pair of "agreeing" decimal numerals.

Exercises

1. Find the decimal representations of the following fractions. Identify the repeating blocks and tell in which place this block begins to repeat.
   (a) 5/111.   (c) 5/13.   (e) 1111/900.
   (b) 146/99.   (d) 6/13.   (f) 3/17.
2. Find the fractions represented by the following repeating decimal numerals.
   (a) $0.222222 \cdots$.   (e) $12.1622222 \cdots$.
   (b) $4.32323232 \cdots$.   (f) $0.120344444 \cdots$.
   (c) $0.123123123 \cdots$.   (g) $0.13657575757 \cdots$.
   (d) $16.50505050 \cdots$.   (h) $1489.623412412412412 \cdots$.

Uniqueness of Decimal Representations

In Example 4, p. 259, we saw that according to the way we have assigned meaning to nonterminating decimal numerals the two different decimals numerals 1 and $0.99999 \cdots$ each represent the same number. We conclude from this that not all fractions have unique decimal representations. Let us apply the method used above to see once more that $0.99999\cdots$ names the fraction 1.

Put $x = 0.99999\cdots$. Then $10x = 9.99999\cdots$ and
$10x - x = 9.99999\cdots - 0.99999\cdots = 9.00000\cdots = 9$.
Thus $9x = 9$ and so $x = 1$.

The following theorem provides complete information as to the uniqueness of decimal representations. It shows that all the trouble is due to the existence of decimal numerals which have a repeating block consisting of the single digit symbol 9.

Uniqueness of Representation Theorem (1) *If a fraction can be represented by a terminating numeral, then it can also be represented by a repeating numeral whose repeating block consists of the single digit symbol 9.* (2) *If a fraction can be represented by a repeating numeral whose repeating block consists of the single digit symbol 9, then that fraction can also be represented by a terminating numeral.* (3) *All fractions except those mentioned in parts* (1) *and* (2) *have a unique decimal representation.*

EXAMPLE. The decimal numerals $0.347999999999\cdots$ and 0.348 represent the same fraction. We can verify this by finding the fractions represented by these numerals and observing that they are equal. First, to find the fraction represented by the repeating numeral write

$$
\begin{aligned}
x &= 0.34799999\cdots \\
1000x &= 347.9999999\cdots \\
10000x &= 3479.999999\cdots
\end{aligned}
$$

Then subtracting,

$$
\begin{aligned}
10000x &= 3479.9999999\cdots \\
1000x &= 347.9999999\cdots \\
\hline
9000x &= 3132.0000000\cdots = 3132
\end{aligned}
$$

Hence $x = 3132/9000$. Next, to find the fraction represented by the terminating numeral write

$$
\begin{aligned}
0.348 &= \frac{3}{10} + \frac{4}{100} + \frac{8}{1000} \\
&= \frac{300}{1000} + \frac{40}{1000} + \frac{8}{1000} \\
&= \frac{348}{1000}
\end{aligned}
$$

Now observe that $3132/9000 = 348/1000$ since

$$
\frac{348}{1000} = \frac{348 \cdot 9}{1000 \cdot 9} = \frac{3132}{9000}
$$

We conclude that $0.348 = 0.3479999999\cdots$.

In order to avoid the unpleasantness of nonunique decimal numeral names for fractions it is possible to stipulate that one will not allow the use of any numerals which are repeating and have as their repeating block the digit symbol 9*. There is nothing wrong with this approach and once the issues involved are fully understood it is a rather convenient thing to do. We shall have no need to use such repeating numerals and so we shall do this. From now on, we shall not permit the use of decimal numerals which end in 9's. Now that we have agreed to this each fraction has a unique decimal representation.

Review Questions

1. Suppose a fraction has two different decimal representations. What can you say about these representations?
2. Suppose a fraction has a unique representation. What can be said about that representation?
3. If the fraction named by n/m (in lowest terms) has a unique representation, what can you say about m? What can you say about m if the fraction has two representations?

Exercises

1. Show that each pair of decimal numerals represent the same fraction.
   (a) 0.1199999 · · · and 0.12.
   (b) 0.8909999999 · · · and 0.891.
   (c) 1.9999999 · · · and 2.
   (d) 1.4999999 · · · and 1.5.
2. By examining the pairs of numerals in Exercise 1, can you say which terminating decimal numeral represents the same fraction as does the repeating decimal numeral
   (a) 0.13699999 · · · .   (c) 0.0001999999 · · · .
   (b) 17.99999 · · · .   (d) 9.9999999 · · · .
3. By examining the pairs of numerals in Exercise 1 can you find the repeating decimal numeral which represents the same fraction as does the terminating decimal numeral
   (a) 1.3.   (c) 78.1042.
   (b) 0.145.   (d) 0.0001.

DECIMAL REPRESENTATIONS OF RATIONAL NUMBERS

Since every rational number is either a fraction or the additive inverse of a fraction, and since we know how to find the decimal representation of a fraction, it is clear how we would find the decimal representation of a rational number.

EXAMPLE.   To represent the rational number $-2/5$ by a decimal numeral we observe that $-2/5$ is the additive inverse of $2/5$ and that the decimal representation of $2/5$ is 0.4. Then the decimal representation of $-2/5$ is -0.4.

---

* We must either outlaw these repeating decimal numerals or outlaw the terminating decimal numerals. The latter course would be decidedly inconvenient.

Are there any decimal numerals which do not represent rational numbers? Surely; all we have to do is to write out a nonterminating and nonrepeating decimal numeral. Such a numeral cannot represent a rational number. But then a very good question is, "If a nonrepeating and nonterminating numeral does not represent a rational number, then why is it called a numeral, for the only numbers we know of are the rational numbers?" It is in fact true that each of these nonterminating and nonrepeating decimal numerals represents a new kind of number which we have not yet studied. These new numbers are called *irrational numbers* and we shall discuss them in the next chapter.

Review Questions

1. How can you identify a rational number from its decimal representation?
2. Assuming that every decimal numeral represents some kind of number, how can you prove that there exist numbers which are not rational numbers by using decimal numerals?
3. Give an example of a nonrepeating and nonterminating decimal numeral.
4. What are numbers called which are represented by nonterminating and nonrepeating decimal numerals?

Exercises

1. Represent the following rational numbers by decimal numerals.
    (a) $-5/7$.   (c) $-(8/3)$.
    (b) $7/-5$.   (d) $-5/3$.
2. What are the rational numbers represented by these decimal numerals?
    (a) $-18.45454545 \cdots$.
    (b) $-8.91349134913491349134 \cdots$.
    (c) -678.901.
    (d) $-0.571428571428571428 \cdots$.
3. It is a fact that $\sqrt{2}$ has a decimal representation. What kind of representation does this number have?

CHAPTER 9

The Real Number System

We have developed the idea of number from its intuitive beginnings through the system of rational numbers. The next step in this development is the *system of real numbers*. The study of this number system lies on the boundary of arithmetic and therefore we shall restrict our attention to the identification of the real numbers and the mention of a few useful and interesting results concerning these numbers which relate to questions we have already considered in the other number systems we have studied.

THE REAL NUMBERS

Recall that an *irrational number* is a number which is represented by a nonterminating and nonrepeating decimal numeral. For example, the numbers represented by these numerals are irrational:

156.101201230123401234501234560123456701234567801 2 · · ·
1037.151151115111151111151111115111111151111111511 · · ·
−7.123456789101112131415161718192021222324252627 28 · · ·

It may be observed that there is a pattern to the occurrence of the digit symbols in these numerals. It is because of this pattern that we are able to decide that these numerals are nonrepeating. But not all irrational numbers have numerals displaying such a pattern, or if they do the pattern has yet to be identified. Consider the number $\sqrt{2}$. We know that this number is not a rational number and thus its decimal representation must be nonterminating and nonrepeating. By any one of the standard procedures for finding square roots it can be seen that the decimal representation of $\sqrt{2}$ begins like this: 1.41213565 · · · . In fact many thousands of the digit symbols in this decimal representation have been computed but no pattern to the occurrence of these digit symbols has been discerned. Another irrational number whose decimal numeral has no discernible pattern to the occurrence of the digit symbols is the irrational number $\pi = 3.1415926536 \cdots$.

The next system of numbers in the hierarchy of number systems is the *real number system*. A *real number* is a number which is either a rational number or an irrational number. In other words, *a real number is a number which is representable by a decimal numeral.* Our investigations into the real number system will be limited to a study of the real number line. Some interesting facts about the real numbers can be visualized by using this line.

However before we take up the real number line let us note that the set of real numbers is an infinite set (obviously, since it contains the rational numbers) which is *not* equivalent to the set of all counting numbers. The other sets of numbers (fractions, integers, and rationals) were all equivalent to the set of counting numbers and because of this they are called *countably infinite* sets. Infinite sets which are not equivalent to the set of counting numbers are called *uncountably infinite* sets.

Theorem *The set of real numbers is uncountably infinite.*

The Proof: We shall prove this theorem by using the indirect method of proof. Thus we begin by assuming that the set of real numbers is equivalent to the set of counting numbers and proceed from this assumption to argue in such a way that a contradiction is obtained.

For the purposes of this proof let us agree to regard each terminating decimal numeral as a nonterminating numeral by inserting zeros in the empty places to the right of the units place. Next, recall that some real numbers do not have unique decimal representations. To avoid this non-uniqueness of representation let us also agree that we shall never represent a real number by a repeating numeral with a repeating block consisting of the single digit symbol 9. These real numbers will always be represented by decimal numerals ending in 0's. With these agreements in effect each real number has a unique representation as a nonterminating decimal numeral. In this proof we will not distinguish between real numbers and their unique nonterminating numerals.

With these understandings in mind let us assume that the theorem is false; that is, we take as an initial assumption that the set of all real numbers is equivalent to the set of all counting numbers. Now since the set of real numbers is equivalent to the set of counting numbers, there is a one-to-one correspondence between these sets. For concreteness let us suppose that this correspondence pairs

$$-56.51687012300000\cdots \quad \text{with} \quad 0$$
$$156.14141414141414\cdots \quad \text{with} \quad 1$$
$$0.60000000000000\cdots \quad \text{with} \quad 2$$
$$-11.45645674567845\cdots \quad \text{with} \quad 3$$
$$14567.34000000000004\cdots \quad \text{with} \quad 4$$
$$-0.00000400000000\cdots \quad \text{with} \quad 5$$
$$0.00000600000000\cdots \quad \text{with} \quad 6$$

and so on. (Our argument will work no matter which real numbers are paired with these counting numbers, but by specifying the real numbers to be paired with the first few counting numbers we can do what we have to do on a more concrete level than would otherwise be possible.) We are going to use this one-to-one correspondence to define a "special" real number. We define this special real number by stipulating which digits should appear in the various places of its decimal numeral as follows:

1. All places to the left of the units place are empty.
2. To find the digit in the units place look at the digit in the units place of the real number corresponding to the counting number 0. If this digit is nonzero, then put 0 in the units place of the special real number. If the digit in the units place of the real number corresponding to 0 is 0, then put 1 in the units place of the special real number.
3. The digit in the nth place to the right of the units place in the special real number is

    0 if the digit in the nth place to the right of the units place in the real number corresponding to the counting number n is nonzero.

    1 if the digit in the nth place to the right of the units place in the real number corresponding to the counting number n is 0.

Thus if the correspondence between the real numbers and the counting numbers begins as shown above, then the special real number we have defined would look like this:

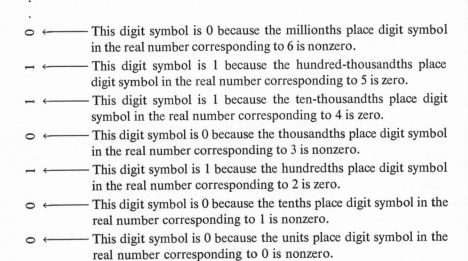

.
.
.

0 ⟵——— This digit symbol is 0 because the millionths place digit symbol in the real number corresponding to 6 is nonzero.

1 ⟵——— This digit symbol is 1 because the hundred-thousandths place digit symbol in the real number corresponding to 5 is zero.

1 ⟵——— This digit symbol is 1 because the ten-thousandths place digit symbol in the real number corresponding to 4 is zero.

0 ⟵——— This digit symbol is 0 because the thousandths place digit symbol in the real number corresponding to 3 is nonzero.

1 ⟵——— This digit symbol is 1 because the hundredths place digit symbol in the real number corresponding to 2 is zero.

0 ⟵——— This digit symbol is 0 because the tenths place digit symbol in the real number corresponding to 1 is nonzero.

0 ⟵——— This digit symbol is 0 because the units place digit symbol in the real number corresponding to 0 is nonzero.

Now according to our initial assumption there is a one-to-one correspondence between the set of all real numbers and the set of counting numbers. Hence in particular the special real number corresponds to some counting number. *But this is impossible!* The special real number was constructed in just such a way that it would not correspond to any counting number. For example, the special real number does not correspond to the counting number 0 because it differs in the units place from the real number corresponding to 0. The special real number does not correspond to the counting number 1 since it differs in the tenths place from the real number corresponding to 1. The special real number does not correspond to 2 because it differs in the hundredths place from the real number corresponding to 2. More generally, the special real number does not correspond to the counting number n ($n > 0$) because it differs in the nth place to the right of the units place from the real number corresponding to the counting number n.

Thus we have obtained a contradiction. Upon close examination it will be observed that this contradiction did not arise from an error in the argument and so it must have arisen because the assumption made at the beginning is false. This means that the set of real numbers is not equivalent to the set of counting numbers.

❈

Exercises

1. Illustrate the relations between the sets of counting numbers, fractions, integers, rational numbers, irrational numbers, and real numbers by using Euler circles.
2. Explain why the decimal numeral

   $$0.10100100010000100000100000010000000100000000001000 \cdots$$

   names an irrational number. (*Suggestion:* Use an indirect proof. Assume the numeral is repeating. Explain why the digit symbol 1 must occur at least once in the repeating block. Suppose the repeating block contains n digit symbols. Go out in the decimal numeral until you get to a place where there are at least $2n$ 0's in succession. Obtain a contradiction.)
3. Suppose (with reference to the proof of the theorem that the set of real numbers is uncountably infinite) that the one-to-one correspondence between real numbers and counting numbers had begun like this:

   $$
   \begin{aligned}
   56.108951607 \cdots &\quad \text{is paired with} \quad 0 \\
   345.102102102 \cdots &\quad \text{is paired with} \quad 1 \\
   -0.123457679 \cdots &\quad \text{is paired with} \quad 2 \\
   -10.000000000 \cdots &\quad \text{is paired with} \quad 3 \\
   8.345678990 \cdots &\quad \text{is paired with} \quad 4 \\
   -18.101203104 \cdots &\quad \text{is paired with} \quad 5
   \end{aligned}
   $$

   What are the first five digit symbols to the right of the units place in the special real number we constructed in the proof? Why does this special real number not correspond to any of the counting numbers 0, 1, 2, 3, 4, or 5?

THE REAL NUMBER LINE

We conclude our study of the real numbers with a discussion of the real number line.

Let a line be drawn and on this line select two distinct points to be called the *origin* and the *unit*. Once these two points are chosen the real numbers which are rational numbers may be paired with points on the line in the same way we paired rational numbers with points to construct the rational number line. The pairing of irrational numbers with points on the line is somewhat more complicated. To illustrate the procedure for pairing irrational numbers with points on the line let us consider an example using the irrational number $\pi = 3.14159265\cdots$. The *partial sums* of this irrational number are rational numbers and thus have already been paired with points on the line. The points corresponding to some of the partial sums of π have been pictured in Fig. 59. Now it is possible to prove (but we shall not do so) that the points pictured in Fig. 59 are converging to the point P shown in that figure. By this we mean that the distances between the point P and the points corresponding to the partial sums are converging to zero. Because the distances between P and the points corresponding to the partial sums are converging to zero and because the differences between π and the partial sums converge to zero, we pair the number π with the point P.

Let us look at another example of how we pair an irrational number with a point on the line.

EXAMPLE.   To find a point to pair with the irrational number $\sqrt{2}$ we first write out the decimal representation of $\sqrt{2}$:

$$1.41213565\cdots$$

and then we locate the points which correspond to the partial sums of this nonterminating numeral (see Fig. 60). It is now possible to prove that there is a unique point Q as shown in Fig. 60 such that the distances between Q and the partial sums of $\sqrt{2}$ are converging to zero. This is the point that we pair with the irrational number $\sqrt{2}$.

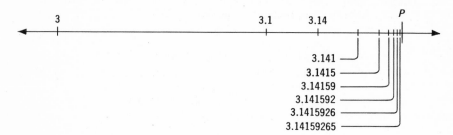

Figure 59   The partial sums of π. (Distorted scale.)

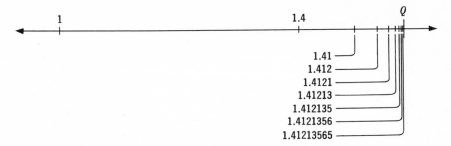

Figure 60 The partial sums of $\sqrt{2}$. (Distorted scale.)

As these two examples illustrate, given an irrational number n it is possible to find a unique point N on the line such that the distances between N and the points corresponding to the partial sums of the number n converge to zero. The point N is then paired with the number n.

This shows that there is a one-to-one correspondence between the set of all real numbers and a certain set of points on the line. This correspondence is in fact between the set of all real numbers and the set of *all* points on the line. This means that there are no "holes" in the real number line as there were in the rational number line. *Every point on the line corresponds to a real number.* Let us see how we could find the real number corresponding to a given point.

In Fig. 61 we show a point P chosen arbitrarily on the line. (In Fig. 61 the point P happens to lie to the right of the origin but our statements will work no matter where the point P is located with respect to the origin.) Here is how we find the real number that is paired with this point. Locate the integers on the line. The point P will either coincide with one of these integer-points or will lie between some pair of adjacent integer points. If P coincides with one of the integer points, then we will have found the real number to which P corresponds. So suppose that P lies between some pair of adjacent integer points, for example, the points 7 and 8 (see Fig. 62).

Figure 61

Figure 62

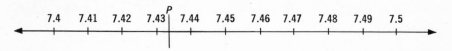

Figure 63

Figure 64

Now subdivide the interval between the points 7 and 8 into tenths (see Fig. 63.) If the point P coincides with one of these subdivision points, we will have found the real number to which P corresponds. So suppose that P lies between some two adjacent subdivision points. For concreteness, suppose that P lies between the subdivision points 7.4 and 7.5. Repeat this process of subdivision into tenths. Subdivide the interval between 7.4 and 7.5 into tenths. If P coincides with one of the subdivision points, then we will have found the real number to which P corresponds. Otherwise P will lie between some pair of adjacent subdivision points. Suppose for concreteness that P lies between 7.43 and 7.44 (see Fig. 64.)

This process of subdividing intervals can be repeated indefinitely. If at any stage the point P coincides with one of the subdivision points, then we will have found the real number to which P corresponds and P will correspond to a number with a terminating decimal numeral. Otherwise P will never (no matter how many times the process of subdividing intervals is repeated) coincide with a point of subdivision and in this case P will correspond to a number with a nonterminating decimal representation.

In our example we see that the number x which corresponds to P satisfies the inequalities

$$7 < x < 8$$
$$7.4 < x < 7.5$$
$$7.43 < x < 7.44$$

and so we know that the decimal representation of the number corresponding to the point P begins with the digits $7.43 \cdots$. To determine more digit symbols in this numeral it is necessary to continue the process of subdividing intervals. The longer this process of subdividing is carried on, the more digit symbols in the numeral will be determined.

We have shown how to construct a one-to-one correspondence between the set of real numbers and the set of points on a line, and so the set of real numbers is equivalent to the set of points on a line. This fact has many important and useful consequences. For instance, it follows from this equivalence that there are no "holes" in the real number line as there were in the rational number line and so it is possible to measure the length of any line segment by using real numbers. Another consequence of this equivalence is that the set of all points on a line is an uncountable set. For the real numbers are uncountable, and since they are equivalent to the set of points on a line, the set of points on a line must also be uncountable.

Another property of the set of all real numbers is that this set possesses the density property. We leave the discussion of this property of the real numbers to the reader.

Exercises

1. Determine the units and tenths places in the decimal representation of the real number which corresponds to the point P shown in the figure below.

2. The following real numbers correspond to points on the real number line. As nearly as you can locate these points.
   (a) $1.23456 \cdots$.   (b) $-5.1647921 \cdots$.   (c) $-\pi$.
3. Construct a rectangle of dimensions 1 inch by 2 inches. Draw a diagonal of this rectangle. The length of this diagonal is $\sqrt{5}$. Now lay off this diagonal on a number line (with unit distance equal to 1 inch) so that one end lies at the origin and the other end lies to the right of the origin. Label the point of the line which coincides with this other end P. Find the units and tenths place digit symbols in the real number which corresponds to P by subdividing intervals.
4. Draw a line segment whose length can be measured in the system of real numbers but not in the system of rational numbers.
5. (a) Define what it ought to mean to say that one real number is *less than* another. (*Suggestion:* Phrase the definition of *less than* in terms of the decimal numerals which represent the real numbers.)
   (b) Define the relation of *greater than* for real numbers.
   (c) Find a real number which is greater than the smaller of the given pair of real numbers and less than the larger of the given real numbers.
      (i) $1.23456789 \cdots$ and $1.234566897 \cdots$.
      (ii) $23.141414141414 \cdots$ and $23.141414151414 \cdots$.
      (iii) $16.000000000 \cdots$ and $15.999999999992999 \cdots$.
   (d) If $1.0000000 \cdots$ and $0.9999999 \cdots$ were different real numbers, then it ought to be possible to find a real number between them. Try to find a real number between these two. Conclude that $1.0000 \cdots = 0.9999 \cdots$.
   (e) Generalize all of the above and write out a proof that the real numbers possess the density property. (*Suggestion:* It will probably make things easier if you outlaw terminating numerals and repeating numerals ending in 9's.)

Review Questions

1. What is an irrational number? What is a rational number? What is a real number?

2. Give examples of irrational numbers by giving examples of nonterminating and nonrepeating decimal numerals.
3. What are the first five digit symbols in the decimal representation of $\sqrt{2}$? Of π?
4. What does it mean to say that a set is countably infinite? That it is uncountably infinite?
5. Give two examples of uncountably infinite sets.
6. What method of proof was used to prove that the set of all real numbers is uncountably infinite? Can you describe in general terms how this theorem was proved?
7. How are the irrational numbers located on the line?
8. Given a point on the line, how is the real number to which it corresponds determined?

CHAPTER 10

Systems of Numeration

The decimal system is the most widely used system of numeration in the world today. In fact, except for a few isolated exceptions, no other system has any application at all. Nevertheless there are other systems which are in many respects just as good as the decimal system and in some respects even better. In this chapter we are going to examine some of these systems.

In discussing these systems of numeration we shall limit ourselves to the counting numbers. It is possible to use any one of them to name each of the real numbers, but to do this would draw us more deeply into the topic than we wish to go. We want to make only a brief survey, for these systems per se do not interest us. We are concerned with them mainly because by studying them and noting their similarities to the decimal system we can put the decimal system into proper perspective.

POLYNOMIALS IN n

In the decimal system the counting numbers are represented by numerals which are abbreviations for certain sums (of place values). These sums are examples of what we shall call *polynomials in ten*.*

Definition of Polynomial in Ten *A polynomial in ten is a sum of finitely many summands each of which has the special form*

$$d(10^m)$$

where the counting number d, called the coefficient of the summand in which it occurs, is less than ten and where m is a counting number.

EXAMPLE. The counting number represented in the decimal system by the numeral 234 can be expressed as a polynomial in ten by writing out the sum of which the numeral 234 is the abbreviation:

$$234 = 2(10^2) + 3(10^1) + 4(10^0)$$

* The word *nomial* means "summand" so *polynomial* means "many summands."

The polynomial in ten is the sum of the place values of the digit symbols occurring in the decimal numeral.

Now it is not unreasonable to wonder, after having defined *polynomial in ten*, why we should not also define polynomials in six, in eight, or even in thirty-four. There is nothing about the definition of *polynomial in ten* which depends upon the particular nature of the counting number ten. In fact, if *n* is any counting number greater than one we can define *polynomial in n*.

Definition of Polynomial in *n*   *A polynomial in n (where n is a counting number greater than* 1) *is a sum of finitely many summands each of which has the special form*

$$d(n^m)$$

where the coefficient d is a counting number less than n and where m is a counting number.

EXAMPLES.   The sum

$$5(8^3) + 6(8^2) + 0(8^1) + 4(8^0)$$

is a polynomial in eight. Each coefficient is a counting number less than eight and each summand involves a power of eight. The sum

$$1(2^5) + 1(2^4) + 0(2^3) + 0(2^2) + 1(2^1) + 1(2^0)$$

is a polynomial in two since each summand is the product of a coefficient less than two and a power of two.

We already know that every counting number can be written as a polynomial in ten. The fundamental observation that enables us to invent new systems of numeration is that the number ten is not unique in this regard. Every counting number can be written as a polynomial in *n* where *n* is *any* counting number greater than 1. To illustrate this important fact in Fig. 65 we have written certain counting numbers as polynomials in ten, five, eight, and two.

A Computational Tool

We can write small counting numbers as polynomials in *n* without any special computational tool. But for larger counting numbers, finding the polynomial in *n* may involve more work and greater difficulty. It is therefore convenient to have available some sort of purely computational procedure for finding polynomials in *n* for those cases where the polynomial is not evident simply by inspection. There is a simple way to find this polynomial which involves only the ability to perform long division. We shall introduce this procedure by means of two examples.

Counting Number	Polynomial in Ten	Polynomial in Five	Polynomial in Eight	Polynomial in Two
Zero	$0(10^0)$	$0(5^0)$	$0(8^0)$	$0(2^0)$
One	$1(10^0)$	$1(5^0)$	$1(8^0)$	$1(2^0)$
Two	$2(10^0)$	$2(5^0)$	$2(8^0)$	$1(2^1) + 0(2^0)$
Three	$3(10^0)$	$3(5^0)$	$3(8^0)$	$1(2^1) + 1(2^0)$
Four	$4(10^0)$	$4(5^0)$	$4(8^0)$	$1(2^2) + 0(2^1) + 0(2^0)$
Five	$5(10^0)$	$1(5^1) + 0(5^0)$	$5(8^0)$	$1(2^2) + 0(2^1) + 1(2^0)$
Eight	$8(10^0)$	$1(5^1) + 3(5^0)$	$1(8^1) + 0(8^0)$	$1(2^3) + 0(2^2) + 0(2^1) + 0(2^0)$
Ten	$1(10^1) + 0(10^0)$	$2(5^1) + 0(5^0)$	$1(8^1) + 2(8^0)$	$1(2^3) + 0(2^2) + 1(2^1) + 0(2^0)$
Fourteen	$1(10^1) + 4(10^0)$	$2(5^1) + 4(5^0)$	$1(8^1) + 6(8^0)$	$1(2^3) + 1(2^2) + 1(2^1) + 0(2^0)$
Fifteen	$1(10^1) + 5(10^0)$	$3(5^1) + 0(5^0)$	$1(8^1) + 7(8^0)$	$1(2^3) + 1(2^2) + 1(2^1) + 1(2^0)$
Sixteen	$1(10^1) + 6(10^0)$	$3(5^1) + 1(5^0)$	$2(8^1) + 0(8^0)$	$1(2^4) + 0(2^3) + 0(2^2) + 0(2^1) + 0(2^0)$
Twenty-five	$2(10^1) + 5(10^0)$	$1(5^2) + 0(5^1) + 0(5^0)$	$3(8^1) + 1(8^0)$	$1(2^4) + 1(2^3) + 0(2^2) + 0(2^1) + 1(2^0)$
Sixty-four	$6(10^1) + 4(10^0)$	$2(5^2) + 2(5^1) + 4(5^0)$	$1(8^2) + 0(8^1) + 0(8^0)$	$1(2^6) + 0(2^5) + 0(2^4) + 0(2^3) + 0(2^2) + 0(2^1) + 0(2^0)$
One hundred	$1(10^2) + 0(10^1) + 0(10^0)$	$4(5^2) + 0(5^1) + 0(5^0)$	$1(8^2) + 4(8^1) + 4(8^0)$	$1(2^6) + 1(2^5) + 0(2^4) + 0(2^3) + 1(2^2) + 0(2^1) + 0(2^0)$

Figure 65

EXAMPLE 1. To write the counting number 257 as a polynomial in eight we carry out a sequence of long divisions as shown below:

$$257 = 8(32) + 1$$
$$32 = 8(4) + 0$$
$$4 = 8(0) + 4$$

The idea is to continue dividing the quotients by 8 until a quotient of 0 is obtained. Now consider the remainders in reverse order from the order in which they were obtained:

$$4, \quad 0, \quad \text{and} \quad 1$$

These numbers are the coefficients of the desired polynomial in eight. That is, the polynomial in eight that we want is $4(8^2) + 0(8^1) + 1(8^0)$.

EXAMPLE 2. To write 1479 as a polynomial in five we proceed with the long divisions as shown below:

$$1479 = 5(295) + 4$$
$$295 = 5(59) + 0$$
$$59 = 5(11) + 4$$
$$11 = 5(2) + 1$$
$$2 = 5(0) + 2$$

Observe that we have continued to long divide quotients by 5 until a quotient of 0 was obtained. The remainders (in reverse order from the order in which they were obtained) are

$$2, \quad 1, \quad 4, \quad 0, \quad \text{and} \quad 4$$

These numbers are the coefficients of the desired polynomial which is $2(5^4) + 1(5^3) + 4(5^2) + 0(5^1) + 4(5^0)$.

Now let us reexamine each of these examples and verify that this procedure has provided us with the polynomials we wanted. In Example 1 we obtained equations which can be combined as follows:

$257 = 8(32) + 1$	(First equation)
$= 8[8(4) + 0] + 1$	(Substituting the second equation)
$= (8^2)(4) + (8)(0) + 1$	(Rewriting)
$= 4(8^2) + 0(8^1) + 1(8^0)$	(Rewriting)

This is exactly the polynomial obtained by using the procedure. Hence the procedure has given us the correct polynomial. In Example 2 we combine the equations as follows:

$1479 = 5(295) + 4$	(First equation)
$= 5[5(59) + 0] + 4$	(Substituting the second equation)
$= (5^2)(59) + (5)(0) + 4$	(Rewriting)
$= (5^2)[5(11) + 4] + (5)(0) + 4$	(Substituting the third equation)

$$= (5^3)(11) + (5^2)(4) + (5)(0) + 4 \qquad \text{(Rewriting)}$$
$$= (5^3)[5(2) + 1] + (5^2)(4) + (5)(0) + 4 \qquad \text{(Substituting the fourth equation)}$$
$$= (5^4)(2) + (5^3)(1) + (5^2)(4) + (5)(0) + 4 \qquad \text{(Rewriting)}$$
$$= 2(5^4) + 1(5^3) + 4(5^2) + 0(5^1) + 4(5^0) \qquad \text{(Rewriting)}$$

The last polynomial (which is a polynomial in five) is the polynomial obtained by using the procedure and thus again we see that the procedure gives the correct result.

We shall not describe a proof that this procedure will always give the desired polynomial, but such a proof can be constructed in a manner similar to the way we have verified the correctness of the procedure in these two examples.

Review Questions

1. What is a polynomial in n?
2. What do we mean by the *coefficients* of a polynomial in n?
3. Why do we not bother defining a polynomial in one or a polynomial in zero?
4. Describe the procedure you would use to write a large counting number as a polynomial in n.

Exercises

1. Write each of the following counting numbers as a polynomial in ten, eight, five, and two. Do not use the procedure for doing this, but find these polynomials by inspection alone.

   (a) 9.   (e) 17.   (h) 20.
   (b) 11.   (f) 18.   (i) 21.
   (c) 12.   (g) 19.   (j) 22.
   (d) 13.

2. Use the procedure to write each of the following counting numbers as a polynomial in eight and in five.

   (a) 2345.   (c) 1000000.   (e) 3456.
   (b) 781.   (d) 11890.   (f) 10145.

3. Use the procedure to find the polynomial in seven which represents the counting number 89. Then combine the equations so obtained and verify that the polynomial is the correct one.

4. The polynomial $5(7^4) + 3(7^3) + 8(7^2) + 0(7^1) + 2(7^0)$ is *not* a polynomial in seven. Explain why it is not. Rewrite this expression as a polynomial in seven.

THE NEW SYSTEMS OF NUMERATION

It may already be evident to the reader how the new systems of numeration are constructed. For after all,

1. We know that to represent a counting number by a decimal numeral we

should first express that counting number as a polynomial in ten and then abbreviate the polynomial by writing down its coefficients.

2. We know that every counting number can be expressed as a polynomial in n ($n > 1$).

All that remains is to say that to obtain the new numerals we should abbreviate the polynomials in n just as we abbreviated the polynomials in ten to obtain the decimal numerals. For no particular reason we shall first discuss the new system of numeration obtained when n is chosen to be eight.

The Octimal System

Let us recall once more how the decimal numeral for a counting number is found. The counting number is first written as a polynomial in ten and then this polynomial is abbreviated by writing down its coefficients. We proceed in exactly the same way in the octimal system except that we begin by expressing the counting number as a polynomial in eight. For example, to find the octimal numeral for the counting number fifteen we write fifteen as a polynomial in eight,

$$1(8^1) + 7(8^0)$$

and then we abbreviate this polynomial by writing down its coefficients:

$$17$$

Hence the octimal numeral* for fifteen is 17. To make it abundantly clear that the numeral 17 is an octimal numeral we shall use a subscript and write 17_8.

Here are some more examples.

EXAMPLE 1.   To represent eleven by an octimal numeral we first write eleven as a polynomial in eight: $1(8^1) + 3(8^0)$. The abbreviation of this polynomial, 13, is the octimal numeral representing eleven. To emphasize that this is a numeral in the octimal system we write 13_8. In the decimal system eleven is represented by the symbol 11 and to emphasize that this is a decimal numeral we shall write 11 as 11_{10}. Since 11_{10} and 13_8 represent the same counting number we can write $11_{10} = 13_8$.

EXAMPLE 2.   The counting number two hundred five is represented by the numeral 205 in the decimal system. To find the octimal representation for this number we must write 205_{10} as a polynomial in eight:

$$205_{10} = 3(8^2) + 1(8^1) + 5(8^0)$$

Consequently the octimal representation of this number is 315 and $205_{10} = 315_8$.

In the decimal system the digits are the counting numbers less than ten—the counting numbers which can occur as coefficients of a polynomial in ten. In the octimal system the digits are the counting numbers 0, 1, 2, 3, 4, 5, 6, and 7

---

* Do not read the octimal numeral 17 as "seventeen." The word "seventeen" does not mean the number represented by the octimal numeral 17. This octimal numeral 17 can be read "one-seven."

since these are the numbers which can occur as coefficients of a polynomial in eight.

EXAMPLE 3.   Learning to count in the octimal system is very much like learning to count in the decimal system. In the octimal system we count from zero through twenty-five as follows:

$$
\left.\begin{array}{c}
0 \\
1 \\
2 \\
3 \\
4 \\
5 \\
6 \\
7
\end{array}\right\}
\text{These are the digits in the octimal system.}
$$

10   That is, eight is $1(8^1) + 0(8^0)$.
11
12
13
14
15
16
17
20   That is, sixteen is $2(8^1) + 0(8^0)$.
21
22
23
24
25
26
27
30   That is, twenty-four is $3(8^1) + 0(8^0)$.
31   That is, twenty-five is $3(8^1) + 1(8^0)$.

It is interesting to note that any difficulties the reader may have experienced in counting in the octimal system parallel very closely the difficulties a child has in learning to count in the decimal system. For example, if the reader has difficulty in understanding why "10" follows "7" in the octimal system, then he is en-countering the same difficulties that a child encounters in understanding that "10" comes after "9" in the decimal system. Studying these different systems of numeration presents an almost unique opportunity for the adult to experience (at least in part) the same difficulties that a child experiences in learning about the decimal system.

Exercises

1. The following are numerals in the octimal system. Write out the polynomials in eight which they abbreviate.
    (a)   7640.   (b)   1000.   (c)   10.   (d)   4561001.

2. Find the octimal numeral which abbreviates each of these sums:
   (a) $6(8^2) + 5(8^3)$.
   (b) $1(8^2) + 1(8^0)$.
   (c) $4(8^3) + 5(8^5) + 1(8^1)$.
3. Count from zero through fifty using octimal numerals. (Keep in mind that the word "fifty" refers to the number represented by the symbol 50_{10} and not the number represented by the symbol 50_8.)
4. Find the octimal numeral representation of each of these counting numbers.

   (a) Thirty-four.   (f) Two hundred eighty-nine.
   (b) Sixty-four.   (g) 2350_{10}.
   (c) Fifty-six.   (h) One million.
   (d) 38_{10}.   (i) 9532_{10}.
   (e) 47_{10}.

5. The concepts of *place holder* and *place value* are meaningful in the octimal system just as they are in the decimal system. Discuss these concepts relative to the octimal system. (*Suggestion:* You might want to review the appropriate parts of Chapter 8 and rephrase these ideas for octimal numerals.)
6. Let us invent some new words. Let us use the word *seight* to mean 8^2 and the word *ceight* to mean 8^3. Using these new words render the following octimal numerals into English.

   (a) 67.   (b) 145.   (c) 7777.

The Binary System

Since every counting number can be written as a polynomial in n (where n is any counting number greater than one) there is a system of numeration corresponding to every counting number greater than one. The *binary system* is the numeration system corresponding to the counting number two and is the system with the least number of digits. The only digits in this system are 0 and 1. This is because the only numbers which can occur as coefficients of a polynomial in two are 0 and 1.

To find the binary numeral for a given counting number it is necessary to first express the counting number as a polynomial in two and then to abbreviate the polynomial. Here are some examples.

EXAMPLE 1.   The counting number thirteen is represented by the binary numeral 111 since $13_{10} = 1(2^3) + 1(2^2) + 1(2^0)$.

EXAMPLE 2.   To find the binary numeral for eighty-seven we first write this counting number as a polynomial in two:

$$87_{10} = 1(2^6) + 0(2^5) + 1(2^4) + 0(2^3) + 1(2^2) + 1(2^1) + 1(2^0)$$

By extracting the coefficients of this polynomial we obtain the binary numeral for eighty-seven, namely, the numeral 1010111_2.

EXAMPLE 3.   Below we have counted from zero through twenty-five in the binary system.

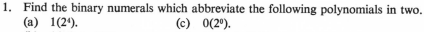

$\left.\begin{matrix} 0 \\ 1 \end{matrix}\right\}$ These are the digits in the binary system.

10   That is, two is $1(2^1) + 0(2^0)$.

11

100   That is, four is $1(2^2) + 0(2^1) + 0(2^0)$.

101

110

111

1000   That is, eight is $1(2^3) + 0(2^2) + 0(2^1) + 0(2^0)$.

1001

1010

1011

1100

1101

1110

1111

10000   That is, sixteen is $1(2^4) + 0(2^3) + \cdots + 0(2^0)$.

10001

10010

10011

10100

10101

10110

10111

11000

11001   That is, twenty-five is $1(2^4) + 1(2^3) + 0(2^2) +$
      $+ 0(2^1) + 1(2^0)$.

Exercises

1. Find the binary numerals which abbreviate the following polynomials in two.
   (a) $1(2^4)$.   (c) $0(2^0)$.
   (b) $1(2^3) + 1(2^0)$.   (d) $1(2^1) + 1(2^4)$.
2. Find the polynomials in two which are abbreviated by these binary numerals.
   (a) 101.   (b) 11010.   (c) 100000.
3. Find binary numerals for the following counting numbers.
   (a) Sixty-seven.   (c) Eighty-nine.
   (b) Six hundred forty-five.   (d) 156_{10}.
4. Discuss the concept of place value as it applies to binary numerals. In particular, what are the place values of the digits in the following binary numerals?
   (a) 1010.   (b) 1000001.   (c) 101110.
5. Invent some words for the first few powers of two and render the following into English.
   (a) 111.   (c) 10010.
   (b) 101.   (d) 1101.

The Duodecimal System

The *duodecimal system* is based upon the fact that every counting number can be written as a polynomial in twelve.* But there is a minor complication. Each of the octimal and binary systems has fewer digits than the decimal system and so it is possible to represent the digits in these systems by using some of the familiar digit symbols used in the decimal system. But the duodecimal system has twelve digits and so it is necessary to invent two new digit symbols to represent the duodecimal digits ten and eleven. We shall use *t* as the duodecimal digit symbol for ten and *e* as the duodecimal digit symbol for eleven. Thus the digit symbols in this system are 0, 1, 2, 3, 4, 5, 6, 7, 8, 9, *t*, and *e*.

We could not use the symbol 10 to represent the counting number ten in the duodecimal system because the symbol 10 in the duodecimal system is the abbreviation of

$$1(12^1) + 0(12^0)$$

and so represents the counting number twelve. Similarly, in the duodecimal system the symbol 11 represents the number thirteen, not eleven, so a new symbol is needed to represent eleven.

EXAMPLE 1. The number twenty-two is represented by the symbol $1t$ in the duo-. decimal system since

$$22_{10} = 1(12^1) + (10)(12^0)$$
$$= 1(12^1) + t(12^0)$$
$$= 1t_{12}$$

EXAMPLE 2. Counting to forty in the duodecimal system we get: 0, 1, 2, 3, 4, 5, 6, 7, 8, 9, *t*, *e*, 10, 11, 12, 13, 14, 15, 16, 17, 18, 19, $1t$, $1e$, 20, 21, 22, 23, 24, 25, 26, 27, 28, 29, $2t$, $2e$, 30, 31, 32, 33, and 34.

Exercises

1. Count to one hundred using duodecimal numerals.
2. Write these counting numbers in the duodecimal system.
    (a) Six hundred and two.   (c) 2409_{10}.
    (b) Eighty-nine.   (d) One million.
3. The duodecimal system has been used in the past as evidenced by the use of the words *dozen* and *gross*. Using these words how would these duodecimal numerals be rendered into English?
    (a) 345.   (c) 12.
    (b) 34.   (d) $1t3$.

There is a system of numeration corresponding to each counting number greater than 1. If *n* is such a counting number, then the numeration system based upon that counting number is called the *n-ary system* and the number *n* is called

---

* Duodecimal derives from *duo* (for two) and *decimal* (for ten).

the *base* for the system. We have discussed only three such systems but the systems are so much alike that understanding one of them is enough to understand them all.

Review Questions

1. Upon what central fact are these new numeration systems based?
2. How is the octimal numeral for a given counting number obtained? Is this process any different from the way the binary numeral for that counting number is obtained? Is it any different from the way the decimal numeral for that counting number is obtained?
3. The word *digit* does not have a meaning independent of the numeration system being used. Explain.
4. In which numeration systems is it necessary to invent new digit symbols? Why is it necessary?
5. Discuss the relative advantages and disadvantages (if any) of using the binary system over the duodecimal system. Discuss the relative advantages and disadvantages (if any) of using each of these in place of the decimal system.
6. In what ways are the new systems of numeration different from the decimal system? In what ways are they similar?

Changing Systems

We have seen how to find the *n*-ary numeral for a counting number given by its decimal numeral. This is a simple two-step process which involves writing the number as a polynomial in *n* and then abbreviating this polynomial. If a number is given by its *n*-ary numeral, then the decimal numeral for that number can be found by reversing this process. Given a number named by its *n*-ary numeral we first replace this *n*-ary numeral by the polynomial in *n* which it abbreviates and then simplify the polynomial by performing the indicated multiplications and additions. The result is the decimal numeral which represents the given number. Here are two examples.

EXAMPLE 1. A certain counting number is represented in the binary system by 101010_2. What is the decimal numeral for this number?

Solution: We replace this binary numeral by the polynomial in two which it abbreviates and then simplify:

$$101010_2 = 1(2^5) + 0(2^4) + 1(2^3) + 0(2^2) + 1(2^1) + 0(2^0)$$
$$= 1(32) + 0 + 1(8) + 0 + 1(2) + 0$$
$$= 32 + 8 + 2$$
$$= 42$$

Hence the decimal numeral we are looking for is 42. That is, $101010_2 = 42_{10}$.

EXAMPLE 2. $513_6 = ?_{10}$.

Solution: We are looking for the decimal numeral that names the same number as is named by the *heximal* numeral 513. We replace 513_6 by the polynomial in six which it abbreviates,

$$513_6 = 5(6^2) + 1(6^1) + 3(6^0)$$

and then simplify this polynomial,

$$\begin{aligned} 5(6^2) + 1(6^1) + 3(6^0) &= 5(36) + 1(6) + 3(1) \\ &= 180 + 6 + 3 \\ &= 189_{10} \end{aligned}$$

Hence the decimal numeral representing this number is 189 and $513_6 = 189_{10}$.

We now know how to change from a decimal numeral to an n-ary numeral (find the polynomial in n and abbreviate) and how to change from an n-ary numeral to a decimal numeral (replace the n-ary numeral by the polynomial in n that it abbreviates and simplify). We can now change from an n-ary numeral to an m-ary numeral by "passing through" the decimal system. For example, to change from an octimal numeral to a pentimal numeral we can change from an octimal numeral to a decimal numeral and then change this decimal numeral into a pentimal numeral.

EXAMPLE. $156_8 = ?_5$.
Solution: First we change from the octimal numeral to a decimal numeral:

$$\begin{aligned} 156_8 &= 1(8^2) + 5(8^1) + 6(8^0) \\ &= 64 + 40 + 6 \\ &= 110_{10} \end{aligned}$$

and then change this decimal numeral to a pentimal numeral:

$$\begin{aligned} 110_{10} &= 4(5^2) + 2(5^1) + 0(5^0) \\ &= 420_5 \end{aligned}$$

Review Questions

1. Describe a general procedure by means of which any decimal numeral may be changed into a n-ary numeral.
2. Describe a general procedure by means of which any n-ary numeral may be changed into a decimal numeral.
3. Let n and m be any two counting numbers greater than 1. Describe a general procedure by means of which any n-ary numeral may be changed into an m-ary numeral.

Exercises

1. $45_7 = ?_{10}$.
2. $234_8 = ?_{10}$.
3. $4t5e_{12} = ?_{10}$.
4. $45_6 = ?_9$.

5. $111_5 = ?_{11}$.
6. $23_5 = ?_6$.
7. $19_{12} = ?_2$.

COMPUTING IN OTHER SYSTEMS

Let us recall what is involved in learning to compute in the decimal system. We begin as children with the memorization of addition and multiplication tables. After these tables have been memorized it is possible to perform certain very simple computations which do not involve "carrying" or "borrowing" by direct application of the tables. Then more difficult problems are introduced which involve "carrying" and "borrowing." The success of the algorithms for addition, subtraction, multiplication, and long division depends not on the decimal numerals themselves but rather on the properties of the operations and relations involved. Since these algorithms depend only upon the operations and relations, it follows that the same algorithms can be used regardless of which numeration system is used to represent the numbers involved in the problem. For example, the addition algorithm works the same way for octimally represented summands as it does for decimally represented summands.

We shall discuss computing in two systems, the pentimal and the binary. Computations in other systems are much the same.

Computing in the Pentimal System

First we must construct the addition and multiplication tables in this system. (All numerals in this subsection are pentimal numerals so we shall omit the subscript 5.)

+	0	1	2	3	4
0	0	1	2	3	4
1	1	2	3	4	10
2	2	3	4	10	11
3	3	4	10	11	12
4	4	10	11	12	13

·	0	1	2	3	4
0	0	0	0	0	0
1	0	1	2	3	4
2	0	2	4	11	13
3	0	3	11	14	22
4	0	4	13	22	31

These tables can be constructed in a number of ways. We can perform the additions and multiplications by using decimal numerals and then change the sums and products to the pentimal system. We can count on our fingers the way children do. We can fill in the addition table in any way we want and then fill in the multiplication table using the fact that multiplication of counting numbers is the same as repeated addition. At any rate, we fill in the tables. Here are some examples of addition and multiplication problems using pentimal numerals.

EXAMPLE 1.   Add 123 and 24.
  Solution: We begin in the usual way by writing

$$\begin{array}{r} 1\,2\,3 \\ 2\,4 \\ \hline \end{array}$$

First we must add 3 and 4 (right column). According to the addition table $3 + 4 = 12$. So put the 2 under the right column and carry the 1. We now have

$$\begin{array}{r} {\scriptstyle 1} \\ 1\,2\,3 \\ 2\,4 \\ \hline 2 \end{array}$$

Next we must add 1, 2, and 2 (middle column). Since, according to the table, $1 + 2 = 3$ and $3 + 2 = 10$, we can put the 0 under the middle column and carry the 1. We now have

$$\begin{array}{r} {\scriptstyle 1} \\ 1\,2\,3 \\ 2\,4 \\ \hline 0\,2 \end{array}$$

Finally, $1 + 1 = 2$ and so we put the 2 under the left column and have

$$\begin{array}{r} 1\,2\,3 \\ 2\,4 \\ \hline 2\,0\,2 \end{array}$$

Hence 202 is the sum.

Example 1 demonstrates that addition by using pentimal numerals is performed in exactly the same way as it is using decimal numerals except that different tables are used.

EXAMPLE 2.   Multiply 23 by 414.
  Solution: We begin by writing

$$\begin{array}{r} 4\,1\,4 \\ 2\,3 \\ \hline \end{array}$$

We first multiply 4 by 3 obtaining 22 (from the table). Put 2 under the right column and carry 2:

$$\begin{array}{r} {\scriptstyle 2} \\ 4\,1\,4 \\ 2\,3 \\ \hline 2 \end{array}$$

Multiply 1 by 3 (obtaining 3) and add 2 (obtaining 10). Write the 0 under the middle column and carry the 1:

$$\begin{array}{r} {\scriptstyle 1} \\ 4\,1\,4 \\ 2\,3 \\ \hline 0\,2 \end{array}$$

Now 4 times 3 is 22 (from the table) and $22 + 1 = 23$. So we get

$$
\begin{array}{r}
4\ 1\ 4 \\
2\ 3 \\
\hline
2\ 3\ 0\ 2
\end{array}
$$

Next multiply 414 by 2 in the same way we just multiplied 414 by 3 and get 1333. Then

$$
\begin{array}{r}
4\ 1\ 4 \\
2\ 3 \\
\hline
2\ 3\ 0\ 2 \\
1\ 3\ 3\ 3
\end{array}
$$

Finally add and obtain

$$
\begin{array}{r}
4\ 1\ 4 \\
2\ 3 \\
\hline
2\ 3\ 0\ 2 \\
1\ 3\ 3\ 3 \\
\hline
2\ 1\ 1\ 3\ 2
\end{array}
$$

Hence the product of 23 and 414 is 21132.

Subtraction and division are performed just as in the decimal system except that the pentimal addition tables and multiplication tables are used.

In order to check a computation in the pentimal system we can change all numerals to decimal numerals, perform the computation in the decimal system (which we can do with some confidence), and then change the answer into the pentimal system. The results should agree. Let us check the multiplication problem in Example 2 in this way.

EXAMPLE.   We determined that the product of 414_5 and 23_5 is 21132_5. But $414_5 = 109_{10}$ and $23_5 = 13_{10}$. We are familiar with multiplication using decimal numerals and can easily determine that $(109_{10})(13_{10}) = 1417_{10}$. If we have performed the multiplication correctly in the pentimal system it should be true that 21132_5 and 1417_{10} are equal. A quick verification will show that they are equal. Assuming that we performed the multiplication correctly in the decimal system, this proves that our solution using pentimal numerals is correct.

Exercises

1. Perform these additions in the pentimal system. Check your answers by changing the summands and sums into decimal numerals and performing the addition in that system.
   (a) $34_5 + 112_5 = \ ?_5$.
   (b) $34_5 + 132_5 + 324_5 = \ ?_5$.
   (c) $234_5 + 112_5 + 3102_5 + 32103_5 = \ ?_5$.
2. Perform these multiplications in the pentimal system and check by changing products and factors into the decimal system.
   (a) $34_5 \cdot 23_5 = \ ?_5$.   (b) $132_5 \cdot 44_5 = \ ?_5$.

Computing in the Binary System

The addition and multiplication tables in this system are quite easy to memorize.

+	0	1
0	0	1
1	1	10

·	0	1
0	0	0
1	0	1

Here are some examples of addition and subtraction worked using binary numerals.

EXAMPLE 1.   Add 1101, 111, 1111, and 1001.
   Solution: First write

$$
\begin{array}{r}
1\,1\,0\,1 \\
1\,1\,1 \\
1\,1\,1\,1 \\
1\,0\,0\,1 \\
\hline
\end{array}
$$

Adding the numbers in the rightmost column we get $1 + 1 + 1 + 1 = (1 + 1) + 1 + 1 = 10 + 1 + 1 = 11 + 1 = 100$.
Write 0 below the rightmost column and carry 10:

$$
\begin{array}{r}
^{10} \\
1\,1\,0\,1 \\
1\,1\,1 \\
1\,1\,1\,1 \\
1\,0\,0\,1 \\
\hline
0
\end{array}
$$

Now add 10, 0, 1, 1, and 0 in the second column:

$$10 + 0 + 1 + 1 + 0 = 10 + 1 + 1 = 11 + 1 = 100$$

Put a 0 under the second column and carry 10:

$$
\begin{array}{r}
^{10} \\
1\,1\,0\,1 \\
1\,1\,1 \\
1\,1\,1\,1 \\
1\,0\,0\,1 \\
\hline
0\,0
\end{array}
$$

Now add 10, 1, 1, 1, and 0 obtaining 101. Then write

$$
\begin{array}{r}
^{10} \\
1\,1\,0\,1 \\
1\,1\,1 \\
1\,1\,1\,1 \\
1\,0\,0\,1 \\
\hline
1\,0\,0
\end{array}
$$

Finally add 10, 1, 1, and 1 obtaining 101. Write

$$\begin{array}{r} 1\,1\,0\,1 \\ 1\,1\,1 \\ 1\,1\,1\,1 \\ \underline{1\,0\,0\,1} \\ \hline 101\,1\,0\,0 \end{array}$$

Hence the sum of these counting numbers is 101100_2. We can check this answer by changing the summands and sum to decimal numerals. The summands are 13_{10}, 7_{10}, 15_{10}, and 9_{10}. Their sum is 44_{10}. Assuming we have worked the addition problem correctly using decimal numerals our solution will be verified if it is true that $44_{10} = 101100_2$. (Is it?)

EXAMPLE 2.   Subtract 111 from 1101.

Solution: Write

$$\begin{array}{r} 1\,1\,0\,1 \\ \underline{1\,1\,1} \end{array}$$

In the first column, $1 - 1 = 0$. We obtain

$$\begin{array}{r} 1\,1\,0\,1 \\ \underline{1\,1\,1} \\ \hline 0 \end{array}$$

In the second column, we cannot subtract 1 from 0 so we borrow and subtract 1 from 10:

$$\begin{array}{r} {\scriptstyle 0\ 10} \\ 1\,\cancel{1}\,\cancel{0}\,1 \\ \underline{1\,1\,1} \\ \hline 0 \end{array}$$

To subtract 1 from 10 look for that number which when added to 1 gives 10. (Definition of subtraction!) Using the addition table we see that $1 + 1 = 10$, so $10 - 1 = 1$. We now have

$$\begin{array}{r} {\scriptstyle 0} \\ 1\,\cancel{1}\,0\,1 \\ \underline{1\,1\,1} \\ \hline 1\,0 \end{array}$$

Next we cannot subtract 1 from 0 so we borrow again and subtract 1 from 10 obtaining (just as before) 1. We have

$$\begin{array}{r} {\scriptstyle 0\ 10} \\ \cancel{1}\,\cancel{1}\,0\,1 \\ \underline{1\,1\,1} \\ \hline 1\,1\,0 \end{array}$$

Hence $1101 - 111 = 110$. We can check this by adding 110 and 111. Another check is to change the minuend and subtrahend to decimal numerals, subtract these decimal numerals (which we can do with little chance of error), and then change the difference back into the binary numeral. When we do we should get 110_2.

Exercises

1. Perform these additions and check by changing summands and sums into the decimal system.
    (a) $101_2 + 110_2 + 11_2 + 1011_2 = ?_2$.
    (b) $101_2 + 111_2 + 1111_2 + 11111_2 + 1011_2 + 110_2 + 1011_2 = ?_2$.
2. Perform these subtraction problems and check in any way that you like.
    (a) $1101_2 - 111_2 = ?_2$.   (c) $342_5 - 132_5 = ?_5$.
    (b) $1111_2 - 1010_2 = ?_2$ (d) $(234012_5 - 3442_5) - 112_5 = ?_5$.
3. Perform these multiplications and check by changing factors and products into the decimal system.
    (a) $(101_2)(111_2) = ?_2$.
    (b) $(1011_2)(101_2)(110_2) = ?_2$.
4. Perform these long divisions and check in any way that you like.
    (a) Long divide 1111_2 by 11_2.   (c) Long divide 314_5 by 3_5.
    (b) Long divide 111_2 by 10_2.   (d) Long divide 1402_5 by 23_5.
5. Construct addition and multiplication tables for the octimal system and work the following problems.
    (a) $45_8 + 157_8 + 403_8 = ?_8$.
    (b) $14_8 - 6_8 = ?_8$.
    (c) $(15_8)(34_8) + 117_8 = ?_8$.
    (d) $200_8 \div 20_8 = ?_8$.
    (e) 200_8 long divided by $7_8 = ?$
6. Construct the addition and multiplication tables for the duodecimal system and work the following problems.
    (a) $134_{12} + 789_{12} = ?_{12}$.
    (b) $eee_{12} + 1589_{12} + t150_{12} = ?_{12}$.
    (c) $eeee_{12} - tttt_{12} = ?_{12}$.
    (d) $34561_{12} - 9t3e_{12} = ?_{12}$.
    (e) $(67_{12})(145_{12}) = ?_{12}$.
    (f) $(56_{12})(9t_{12}) - (4e_{12})(9t_{12}) = ?_{12}$.
    (g) 189_{12} long divided by $67_{12} = ?$
    (h) $136_{12} \div 3_{12} = ?_{12}$.

Answers

Some of the answers which follow are complete and some are only partial answers. Frequently no answer is given but only a suggestion on how to work the exercise. Many exercises have more than one correct answer and so answers different from the ones given here may nevertheless be correct. Many answers can be verified by the reader himself and whenever this is possible he should do so. In a sense, to work an exercise without attempting some sort of verification of the result is to leave the exercise only half finished.

Page 5
1. (a) Using any one of the concepts A, D, or E would involve a circular definition. Using either B or C would not. (d) Defining C in terms of E would involve a circular definition.

Page 7
5. (a) 2×2. (b) $4 + 3$. (c) 3×5.

Page 9
1. Statements b, e, f, h, i, j, l, m, n, and o are true. (In (i) and (j) we have assumed that it is true that dogs bark.) 2. Exclusive or.

Page 13
1. (d) If $4 = 5$, then $3 + 3 = 7$. (e) If $3 + 5 = 1$, then $3 = 17$. 3. (a) i, ii, and v. (b) iii, iv, and vi. 4. (a) Given implication is true and its converse is false. (b) Given implication is true and its converse is false. (c) Given implication is true and its converse is also true.

Page 14
1. (a) A parallelogram is a rectangle if and only if its interior angles are all right angles. (c) A counting number is a digit if and only if it is less than ten. 2. (a) A letter of the Greek alphabet is epsilon if and only if that letter is the fifth letter of the Greek alphabet.

Page 21
1. f is an absolute equation. b, c, d, and e are conditional equations with solutions. g is a conditional equation with no solution. a and h are identities.

Page 26

1. Jim 𝓎 John, Jim 𝓎 Will, Jim 𝓎 Joan, and Jim 𝓎 Hank. Jim 𝓎̸ Jim, Sue 𝓎̸ Jim, Hank 𝓎̸ Jim, and Joan 𝓎̸ Jim. No, because no one is younger than himself.   **3.** Marsha ℜ Sue, Marsha ℜ Nancy, Will ℜ Jim, and four more.

Page 27

1. (a) No.   **(b)** No.

Page 29

1. (a) (i) No matter which person *n* represents, *n* is older than *n*. **(ii)** No matter which people *n* and *m* represent, if *n* is older than *m*, then *m* is older than *n*. **(iii)** No matter which people *n*, *m*, and *p* represent, if *n* is older than *m* and if *m* is older than *p*, then *n* is older than *p*.   **(b)** Only the last statement is true. This relation is only transitive. **4. (a)** Yes.   **(b)** Yes. No.   **(c)** The relation is not symmetric.   **(d)** Yes. Yes. No. **(e)** The relation is not transitive.   **5. (a)** Not reflexive and symmetric, is transitive. **(b)** Not reflexive and not symmetric, is transitive.   **(c)** Reflexive, not symmetric and not transitive.   **(d)** Only transitive.

Page 31

1. E.g., *less than*.   **2.** E.g., *equal to one more than*.   **3.** E.g., *less than*.   **4. (a)** ℜ̸ ℜ ℜ ℜ̸; ℜ ℜ ℜ̸ ℜ; ℜ ℜ ℜ ℜ̸.   **(b)** All odd numbers. All odd numbers. All even numbers including zero (which is even). All even numbers.   **6. (b)** 6, 16, 26, 36, 46, 56, 66, 76, ...   **7.** E.g., *is exactly the same age as*.   **8. (d)** 4 ℜ 12, 12 ℜ 6, but 4 ℜ̸ 6. **11.** Only reflexive. E.g., to show not transitive consider the counterexample: 5 ℜ 4, 4 ℜ 3, but 5 ℜ̸ 3.   **12.** Both.   **13.** *Is parallel to* is an equivalence relation. *Is perpendicular to* is only symmetric.   **14.** Both.

Page 36

1. (a) Rightmost addition.   **2. (c)** Rightmost addition.   **3.** Since 5 = 4 + 1 and addition is well-defined.   **5.** Well-definedness of addition is used.

Page 39

1. *b*, *c*, and *d*.   **2.** Associativity, commutivity, commutivity.

Page 41

1. Converse: If *n* = *m*, then *n* + 3 = *m* + 3. True because of well-definedness of addition.   **2.** Since 7 = 4 + 3, *x* + 3 = 4 + 3 (Why?), so that by cancellation *x* = 4.   **4. (a)** Zero property.   **(c)** Commutivity.   **(e)** Associativity.   **(g)** Associativity, commutivity, associativity.   **(i)** Zero, commutivity.   **(k)** Well-definedness.   **(m)** Associativity, commutivity, well-definedness.

Page 46

3. (a) Unit.   **(c)** Commutivity.   **(e)** Commutivity, Associativity.   **(g)** Unit, well-definedness.   **(i)** Commutivity.   **(k)** Well-definedness.   **(m)** Well-definedness.   **4.** 18 = 6 × 3, so by transitivity *n* × 3 = 6 × 3, and by cancellation *n* = 6.

Page 49

1. No. The numbers *n* = 2, *m* = 3, and *p* = 4 provide a counterexample.   **2. (a)** 3 × (7 + 6).   **(b)** (2 × 4) + (2 × 5).   **7.** *n* × (*m* + *p* + *q*) = (*n* × *m*) + (*n* × *p*) + (*n* × *q*).

Page 53

1. (a) $2x = 30$ (given equation), $30 = 2 \times 15$ (multiplication fact), $2x = 2 \times 15$ (transitivity of equality), $x = 15$ (Theorem 4). **2. (a)** $2x + 15 = 45$ (given equation), $45 = 30 + 15$ (addition fact), $2x + 15 = 30 + 15$ (transitivity of equality), $2x = 30$, (cancellation), $30 = 2 \times 15$ (multiplication fact), $2x = 2 \times 15$ (transitivity of equality), $x = 15$ (Theorem 4).

Page 55

2. (a) Associativity, commutivity, associativity. **(b)** Commutivity, commutivity. **(c)** Associativity, commutivity. **(d)** Associativity, commutivity, associativity. **3. (a)** Theorem A: $(n \times m) \times p = (n \times p) \times m$. (Prove it by using associativity, commutivity, and associativity in that order.)

Page 58

1. (a) $n = 145 - 23$. **2. (a)** $15 = n + 7$. **3.** (2) Definition of subtraction. (3) Commutivity of addition. (4) From (2) and (3) by using transitivity of equality. (5) From (4) by using the definition of subtraction.

Page 60

5. Yes. **7.** (1) Hypothesis. (3) Definition of subtraction. (4) Symmetry and transitivity of equality.

Page 63

1. (a) $(n + 7) - 7 = 10 - 7$; $n = 10 - 7$; $n = 3$. **3. (a)** $n - 6 = 2$; $n = 6 + 2$; $6 + 2 = 8$; $n = 8$. **4. (a)** $n - 6 = 2$; $2 = 8 - 6$; $n - 6 = 8 - 6$; $n = 8$. **5. (a)** First add 3 to both sides, then use Theorem 4. **(c)** First apply Theorem 4 to cancel the 3, then add 1 to both sides, then use Theorem 4 again.

Page 64

1. (2) Definition of subtraction. (3) Same as (2). (5) Transitivity of equality. (6) Definition of subtraction. (7) Same as (6). (8) Symmetry and transitivity of equality. **3.** (2) Definition of equality. (4) Symmetry of equality. (5) Definition of subtraction. (6) Symmetry of equality and commutivity of addition. (7) Definition of subtraction. (8) Theorem 12. (9) Transitivity of equality. **5.** $n \times (m - p) = (n \times m) - (n \times p)$.

Page 69

1. There is no counting number q such that $5 = 2 \times q$. **3.** Each possesses an identity, has the cancellation property and the well-definedness property. Neither has closure, commutivity, nor associativity. **4.** E.g., $n = 8$, $m = 4$, and $p = 1$. **6.** (1) Hypothesis. (2) Another way of saying that $n \div p$ and $m \div p$ are meaningful, which is an unstated but understood part of the hypothesis. (3) From (2) by using the definition of division. (4) From (3) by using symmetry and transitivity of equality.

Page 70

1. (a) $5n = 75$; $(5n) \div 5 = 75 \div 5$; $n = 75 \div 5$; $n = 15$. **2. (a)** $n \div 2 = 5$; $(n \div 2) \times 2 = 5 \times 2$; $n = 5 \times 2$; $n = 10$. **4.** (1) Hypothesis. (3) Definition of division. (4) Well-definedness of multiplication. (5) Transitivity of equality. (6) Symmetry of equality. (7) Commutivity of multiplication and some properties of equality. **5. (a)** First multiply both sides by 3. **(c)** Subtract 4 from both sides, multiply both sides by 3, and use Theorem 4. **(e)** Multiply both sides by 4 and add 2 to both sides.

Page 72

3. (2) Definition of division. (3) Well-definedness of subtraction. (5) Transitivity of equality. (6) Definition of division. (7) Well-definedness of subtraction and transitivity of equality.

Page 73

4. Theorem: If n, m, and p are counting numbers such that p can be subtracted from m, then p can be subtracted from $n + m$. Moreover, $(n + m) - p = n + (m - p)$.

Page 76

1. No. 4 * 5 is meaningless; i.e., 4 * 5 is not the name of a counting number.   **2.** No. Since division by zero is impossible, if either n or m were zero, then there is no least nonzero number divisible by both n and m.   **3.** No. E.g., 0 * 5 is meaningless.   **4.** Yes.

Page 77

1. (b) E.g., if n and m are digits, then $n * m$ is the rightmost digit of the number obtained by multiplying n by m.   **2.** (b) E.g., if n and m are digits, then $n * m$ is the rightmost digit of the number obtained by subtracting m from n. Then, for example, 3 * 6 is meaningless.

Page 78

1. (a) $2 + 3 = 5$, $2 \oplus 3$ is meaningless, $2 \boxplus 3$ is meaningless. (c) $7 + 3 = 10$, $7 \oplus 3$ is meaningless, $7 \boxplus 3$ is meaningless since 10 is not an odd counting number.   (e) $2 + 0 = 2$, $2 \oplus 0 = 2$, $2 \boxplus 0$ is meaningless because $\boxplus$ cannot be applied to even counting numbers.   **2.** (a) Is a binary operation.   (c) Is not. E.g., 4 * 5 is not a digit. (e) Is not.   (g) Is a binary operation.   (i) Is not. It is possible to find two perfect squares whose sum is not a perfect square.   (k) Is not.   E.g., the average of 2 and 4 is not an even counting number.

Page 81

1. E.g., if n and m represent people, let $n * m$ represent a person whose first name is the same as the first name of n and whose last name is the same as the last name of m. Then, for example, *Sam Jones * Bill Smith* is any person whose name is Sam Smith. Since there are many such people and since the instruction for performing the process provides no way to select a unique Sam Smith, the process is not well-defined.   **3.** 4 * 7 is also equal to 19 since $4 = 1 + 3$ and $7 = 1 + 6$.

Page 82 Top

1. (a) Both commutative and associative.   (c) Both commutative and associative. (e) Not commutative. Is associative.

Page 82 Bottom

1. (a) No identity.   (c) The identity is 0.   (e) No identity.   **2.** (a) No identity.   (b) No identity.   (c) No identity.   **3.** (a) Subtraction of counting numbers.   (c) Every right identity is also a left identity and every left identity is also a right identity.

Page 83

1. (a) Does not possess the cancellation property. Counterexample: $18 * 6 = 12 * 6$, but $18 \neq 12$.   (c) No. Counterexample: $5 * 9 = 4 * 9$, but $5 \neq 4$.   (e) No.   **2.** (a) Yes. $n * p = m * p$ implies that $(n + p) \div 2 = (m + p) \div 2$ which in turn implies that $n + p = m + p$ which in turn implies that $n = m$.   (c) Yes. $n * p = m * p$ implies that $np - (n + p) = mp - (m + p)$ which in turn implies that $np - n = mp - m$ which in turn implies that $n(p - 1) = m(p - 1)$ which in turn implies that $n = m$. (Note that p cannot be equal to 1 or else $n * p$ and $m * p$ are meaningless and therefore we can cancel the $p - 1$.)

Page 87

1. **(c)** $\{1, 2, 5, 10, 25, 50\}$. **(e)** $\{0, 5, 10, 15, 20, 25, \ldots\}$. **(g)** $\{0, 1, 2, 3, 4, 5, 6, 7\}$. **(i)** $\{1, 13\}$. **2.** $\{0, 2, 4, 6, 8, 10, \ldots, 999994, 999996, 999998\}$.

Page 90

1. **(a)** $\{x \in C : x < 5\}$, where C denotes the set of all counting numbers. **(c)** $\{x \in C : x > 0,\ x < 9,\ \text{and}\ x\ \text{is even}\}$, where C denotes the set of all counting numbers. **(e)** $\{x \in C : x\ \text{is divisible only by itself and}\ 1\}$, where C denotes the set of all counting numbers. **2.** **(a)** $\{6\}$. **(c)** $\{5, 7, 9, 11, 13, 15, 17, 19, 21, 23, \ldots\}$. **(e)** $\{3, 12\}$. **(f)** $\{0, 1\}$. **3.** **(a)** $\{3, 4, 5, 6, 7, 8, 9, 10, 11, 12, 13, 14\}$. **(c)** $\{5, 10\}$.

Page 92

1. **(a)** There are 34 such relations. **(b)** There are 21 such relations. **2.** **(a)** $\{0\}$ and $\varnothing$. **4.** Yes. Not necessarily.

Page 94 Top

1. **(a)** $\{0, 1, 2, 4\}$. **2.** **(a)** No. **(b)** No. **(c)** No. **4.** **(b)** $\varnothing, \{a\}, \{b\}, \{a, b\}$. **(c)** There are eight subsets. **5.** 2^6 or 64. 2^7 or 128. 2^n.

Page 94 Bottom

1. $\{7\}, \{8\}, \{9\}, \{7, 8\}$, and four more. **4.** $A = \varnothing$. **5.** Yes if and only if the set is the empty set.

Page 102

1. **(b)** Pair $n \in A$ with $5n \in B$. **3.** **(b)** 6. **5.** The set of all married men should be equivalent to the set of all married women. There must be a one-to-one correspondence between husbands and wives. **6.** Equality of sets and equivalence of sets. Equal sets are necessarily equivalent, but equivalent sets are not in general equal. **7.** **(a)** $n < m$ means that the point corresponding to n lies to the left of the point corresponding to m. **(b)** Given two points n and m, either n lies to the left of m, coincides with m, or lies to the right of m.

Page 105

1. **(a)** The given set can be put into one-to-one correspondence with its proper subset $\{7, 14, 21, 28, 35, 52, \ldots\}$. **3.** **(a)** Put $\{a, b, c\}$ into one-to-one correspondence with the set $\{1, 2, 3\}$.

Page 107

1. $c(A) = c(C) < c(B)$. **3.** Any infinite subset of the set of all counting numbers can be put into one-to-one correspondence with the set of all counting numbers. **4.** Establish a one-to-one correspondence between the counting numbers and the points of the counting number line. **5.** The counting process "terminates" at some stage.

Page 110

1. **(a)** $A \cup B = \{0, 1, 2, 3, 4, 5, 6\}$. $A \cap B = \{0, 2, 3\}$. **(c)** $A \cup B = A$. $A \cap B = B$. **(e)** $A \cup B = B$. $A \cap B = A$. **2.** **(a)** $\{1, 2, 3, 4, 5, 7, 8\}$. **(c)** $\{2\}$. **(e)** $\{2, 3\}$. **4.** **(a)** $B \subseteq A$. **(b)** $B = \varnothing$. **(c)** $B \subseteq A$. **(d)** $B = \varnothing$. **(e)** Yes, select A to be any set at all and B to be the empty set. **(f)** Equal to U. Equal to A. **5. (a)** No. No. **(b)** The union has at least 7 elements and not more than 13 elements. **6. (a)** $c(A) \leq c(B)$. **(c)** A and B are disjoint. **(d)** $B \subseteq A$. **(f)** $A \subseteq B$. **(h)** No. **(j)** They are equal. **7. (a)** They are equal. **(b)** No.

Page 114

1. (a) 0 and 111, 1 and 83, 2 and 55, 3 and 27. **2.** $n = 4$ and $m = 5$. Only $q = 0$ and $r = 4$ will satisfy. **3 (a)** $q = 1$ and $r = 0$. **(c)** $q = 5$ and $r = 6$. **5** The long division process results in a pair of counting numbers q and r with r less than the divisor m. If $m = 0$, then no such remainder can be obtained since there are no counting numbers less than 0.

Page 122

1. (a) 3. **(c)** 2^4 or 16. **(e)** 4. **(g)** 2. **(i)** 3. **(k)** 36. **(m)** 5^2 or 25. **(o)** 3. **(q)** s. **(s)** 6. **(u)** $2 \cdot 3$ or 6. **3.** $E = mcc$. In $2 \cdot 3^2$ the exponent applies only to the 3. In $(2 \cdot 3)^2$ the parentheses are being used to indicate that the exponent should be applied to $2 \cdot 3$.

Page 123

3. $\{1, 2, 5, 10\}$. $\{0, 10, 20, 30, 40, 50, \ldots\}$. $\{1, 2, 5, 10\}$. $\{0, 10, 20, 30, 40, 50, \ldots\}$. **5.** Yes. Yes. Yes. 0. n. No. **6.** No. 1. Yes, n itself.

Page 126

1. (a) $2 \cdot 3 \cdot 7$. **(c)** $2^2 \cdot 3^2 \cdot 5 \cdot 7^2$. **(e)** $2^3 \cdot 5^2$. **(g)** $2^2 \cdot 53$. **4. (a) (i)** Divisible by 2, 3, 4, 8. **(b) (i)** $2^3 \cdot 3^4 \cdot 5$.

Page 128

1. (a) $2^3 \cdot 3^3 \cdot 5^2 \cdot 7^6 \cdot 11^1 \cdot$ **(c)** $2^8 \cdot 3^{11} \cdot 5^{12} \cdot 7^{11}$. **(e)** $212 \cdot 100 \cdot 64 = (2^2 \cdot 53)(2^2 \cdot 5^2)$ $(2^6) = 2^{10} \cdot 5^2 \cdot 53^1$. **2. (a)** $2^6 \cdot 3^2 \cdot 5^4 \cdot 7^2$. **(c)** $2^{12} \cdot 3^4 \cdot 5^8 \cdot 7^4$. **3. (a)** It contains the prime 2 raised at least to the second power. **(b)** It contains the prime 2 raised at least to the first power. **(c)** It contains the prime 2 raised at least to the second power. It contains the prime 2 raised at least to the fourth power. **4. (a)** $2^4 \cdot 3^8 \cdot 5^4 \cdot 7^{12}$. **5.** It contains the primes 2, 3, and 11 raised at least to the first, second, and first powers, respectively. It contains the primes 2 and 3 raised at least to the fourth and second powers, respectively.

Page 129

1. (a) Choose a less than or equal to 2, b either 0 or 1. **(c)** $a = 0$. **2. (a)** Either choose a greater than 2 or b greater than 2. **3. (a)** $m = 2^a \cdot 3^b \cdot 5^c$, where $a \leq 1$, $b \leq 1$, and $c \leq 1$. **4. (a)** $\{1, 3, 5, 5^2, 3 \cdot 5, 3 \cdot 5^2\}$. The idea is to fill in the exponents a and b in $3^a \cdot 5^b$ in all possible ways subject to the restrictions $a \leq 1$ and $b \leq 2$. **(c)** There are a total of 16 different divisors. **5. (c)** $(3 + 1)(2 + 1)(4 + 1)$.

Page 131

1. (a) $2^{3-0} \cdot 3^{2-2} \cdot 11^{4-4} \cdot 13^{6-2}$ or $2^3 \cdot 13^4$. **(c)** $1188 \div 198 = 2^2 \cdot 3^3 \cdot 11 \div 2 \cdot 3^2 \cdot 11 = 2^1 \cdot 3^1$. **2. (a)** $(2^3 \cdot 3^1 \cdot 7^1 \cdot 11) \cdot (2 \cdot 5^3 \cdot 7 \cdot 11^9) = 2^4 \cdot 3 \cdot 5^3 \cdot 7^2 \cdot 11^{10}$. **3.** Multiply $n \div m$ by m, obtain n, and then appeal to the definition of division of counting numbers.

Page 134

1. (a) $3 \cdot 5$. **(b)** $2^1 \cdot 3^2$. **2. (a)** 2. **(b)** $2 \cdot 5$. **3.** Because a common divisor of n and m cannot be any larger than the minimum of n and m. Hence the largest that the GCD could be is min $[n, m]$. There are only finitely many counting numbers less than min $[n, m]$. **4.** (a) Yes. (Why?) **7.** It is a prime number. **8.** p must divide b. **10.** (a) Divisibility Test for Six: A counting number is divisible by 6 if it is divisible by both 2 and 3. Divisibility Test for Eighteen: A counting number is divisible by 18 if it is divisible by both 2 and 9.

Page 136

1. (a) $2^2 \cdot 3^3 \cdot 5^3 \cdot 7^2 \cdot 11^7 \cdot 13^4$. (b) $2^6 \cdot 3^2 \cdot 11$. **2.** (a) $2^2 \cdot 3^2 \cdot 5^2 \cdot 7 \cdot 11 \cdot 13$. (b) $2^4 \cdot 3^2 \cdot 5 \cdot 11$. **3.** The set of all common multiples of n and m contains the numbers $1nm, 2nm, 3nm, 4nm, 5nm, 6nm, \ldots$. **4.** (a) Yes. (Why?) (c) Yes, the number 1. **5.** (a) n and m are relatively prime. (b) nm. **6.** (a) $nm = gd$.

Page 142

1. Not necessarily; e.g., the symbol 2/3 is meaningful but $2 \div 3$ is meaningless in the system of counting numbers. If both $n \div m$ and n/m are meaningful, then $n \div m = n/m$. **2.** No. No. Yes, $0/6 = 0$. a is a counting number and b is a nonzero counting number.

Page 145

1. (a) (1) Reflexivity of equality of counting numbers. (2) Definition of equality of fractions and (1). (b) (1) Hypothesis. (2) From (1) by using definition of equality of fractions. (3) From (2) by using symmetry of equality of counting numbers. (4) From (3) by using definition of equality of fractions. **3.** Because equality of counting numbers is not defined on all fractions.

Page 146

1. (a) 6/9. (e) 25/3. **2.** (a) 20/42. (b) 8/9. **3.** (a) 32/48 and 42/48. **4.** (b) (i) $n/3 = 5n/15$ so that $7/15 = 5n/15$ and therefore $7 = 5n$ so that $n = 7/5$. **6.** The tabulation of the fractions discussed in Exercise 5 effectively produces a one-to-one correspondence between the fractions and the counting numbers. The first fraction tabulated is paired with 0, the second fraction with 1, the third fraction with 2, and so on.

Page 149

1. (a) $15/21 = 5/7 = 2^2 \cdot 5^2/2^2 \cdot 5 \cdot 7$ and $7/20 = 7^2/2^2 \cdot 5 \cdot 7$. (c) $2 \cdot 5 \cdot 7/3 \cdot 5 \cdot 7$, $2^2 \cdot 5/3 \cdot 5 \cdot 7$, and $3^3/3 \cdot 5 \cdot 7$. (e) $2 \cdot 3 \cdot 7 \cdot 11/3^3 \cdot 5^4 \cdot 7^2 \cdot 11$ and $2 \cdot 5^3/3^3 \cdot 5^4 \cdot 7^2 \cdot 11$.

Page 150

1. (a) $18/42 = 3 \cdot 6/7 \cdot 6 = 3/7$ by the Renaming Theorem. (c) $36/18 = 2 \cdot 18/1 \cdot 18 = 2/1 = 2$.

Page 152

1. (a) $15/32 < 21/32$ since $15 < 21$. (c) $4/21 < 9/35 < 2/3$. **4.** Write $n = a/b$ and $m = c/b$. Then since exactly one of $a < c$, $a = b$, and $a > c$ is true, exactly one of $a/b < c/b$, $a/b = c/b$, and $a/b > c/b$ is true. **5.** (d). E.g., $a/b \geq c/d$ if and only if $da \geq bc$. **6.** Denote less than for counting numbers by $\overset{C}{<}$ and less than for fractions by $\overset{F}{<}$. Then to say that $\overset{C}{<}$ and $\overset{F}{<}$ agree on the counting numbers means that if n and m are counting numbers, then $n \overset{C}{<} m$ if and only if $n \overset{F}{<} m$.

Page 156

1. (a) $1/3 + 17/39 = 1 \cdot 13/3 \cdot 13 + 17/39 = 13/39 + 17/39 = (13 + 17)/39 = 30/39 = 10 \cdot 3/13 \cdot 3 = 10/13$. (c) 45/82. (f) 7577/2100. (h) $(2^2 + 3 \cdot 7)/2 \cdot 3^2 \cdot 5$.

(j) 631/792. **2.** (a) $a/b + cb/d = ad/bd + bcb/bd = (ad + cb^2)/bd$. (c) $(bc + 2c^2 + 4b)/2bc$. **3.** (1) Definition of addition of fractions. (2) Same as (1). (3) Associativity of addition of counting numbers. (4) Definition of addition of fractions. (5) Same as (4). **6.** $a/b + c/d = ad/bd + bc/bd = (ad + bc)/bd = (da + bc)/bd$. **8.** (a) $2/3 = 4/6 = 1/6 + 3/6 = 1/6 + 1/2$. So $n + 1/2 = 1/6 + 1/2$ and so $n = 1/6$.

Page 160
1. (a) $9/11 - 9/14 = 3^2 \cdot 2 \cdot 7/2 \cdot 7 \cdot 11 - 3^2 \cdot 11/2 \cdot 7 \cdot 11 = (3^2 \cdot 2 \cdot 7 - 3^2 \cdot 11)/ 2 \cdot 7 \cdot 11 = 27/154$. (g) $(48/96 - 40/96) - 6/96 = (48 - 40)/96 - 6/96 = 8/96 - 6/96 = 2/96 = 1/48$. **2.** (a) $n = 25/3$. (c) Cannot be solved in the system of fractions. (e) Cannot be solved in the system of fractions. (g) $n = 0$. (i) $n = 2$. **5.** Let a/b represent any fraction and write $0 = 0/b$. Then $a/b - 0/b = (a - 0)/b = a/b$. Depends upon the fact that 0 is the identity for subtraction of counting numbers.

Page 163
1. (a) $2/5 \cdot 4/9 = 2 \cdot 4/5 \cdot 9 = 8/45$. (e) $2 \cdot 7^2/3 \cdot 11$. **2.** (a) $n = 49/15$. (c) $17/60 = n$. (g) $n = 3$. **3.** (a) $ab/bc = a/c$. (b) a^2. (c) 1. (d) $c(a + b)/ba$. **5.** (d) (1) Hypothesis. (2) From (1) by using definition of multiplication. (3) From (2) by using definition of equality. (4) From (3) by using cancellation of multiplication of counting numbers. (5) From (4) by using definition of equality of fractions. **6.** (1) Addition of fractions. (2) Multiplication of fractions. (3) Distributivity of addition and multiplication of counting numbers. (4) Addition of fractions. (5) Renaming Theorem. (6) Multiplication of fractions. (7) From (1) through (6) by using transitivity of equality of fractions. **9.** No. $4 \cdot 3$ means to add 4 to itself 3 times. But $4/5 \cdot 1/2$ cannot be similarly interpreted.

Page 166
1. (a) 1. (c) 18/7. (e) 21/31. **2.** Set up the correspondence by pairing an element in S with its multiplicative inverse in T. Explain why this is a one-to-one correspondence. **5.** (a) First multiply both sides by the multiplicative inverse of 2/3. Obtain $(n \cdot 3/2)(2/3) = 5/9 \cdot 2/3$. Then associate and write $(n)(3/2 \cdot 2/3) = (5/9)(2/3)$ so that $n(1) = 10/27$ and so $n = 10/27$.

Page 172
1. (a) $2/3 \div 4/5 = 2/3 \cdot 5/4 = 5/6$. (c) 7/32. (e) $3 \cdot 7^2/5^3 \cdot 13^2$. **3.** (a) 32/7. (c) 9/4. (e) 6/7. **7.** Assume that $a/b \div c/d = e/f \div c/d$. Then this implies that $a/b \cdot d/c = e/f \cdot d/c$ so that $ad/bc = ed/fc$. Then $fcad = bced$ implies $fa = be$ whence $a/b = e/f$.

Page 175
1. $(2bc + ad)/3bd$. **2.** $2/3 = 10/15$. So 8/15 and 9/15 lie between 10/15 and 7/15. **3.** Make denominators equal to 90. **6.** (a) Has density property. (b) Does not possess density property. (c) Possesses density property.

Page 178
5. The proof breaks down at steps 6 and 12 because the Preliminary Theorem itself is false when 2 is replaced by 4.

Page 182
1. (b) Tabulate the set of all integers as $\{0, 1, -1, 2, -2, 3, -3, \ldots\}$. Then pair 0 with 0, 1 with 1, -1 with 2, 2 with 3, -2 with 4, 3 with 5, -3 with 6, and so on. This shows that $C \sim I$.

Page 185
4. No. E.g., there is no integer between the integers 1 and 2.

Page 187
2. Reflexive: Every integer has the same algebraic sign and the same absolute value as itself. Symmetry: If n has the same algebraic sign and the same absolute value as m, then m has the same algebraic sign and same absolute value as n.

Page 190
1. (a) $3^- + 1^- = (3 + 1)^- = 4^-$. Used Part 4 and Part 1.   (c) 9.   (e) 0.   (g) 0.
2. (a) $5^- + 5 = 0$ and $4^- + 4 = 0$. Then $(5^- + 5) + (4^- + 4) = 0 + 0 = 0$, $5^- + [5 + (4^- + 4)] = 0$, $5^- + [(5 + 4^-) + 4)] = 0$, $5^- + [(4^- + 5) + 4] = 0$, $5^- + [4^- + (5 + 4)] = 0$, $(5^- + 4^-) + (5 + 4) = 0$, $(5^- + 4^-) + 9 = 0$. So $5^- + 4^-$ is equal to 9^-.

Page 192
1. (a) 2. Used Parts 4, 1, and 5a.   (c) 47.   **2.** (a) Since $18 = (18 - 15) + 15$, $18 + 15^- = [(18 - 15) + 15] + 15^- = (18 - 15) + (15 + 15^-) = (18 - 15) + 0 = 18 - 15 = 3$.

Page 193
1. (a) $13^- + 6 = (13 - 6)^- = 7^-$.   (c) 14^-. Used Parts 4, 1, and 5b.   (e) 15.   (f) 37^-.
(i) 0.   **2.** (a) Know that $15^- = 6^- + (15 - 6)^-$. So $15^- + 6 = [6^- + (15 - 6)^-] + 6 = [(15 - 6)^- + 6^-] + 6 = (15 - 6)^- + (6^- + 6) = (15 - 6)^- + 0 = (15 - 6)^- = 9^-$.

Page 194
2. An abbreviated proof is: $n^- + m^- = (n + m)^- = (m + n)^- = m^- + n^-$. Commutivity of addition of counting numbers.   **5.** Use the well-definedness of addition of integers to add p to both sides. Then use associativity and zero property.   **6.** (a) Write $14 = 21 + 7^-$, use transitivity of equality and cancellation property of addition. $n = 21$.   **7.** (a) $n + 6 = 25^-$; $(n + 6) + 6^- = 25^- + 6^-$; $n + (6 + 6^-) = 25^- + 6^-$; $n + 0 = 25^- + 6^-$; $n = 25^- + 6^-$; $n = (25 + 6)^-$; $n = 31^-$.   **8.** $|n + m| \leq |n| + |m|$. (This inequality is called the Triangle Inequality.)

Page 197
1. 6^-. 6^-. n. n^-.   **2.** Positive. Negative.   **3.** (a) 5^-.   (b) 1^-.

Page 198
1. (a) If n is an integer, then $0 + n = n$.   **2.** (1) Commutivity of addition. (2) Associativity of addition. (3) Additive Inverses. (4) Zero property of addition. (5) Additive Inverses. (6) From (1) through (5) by transitivity of equality.   **3.** The multiplicative inverse of $n \cdot m$ is the product of the multiplicative inverse of n and the multiplicative inverse of m. That is, $1/nm = 1/n \cdot 1/m$.

Page 199
1. (a) $6^- < 5^-$ since $6^- + 1 = 5^-$.   (b) $6^- < 6$ since $6^- + 12 = 6$.   **3.** The absolute value of n is greater than the absolute value of m.   **4.** n is negative and m is positive. **5.** We say that $n > m$ if and only if there is a positive integer p such that $n = m + p$. **8.** $n \leq m$ means (by definition) that there is a non-negative integer p such that $n + p = m$. This means that either p is positive (in which case $n < m$) or p is zero (in which case $n = m$).

Page 200

1. (a) $6^- - 9 = d$; $6^- = 9 + d$; so d must be 15^-.

Page 202

1. (a) $5^- - 6 = 5^- + 6^- = (5 + 6)^- = 11^-$.   (c) 37.   (e) 11.   2. (a) $6 - (5 + 7^-)^-$
$= 6 + (5 + 7^-)^{--} = 6 + (5 + 7^-) = 6 + 2^- = 4$.   (c) 8^-.   (e) 1^-.   3. (a) $n -$
$(m - p) = n + (m - p)^- = n + (m + p^-)^- = n + (m^- + p^{--}) = n + m^- + p$.
(c) $a + b^- + c + d^-$.   (e) $b + c^- + a + x + y^-$.   (g) $a + b^- + c + d$.   (i) $e + a^-$
$+ b + c + d$.   4. In going from (1) to (2).

Page 203

4. (a) If n, m, and p are integers, then $(n - m) + p = (n + p) - m$. (We do not have
to worry now about the meaningfulness of the differences as we did in the system of
counting numbers.)   6. (a) Is a theorem.   (b) Is a false statement. To make it true
replace $p - n < p - m$ by $p - n > p - m$.

Page 206

1. (a) $(5)(7^-) + 35 = (5)(7^-) + (5)(7) = (5)(7^- + 7) = (5)(0) = 0$. So $(5)(7^-) = 35^-$.
2. (a) 42^-.   (d) 12^-.   (h) 24^-.   3. By Part 1 of the definition of multiplication of
integers and the fact that the product of the *counting numbers* 3 and 7 is the *counting
number* 21.

Page 208

1. (a) $(5^-)(7^-) + 35^- = (5^-)(7^-) + (5^-)(7) = (5^-)(7^- + 7) =$ etc.   2. (a) 36.   (c) 7^-.
(e) 5^-.   (g) 2^-.

Page 210

4. Because multiplication of counting numbers is associative and multiplication of
integers agrees with multiplication of counting numbers.   7. (a) The theorem *If at
least one of n and m is zero, then nm = 0* is true by virtue of the definition of multipli-
cation.   (b) Suppose $nm = 0$. Then $|nm| = 0$ and therefore $|n| \cdot |m| = 0$. Since $|n|$ and
$|m|$ are counting numbers according to Theorem 8 of Chapter 2 at least one of these
numbers is zero. But if the absolute value of an integer is zero, then the integer itself
is zero. Therefore at least one of n and m is zero.

Page 213

1. (a) 6^-.   (c) 2^-.   (e) 9.   (g) 2^-.   (i) 29.   (k) 158^-.   5. (a) Set $n^- \div m^- = q$. Then
$n^- = m^- q$ and upon multiplying both sides by 1^- obtain $n = mq$ from which it follows
that $n \div m = q$. Use transitivity of equality to finish.

Page 214

1. (a) $-5 - 6$.   (c) $-(-3 - -4)$.   2. (a) $3^- - 2$.   (c) $3 + 2^-$.   (f) $3^- - 4^{--}$.
(j) $(3^- + 4^-)^- - (4^- - 6^-)$.

Page 219

1. (a) $-27/-3 = (-27(-1)/(-3)(-1) = 27/3 = (9)(3)/(1)(3) = 9/1 = 9$.   3. (a)
$2/5 = (2)(-5)/(5)(-5) = -10/-25$.   (e) $-n/-m$.   5. Pattern a proof after the
proof of the Renaming Theorem for fractions.

Page 221

2. If a/b and c/b are rational numbers written with the same positive denominators
then we say that a/b is greater than c/b, and write $a/b > c/b$, if and only if $a > c$.

This relation is only transitive. This relation agrees with *greater than* for counting numbers and with *greater than* for fractions and with *greater than* for integers. **3.** (a) $2/-1 < -1 < -2/3 < 0 < 2/5 < 1/2 < 1$. **4.** Without the restriction on b the rational number $-7/-2$ would be less than the rational number $-6/-2$ (since $-7 < -6$). But $-7/-2 = 7/2$ and $-6/-2 = 3$. That is, $7/2$ would be less than 3. But regarded as fractions $7/2$ is greater than 3. So without the restriction on the denominator *less than* for rational numbers and *less than* for fractions would not agree on the fractions. **6.** If x and y represent rational numbers, then exactly one of these is true: $x < y$, $x = y$, $x > y$.

Page 222

1. (a) $-12/18 + -2/18 + -3/18 = -17/18$. (c) $(-np^2 + 2mp - p - m)/mp^2$.
2. (c) $(nm - 2m)/-m^2$. This is not in lowest terms.

Page 224

1. (a) $-(-2/3), 2/3, -2/-3$. (c) $-(2/3), -2/3, 2/-3$. **2.** (a) $-(2/3 + -7/2) = -(2/3) + -(-7/2) = -2/3 + 7/2 = -4/6 + 21/6 = (-4 + 21)/6 = 17/6$.
3. Only symmetry.

Page 226

1. If a/b is positive, then if necessary rewrite a/b so that both a and b are positive integers. Then compare a/b and $0/b$. Since a is positive, $a > 0$ whence $a/b > 0/b = 0$.
2. (a) Write $n = a/b$ and $m = c/b$. Then $n < m$ means $a/b < c/b$ and this means that $a < c$. By definition of less than for integers there is a positive integer k such that $a + k = b$. Then consider the positive rational number k/b and show that if we let $p = k/b$, then $n + p = m$.

Page 229

1. (a) $-2/3 - 4/5 = x$ and so $-2/3 = 4/5 + x$. Rename and get $-10/15 = 12/15 + x$. Then $x = -22/15$ since $12 + -22 = -10$. **2.** Proof of Theorem 1: $(a/b + c/d) - c/d = (ad + bc)/bd - cb/bd = [(ad + bc) - cb]/bd = ad/bd = a/b$. **3.** (a) $(n - 2/3) + 2/3 = (4/5 - 2/4) + 2/3$; $n = (4/5 - 2/4) + 2/3$; $n = 4/5 + -1/2 + 2/3 =$ etc. (d) $(1/2)n = 1/3 - 5$; $n = -28/3$. (g) $n = -37/30$. **7.** (a) $2 + -2/3 + -4/5$. **9.** Let x, y, and z be rational numbers such that $x - z = y - z$. Then $x + -z = y + -z$ and by cancellation for addition, $x = y$.

Page 230

1. $(a/b)(c/d + e/f) = (a/b)[(cf + de)/df] = a(cf + de)/bdf = (acf + ade)/bdf = acf/bdf + ade/bdf = ac/bd + ae/bf = (a/b)(c/d) + (a/b)(e/f)$. **3.** Let x be a nonzero rational number and assume that both y and z are multiplicative inverses of x. Then $xy = 1$ and $xz = 1$. Use transitivity of equality and the cancellation property of multiplication to conclude that $y = z$.

Page 231

2. $a/b \div c/d = q$ and so $a/b = c/d \cdot q$. Multiply both sides by d/c and obtain $q = a/b \cdot d/c$. Use transitivity of equality to obtain the theorem. **6.** (a) $1/3 \div -2/5 = q$ implies $1/3 = -2/5 \cdot q$. So q must be $5/(3)(-2)$ or $-5/6$. **7.** (a) $(a/b \cdot c/d) \div c/d = (a/b \cdot c/d)(d/c) = (a/b)(c/d \cdot c/d) = (a/b)(1) = a/b$. **9.** (a) $(ade + bce)/bdf$. (c) $(a^2d^2 - b^2c^2)/b^2d^2$. **11.** (a) $x = -10$. (d) $n = -8$. (g) $s = 15/4$. (j) $x = -11/2$.

Page 237

1. (a) Counting numbers: $\{8, 9, 10, 11, 12, \ldots\}$. Fractions: $\{x \in F : x > 7\}$, where F denotes the set of fractions. Integers: $\{8, 9, 10, 11, 12, \ldots\}$. Rationals: $\{x \in R : x > 7\}$, where R denotes the set of rational numbers.   (c) Counting numbers and integers: $\{1, 2, 3, 4, 5, \ldots\}$.   (e) Counting numbers: $\{0, 1\}$. Integers: $\{0, 1, -1, -2, -3, -4, \ldots\}$. Fractions: $\{x \in F : x < 2\}$.   (g) Rational numbers: $\{x \in R : x \leq -1\}$.   (i) Counting numbers: $\{1, 2, 3, 4, 5, \ldots\}$. Integers: $\{1, -1, 2, -2, \ldots\}$.   2. (a) $3 \leq n$ and $n < 7$. $\{3, 4, 5, 6\}$.   (c) $\{-2, -1, 0, 1, 2, 3, 4, 5\}$.   (e) $\{-3, -2, -1, 0, 1, 2, 3, 4\}$.   (g) $\{-3, -4, -5, -6, -7, \ldots\}$.   (i) $\varnothing$.

Page 240

1. (a) Multiply both sides by 4 to obtain $8/3 > 1$.   (c) Add $1/3$ to both sides. (f) Multiply both sides by -3 to obtain $9 < 15$.   7. (a) Proof of first theorem: Since b and d have the same algebraic sign, the number bd is positive. Multiply both sides of $a/b < c/d$ by the positive number bd obtaining $bda/b < bdc/d$ or $da < bc$. To prove converse, divide both sides of $da < bc$ by the positive number bd.   8. (a) True because can add the integer $-y$ to both sides by Theorem 1.   (c) Theorem 3.   (e) Theorem 2. (Divide both sides by x.)   (g) From (e) and (f).   (i) Theorem 2.   (k) From (g) and (j).   (m) From (l).

Page 243

1. (a) $\{x \in R : x \leq -1\}$, where R denotes the set of all rational numbers.   (c) $\{x \in R : x \geq -11\}$.   (e) $\{x \in R : x \leq 33/2\}$.   (f) $\{x \in R : -13/20 \leq x < 11/4\}$.   (h) $\{x \in R : x > 14\}$.   (j) $\{x \in R : x \geq 13/6\}$.

Page 252

1. Terminating decimal numerals: $b, c, d, f, g, i, j, k, l$.   2. (a) $1/125 = 7/5^3 = 2^3/2^3 5^3 = 2^3/(10)^3 = 2^3/1000 = 8/1000 = 0/10 + 0/100 + 8/1000 = 0.008$.   3. (a) $17.78 = 10 + 7 + 7/10 + 8/100 = 1000/100 + 700/100 + 70/100 + 8/100 = (1000 + 700 + 70 + 8)/100 = 1778/100 = 889/50$.

Page 257

1. (a) (i) $1/101$. (ii) $1/1001$.   (b) (i) $1/128$. (ii) $1/1024$.   2. $3, 3 - 1/10, 3 - 1/100, 3 - 1/1000, 3 - 1/10000, \ldots$ $4 + 1/10, 4 + 1/100, 4 + 1/1000, 4 + 1/10000, \ldots$

Page 261

2. The partial sums are getting closer and closer to $7/6$ but they are not getting arbitrarily close to $7/6$. It can be shown that the partial sums never get to the right of the point $5/6$ and that they in fact are getting arbitrarily close to this point.

Page 262

1. (a) Block: 134. Begins to repeat in the ten thousandths place.   3. One is the set of all nonterminating but repeating decimal numerals.   4. Nonterminating.

Page 265

1. (a) $0.11111 \cdots$.   (c) $0.833333 \cdots$.

Page 268

1.   (a) $0.045045045045 \cdots$.   (c) $0.38465384653846538465 \cdots$.   2. (a) $2/9$.   (c) $41/333$.   (e) $5473/450$.   (g) $4507/3300$.

Page 270

2. (a) 0.137.   (b) 18.   **3.** (a) 1.299999 · · · ·.   (b) 0.14499999 · · · ·.

Page 271

1. (a) -0.714285714285 · · · ·.   (b) -1.4.   **2.** (a) $-203/111$.   (b) $-89126/9999$.
3. Since $\sqrt{2}$ is not a rational number, the decimal representation must be nonterminating and nonrepeating.

Page 275

3. 0.010101.

Page 279

5. (c) (i) 1.2345669.

Page 285

1. (a) $9(10^0)$; $1(8^1) + 1(8^0)$; $1(5^1) + 4(5^0)$; $1(2^3) + 0(2^2) + 0(2^1) + 1(2^0)$.   (c) $1(10^1) + 2(10^0)$; $1(8^1) + 4(8^0)$.   (e) $3(5^1) + 2(5^0)$.   (f) $1(2^4) + 0(2^3) + 0(2^2) + 1(2^1) + 0(2^0)$.
2. (a) $4(8^3) + 4(8^2) + 5(8^1) + 1(8^0)$. $3(5^4) + 3(5^3) + 3(5^2) + 4(5^1) + 0(5^0)$.   **4.** One of the coefficients is greater than 6. $5(7^4) + 4(7^3) + 1(7^2) + 0(7^1) + 2(7^0)$.

Page 287

1. (a) $7(8^3) + 6(8^2) + 4(8^1) + 0(8^0)$.   (c) $1(8^1) + 0(8^0)$.   **2.** (a) 5600.   **4.** (a) 42.
(c) 70.   (e) 57.   (g) 4456.   (i) 22474.

Page 289

1. (a) 10000.   (c) 0.   **2.** (a) $1(2^2) + 0(2^1) + 1(2^0)$. $1(2^5) + 0(2^4) + 0(2^3) + 0(2^2) + 0(2^1) + 0(2^0)$.   **3.** (a) 1000011.   (c) 1011001.

Page 290

2. (a) 422.   (c) 1489.   **3.** (a) Three gross four dozen and five.

Page 292

1. 33_{10}.   **3.** 8423_{10}.   **5.** 29_{11}.   **7.** 10101_2.

Page 298

5. (a) 3226_8.   (c) 206_8.   **6.** (a) $468t6_{12}$.   (c) 71080_{12}.

Index